D1272842

The Constitution of Glasses

A Dynamic Interpretation
IN TWO VOLUMES

Volume I: *Fundamentals of the Structure of Inorganic Liquids and Solids*

Volume II: *Constitution and Properties of Some Representative Glasses*

The Constitution of Glasses

A DYNAMIC INTERPRETATION

Woldemar A. Weyl

Evan Pugh Research Professor in Physical Science
College of Mineral Industries
The Pennsylvania State University
University Park, Pennsylvania

Evelyn Chostner Marboe

Associate Professor of Mineral Science
College of Mineral Industries
The Pennsylvania State University
University Park, Pennsylvania

VOLUME I:

Fundamentals of the Structure
of Inorganic Liquids and Solids

1962 INTERSCIENCE PUBLISHERS

a division of John Wiley and Sons
New York and London

Library of Congress Catalog Card Number 62–19684

Printed in the United States of America

Foreword

By Emeritus Professor W. E. S. Turner, F.R.S.

When Professors Weyl and Marboe invited me to write a foreword to their new book on the constitution of glass, I accepted with great pleasure for I had for many years admired the persistence, skill, and critical ability with which, in a long series of papers, they had kept the subject under periodic survey.

With Professor Weyl and his work I had been intimate for more than 30 years. In 1939 he accepted an invitation from the Society of Glass Technology to prepare a monograph on the subject of coloured glasses. He had then settled at The Pennsylvania State University; but, from 1926 to 1938, he had been an active member of the Kaiser Wilhelm Institut für Silikatforschung under the direction of Dr. Wilhelm Eitel at Berlin-Dahlem. At this research centre, with its adequate technical resources, he had carried out and published a number of researches on the colours produced by metallic ions in glasses and in aqueous solutions; on the state of manganese in glasses at varying oxygen pressures; on the behaviour of arsenic and antimony oxides in glasses, and on the spectral transmission of glasses containing relatively high concentrations of iron and manganese. His training had been that of a physical chemist and he was well fitted to write on coloured glasses.

When, in 1942, Dr. Weyl's manuscript began to arrive in instalments I found myself, as editor, faced with a serious problem for, in order to expound the subject of coloured glasses on modern lines, he had thought it essential to prepare an extensive introduction which presented the most up to date views about the nature and constitution of glasses. At that time, paper suitable for the printing of scientific publications was difficult to obtain. Yet the value of Dr. Weyl's introductory review was, in my opinion, well worth a special effort to overcome the difficulties. I accepted the full text therefore and I believe this introduction proved very stimulating to a large circle of readers as it appeared in instalments in the Society's Journal between 1943 and 1946.

The Monograph in book form did not appear until 1951, but the long delay was due only partly to continuing printing difficulties; there was also the fact that the author wished to make extensive alterations and additions as the result of the substantial advances in knowledge since the initial sections of the monograph were written. The demand for the Monograph in book form on its first appearance was such that the Society consented to a reprinting and re-issue without revision: a testimony to the authority which Dr. Weyl had achieved in the field of knowledge of the properties and constitution of glass.

In 1944, Dr. Weyl found an enthusiastic collaborator in Mrs. Evelyn C. Marboe, now Associate Professor of Mineral Sciences in the College of Mineral Industries at The Pennsylvania State University. During 11 of their 18 years of partnership they have been engaged in basic research problems for the Office of Naval Research; but they have nevertheless continued to write with imaginative insight on widely diverse subjects relating to the properties and constitution of glass, and they have not hesitated to criticise faulty concepts. In particular, they have strongly challenged the correctness of the principles governing glass formation laid down by W. H. Zachariasen in 1932 and seemingly confirmed and entrenched by the X-ray measurements of B. E. Warren. Immediately before the war Zachariasen's views had been widely accepted and cases of deviation from his rules were treated as exceptions to be explained by new hypotheses. During the decade following the war, however, as the result of many experimental determinations of the conditions governing glass formation for a wide range of elements, it became clear that the supposed sharp differentiation into glass-forming and glass-modifying elements had so many exceptions that Zachariasen's rules had become cumbersome and of limited value.

The authors have come to the conclusion, which they present in this two-volume work, that the nature of glass is most likely to be established by reverting to the old definition that a glass is a supercooled liquid and by studying the structure of the liquid from which it is formed. This new approach by the authors is bound to create widespread interest; and, whatever the measure of its acceptance, I have no doubt that the book will be warmly welcomed and widely read.

Sheffield, August 1962

Preface

As the title of this book emphasizes, our approach to the constitution of glasses is based upon the dynamics of glass formation. Glasses form from supercooled liquids. Therefore, in contrast to present approaches based on crystal structures, we prefer to discuss the formation of glasses on the basis of the structures of those liquids from which they have formed on cooling. The structure of a liquid calls for a dynamic description. In contrast to crystals, the structures of liquids cannot be described by static models. Hence, in order to describe the structure of glasses we have developed a model which is dynamic rather than static: we have chosen three idealized liquid structures, two of which can form glasses and one which cannot. All glasses can be described in terms of these three extreme liquid structures. The constitution of a glass involves not only the atomic structure of the liquid from which it has formed but also its change with temperature and thermal history. The constitution of a glass should incorporate also its response to external mechanical or electrical forces.

The immediate aim of this book is to focus attention on the relationship between properties of glasses and their constitution. However, we have no intention of presenting a comprehensive treatment of glasses covering all of their properties. Certain aspects are emphasized at the expense of others, and in many cases it was necessary to make an arbitrary decision concerning which subjects to include. Even with respect to those properties which are discussed, our intention is not to present a complete bibliography.

We found it advisable to divide the material into two parts. Volume I is of a rather general nature and concerns itself with the constituents of inorganic solids and liquids and the mutual interaction of these constituents. We have chosen to describe our systems on the basis of ions and their mutual polarization. This description permits us to deal with rate phenomena. The pictures which we present are qualitative in nature. It would be desirable to develop some of the aspects discussed in our work on a more quantitative basis, however, this was not our immediate aim.

Volume I includes a description of those experimental approaches which we think have proved most useful in arriving at a consistent picture of the constitution of glasses. The viscosity of glasses and their electrical conductivities are properties of great practical importance. However, we did not include these properties in Volume I because they are of such a complex nature that they cannot be used for deriving the constitution of glasses. The best one can hope for is to attempt a structural interpretation of these properties which is based on the constitution of glasses as derived from other, better understood, properties. This is done in the second volume. Volume II deals with the constitution of representative types of glasses and their properties as functions of composition and temperature. Also included are discussions of the surface tension of glasses and their responses to mechanical forces. The surface chemistry of silicate glasses is discussed in some detail whenever it contributes to a better understanding of their constitution.

Nearly 30 years have gone by since the early work on the atomic structure of glasses caused us to abandon our molecular description as well as our ideas that glasses were heterogeneous in a submicroscopic way. Today, experimental evidence is accumulating rapidly, compelling us to return to molecular concepts and to the existence of complex ions. Today, we know that most glasses are heterogeneous in a submicroscopic way.

The historical aspects included have been chosen so that the reader can see that science is not a road which leads steadily uphill and reaches its goal asymptotically. Theoretical approaches move more like a pendulum swinging back and forth so that certain views which are considered obsolete today may become modern again tomorrow.

Our aim is to correlate existing experimental material and theoretical approaches and to present a new approach to the constitution of glasses consistent with their properties. We hope that our approach will aid in broadening the views of those engaged in glass technology research and will be stimulating to those who are generally concerned with the physical chemistry of the solid and liquid states. It is our hope that it will prove to be of value to those engaged in teaching, research, and development.

August, 1962
University Park, Pa.

W. A. Weyl
E. C. Marboe

Contents

INTRODUCTORY REMARKS

The development of glass technology was very different from the development of the organic chemical industry. The organic chemical industry is rather young. It began to make great advances only after chemists were able to determine the constitution of organic compounds. The synthesis of desirable naturally occurring compounds, such as indigo, usually followed rapidly the knowledge of their constitution. In organic chemistry, a quantitative analysis of a compound does not reveal much about its nature: one has to know the constitution of the compound in order to obtain clues to its behavior and its properties.

Glass technology developed over a period of several thousands of years. Any developments by necessity had to be empirical. Even today, the important discoveries in the field of glass technology are made by chance. One finds little information concerning the properties of glasses correlated with their constitution. The inventors of the Pyrex brand glass did not know why the combination of silica with boric oxide and a few minor constituents led to a glass that had so many valuable properties and that could be melted at a reasonable temperature. The inventors of the Vycor glass could not possibly have predicted that certain sodium boro-silicate glasses would undergo phase separations into sodium borate and nearly pure silica. Neither could they predict that the siliceous phase (96% SiO_2), obtained after leaching out the soluble sodium borate, could be densified at temperatures 500 degrees below the softening point of the final product. From the viewpoint of the technologists, the Pyrex brand and the Vycor glass involve relatively simple systems.

At the present time efforts are being made to better understand and control those complex phenomena responsible for the formation and the properties of Corning's Pyroceram, another important glass technological discovery which was made on an empirical basis.

The rapid automation in glass molding called for glasses that met certain temperature-viscosity relations. Suitable glasses were developed that met the rapidly changing demands of the industry. However, the development of new glasses and the modification of existing ones proceeded on a strictly empirical basis.

Glass technologists need a better understanding of rate phenomena. Viscosity, refractory attack, and chemical durability, as well as devitrification, are rate phenomena. Physical chemistry can deal with equilibria, but rate phenomena are not so well understood.

Further rapid industrial progress in the field of glass technology may be expected as soon as glass technologists are in a better posiion to understand the fundamentals of the methods and the processes that they are using. The present rapid expansion of industrial research facilities is ample proof of the fact that the glass industry now realizes the value of fundamental research. In any industry, progress will be faster when the fundamentals of the processes used are better understood.

G. Tammann (1) and his school contributed much to our present knowledge of the glassy state by making use of low-melting organic compounds. How is it possible to gain insight into characteristic features of glasses, e.g., nucleation and crystal growth, by studying systems which, from a structural point of view, have nothing in common with the most important group of glasses, the silicates?

Today we know that the differences between organic and inorganic substances are not quite as drastic as first appeared. Some amorphous organic solids, e.g., the phenol-formaldehyde resins, are essentially three-dimensional networks and do not contain discrete molecules as building units. Some alkali phosphate glasses, on the other hand, consist of long chain polymers, and their constitution can be treated successfully on the same basis as can organic polymers. We believe that the determination of the constitution of vitreous alkali phosphates represents an important milestone in our present search for the constitution of glasses primarily because it reintroduces molecular concepts into the description of inorganic glasses.

We emphasize in the title of this treatise that our approach to the constitution of glasses is a dynamic one. We begin with Tammann's description of glasses as supercooled liquids, and we prefer to discuss the formation of glasses on the basis of the structure of those liquids from which they form, rather than on the basis of crystals. The constitution of a crystal can be described by a static picture, but no static picture can help us in the understanding of the liquid state; hence, a dynamic rather than a static model had to be developed.

Tammann was interested in the vitreous state of glass, and its relation to other states of aggregation, liquids and solids. His experiments rarely dealt with silicate glasses, and he made no effort to vary chemical composition systematically.

As far as the constitution of technical glasses, in particular silicates, boro-silicates, and alumino-silicates, is concerned, to a large extent we still depend on the work which W. E. S. Turner (2) started in Sheffield in 1915 and conducted for many years with a group of outstanding scientists. This accumulation of much needed information on silicate glasses, the chemical compositions of which were varied systematically, was directed by thoughts based on physical chemistry. Turner thought in terms of molecules, and even went so far as to talk about a "sponge structure" of glasses. With the application of X rays to glasses Turner's theory was considered to be obsolete. However, present-day research is proving his ideas correct.

There is a definite need for a description of the structure of fused ionic substances, such as silicates, phosphates, and borates, that, in addition to ions or atoms, introduces some larger particles or aggregates that have widely different lifetimes. This the authors have attempted to do.

W. H. Zachariasen (3) expanded on some ideas of V. M. Goldschmidt (4) on the conditions of glass formation, and presented some simple rules concerning the structure of oxide glasses. Zachariasen found wide acceptance of his concept that oxide glasses are three-dimensional, random, and continuous networks in which the network-forming cations form either triangles or tetrahedra with oxygen. B. E. Warren (5) stated that the X-ray diffraction work that he and his associates carried out on simple glasses could be interpreted on the basis of Zachariasen's picture, but he also warned, repeatedly, that his own work proved neither that Zachariasen's picture was correct nor that it was the only one which could agree with his data. Nevertheless, some scientists have fully embraced this concept and have even distorted their findings to make them compatible with the concept of Zachariasen.

We are convinced that a continuation of research concerning the constitution of glasses along these established lines cannot deepen our understanding of the constitution of glasses, not even of glasses that have very simple chemical compositions. What we need is much more than a refinement of this picture if we want to understand the behavior of glasses.

Conventional approaches have not helped us to understand the simplest of all facts concerning the structures of silicate glasses; namely, the phase relationships in the alkali oxide–silica systems. G. W. Morey (6), who has contributed so much to our knowledge of the phase relations of glass-forming systems, was fully aware of the present situation when he wrote the following:

"In spite of the accumulation of an enormous amount of data, we have not yet any intimation of an hypothesis which will enable us to predict the heterogeneous equilibrium from the properties of a homogeneous equilibrium."

"In no case have we any intimation as to why a compound is formed. From no theoretical knowledge available today could one predict that a compound of the composition $K_2O \cdot 4SiO_2$ would be present in the system K_2O-SiO_2, and no similar compound in the system Na_2O-SiO_2; or that lithium disilicate would have an incongruent melting point, although sodium and potassium disilicates have congruent melting points. The prediction of the heterogeneous equilibrium from the properties of the components of the homogeneous equilibrium, a fundamental object of theoretical chemistry, is far from our capabilities at the present time, and there is no known relationship between the properties of a solution and of the substances which form from it on completion of the process of crystallization."

Morey emphasizes both the importance of the problem and the utter helplessness of conventional approaches to aid in an understanding of these relations.

Volume I of this book deals with the principles that are used in our approach to the constitution of glasses. V. M. Goldschmidt (4), the father of modern solid state chemistry, pointed out that the properties of a crystal are determined by the constituent ions; i.e., their ratio, sizes, charges, and polarization properties. As far as the geometry of the crystals—and the same applies to glasses—is concerned, the parameters are listed approximately in the order of their importance. With respect to the kinetic aspects of crystals, their phase transformations, their melting, and their reaction rates, however, the polarization properties become of major importance. For this reason our concepts of chemical binding forces are based upon the work of K. Fajans (7) and his school and considerable space has been given to the description of the properties of ions and their mutual electrical interactions.

Our interpretation of melting, in particular of its kinetic aspects, is based on the postulate that an ionic solid can melt for different reasons. We postulate that in certain cases the structure of the liquid phase that is in equilibrium with a crystal at its melting point bears much resemblance to that of the crystal; e.g., albite $Na_2O \cdot Al_2O_3 \cdot 6SiO_2$. However, there may also be cases in which no resemblance exists between the structure of the crystals and the liquids; e.g., the alkali halides. On this basis it became apparent that the atomic structures of some vitreous compounds strongly resembled those of their crystalline modifications, whereas the structure of other vitreous compounds show no resemblance to the crystalline forms. This discovery made it possible for us to approach glass structures on a dynamic basis using liquid structures as the starting point.

CHAPTER I

STRUCTURAL PRINCIPLES OF CONDENSED SYSTEMS

Gases at ordinary temperature and pressure have no structure. The size of a hydrogen, oxygen, or nitrogen molecule is of the order of 2 to 3 A. but the average distance between these molecules at ordinary temperature and pressure is of the order of 100 A. Such a system can be treated successfully as consisting of points which are in thermal motion. The kinetic theory of gases requires refinements only if it is to be extended to low temperatures or to high pressures. Only when the molecules come closer together does it become necessary to consider their shapes and dimensions and their mutual attractions as expressed by their van der Waals' constants. Normally, these factors are of no concern and the fundamental gas laws apply to many gases regardless of their chemical nature.

The absence of a structure in gases made it possible for Avagadro to postulate that for a given temperature and pressure equal volumes of all gases contain the same number of particles. The absence of strong intermolecular forces makes all gases miscible.

No such simple relationship can be expected for the condensed state. The particles are close together and exert forces upon one another. The particles in the condensed state cannot be treated as mere points; their dimensions must be considered. This, by itself, introduces a certain order. If one wants to describe the distribution of atoms or molecules in a liquid, the Brownian motion makes it necessary to use an ordinate system, the origin of which moves with the reference particle. The curve that describes the probability of finding a second particle as a function of the distance from the reference particle will then show maxima and minima which become less distinct for larger distances. P. Debye and H. Menke (8) calculated the distribution function for mercury, a monoatomic liquid, on the basis of its X-ray scattering. Molecular liquids which consist of spherical molecules assume similar structures. The spheres are fairly close packed so that some order is established for close distances. In contrast to the structures of crystals, the structures of liquids and glasses have only short range order.

1. Nature of Chemical Binding Forces

As far as the structures of crystals are concerned, our knowledge is on firmly established grounds. Most discussions of crystals are restricted to "ideal crystals," and ignore the mosaic or block structure as well as vacant lattice sites. This is a useful approximation which is derived from X-ray diffraction patterns. The analysis of the X-ray diffraction patterns can give us not only the geometry of the crystal but also the electron density distribution. A crystal of NaCl can be described as an array of Na^+ and Cl^- ions. Such a description does not apply to a crystal of SiO_2. Here, too, we refer to Si^{4+} and O^{2-} ions but the electron density in such a crystal tells us that the nuclei of the oxygens are surrounded by a lower electron density than would correspond to the quantum state O^{2-}. The electron density around the nuclei of silicon, on the other hand, is higher than would correspond to Si^{4+}. This deviation from the ideal ionic structure has been interpreted in different ways. It has been attributed to partial covalency, meaning that the quantum state is somewhere between ions and neutral atoms. In this treatise we use the concept of the mutual polarization of the ions instead of the concept of partial covalency. Whereas both descriptions are the same for the crystal as a whole, the polarization picture makes it obvious that the interaction is accentuated by the asymmetry of surfaces and vacancies. As we will see later, the transition of crystals into liquids can be the result of a drastic change in the binding forces due to the formation of vacancies. Furthermore an obvious consequence of the concept of mutual polarization of ions is that this interaction decreases with increasing temperature. As a crystal or a glass expands and the average internuclear distances increase the mutual deformation becomes less important for its properties. Using the concept of the partial covalency we would regard a crystal or a glass at higher temperature as being more ionic.

Shortly after M. von Laue used crystals as diffraction gratings in order to prove the wave nature of X rays this phenomenon was applied to the exploration of the structures of crystals. It was in particular the systematic work of W. H. Bragg and W. L. Bragg which opened the door to modern crystallography. As a result of their work, it became possible to derive the sizes of the ultimate constituents of crystals. The method itself provided only the internuclear distances, i.e., the sum of two ionic radii, but one could make reasonable assumptions concerning the relative contributions of anions and cations. Thus, the determination of the crystal structures of the alkali halides also became the basis for the theory of lattice energies (Born and Lande, in 1918).

The core of the chlorine atom can improve its screening by completing its octet shell and changing into an Cl^- ion if an electron is available. This process

$$Cl + e^- = Cl^- + 86 \text{ kcal.}$$

is exothermic. However, the electron affinity of the chlorine atom (86 kcal.) is not sufficient to remove the outermost or valence electron from a sodium atom. This process

$$Na^0 - e^- + 118 \text{ kcal.} = Na^+$$

requires more ionization energy than can be gained by the formation of Cl^- ions. Hence, a chemical reaction between sodium and chlorine atoms becomes possible only because the potential energy of the system Na + Cl can be lowered considerably by the coulombic interaction between the charged particles Na^+ and Cl^- ions.

The coulombic energy gained by the combination of Na^+ and Cl^- ions amounts to approximately 120 kcal. for the formation of single NaCl molecules. However, the formation of the crystal from the single ions gives 180 kcal. and this value is the lattice energy of NaCl.

On the basis of X-ray scattering, a procedure has been developed which makes it possible to measure the electron density distribution in crystals. The application of this method to a NaCl crystal reveals that the electron density at a certain point on the line that connects the centers of Na^+ and Cl^- ions falls off to a value very close to zero. This result agrees with the concept that an NaCl crystal consists of an array of Na^+ and Cl^- ions that are nearly spherical. NaCl is the prototype of an ionic compound.

An analogous investigation of an MgO crystal that has the same geometry as an NaCl crystal gives somewhat different results. On the connecting line between Mg and O atoms the electron density also goes through a minimum, but the minimum value between Mg and O atoms is much higher than that between Na and Cl atoms. Nowhere in the MgO lattice does the electron density drop to the same level as that found in alkali halides. The mean value of the electron density in space between the alkali and halogen ions is 0.01–0.05 electrons per A^3 whereas in MgO the corresponding minimum is about 0.15–0.2 electrons per A^3. This has been interpreted to mean that electrons are used partly for the formation of a covalent bond between the Mg and O ions. The bond type in MgO cannot be extremely ionic in the sense that the lattice consists of rigid spheres which are bonded by coulomb attractive forces.

In the case of quartz, the "degree of covalency" would even be much larger than that for MgO. R. Brill (9) estimates the bond type of quartz to be approximately 50% covalent and 50% ionic. L. Pauling (10) had come to the same estimate on the basis of the Si-O distance. He interprets the anomalously small distance between Si and O atoms in silica as a shortening of the ionic bond by partial covalency.

We will not use this description of the chemical binding forces as partly ionic and partly covalent. We found it advantageous to follow another school of thought because we need a concept which lends itself to the interpretation of kinetic phenomena and rates of reactions.

According to K. Fajans (7), the deviation from pure ionic binding can be expressed in terms of a mutual deformation of the electron clouds of the ions. The facts which led to the concept of partial covalency can be interpreted as a "pulling over" of the electron clouds of the O^{2-} ions by the Mg^{2+} ions and even more so by the Si^{4+} ions. As a result of this deformation, the electron density does not fall off to zero at any point between the Mg^{2+} or Si^{4+} ions and the O^{2-} ions. This interaction also accounts for the smaller distance or the decrease of apparent radii of the ions.

In this treatise we will use exclusively the approach to chemical binding which has been developed by K. Fajans (7). Instead of treating substances as composed of atoms, we subdivide matter into positively and negatively charged particles. This ionic viewpoint is not generally accepted. A. F. Wells (11), for example, writes: "When extended to bonds between atoms such as carbon and phosphorus it becomes artificial in postulating ions of high charge which cannot exist under ordinary conditions." Wells rejects one concept, that of highly charged ions P^{5+} and C^{4+} or C^{4-}, etc., on the basis that these units cannot exist under "ordinary conditions," but he accepts the concept of C and P atoms, i.e., of units which, too, do not exist under ordinary conditions.

In our approach to the constitution of glasses we have to use a system which applies equally well to the crystalline, liquid, and gaseous states.

Among the books of inorganic chemistry that of A. E. van Arkel (12) on "Molecules and Crystals in Inorganic Chemistry" represents a serious effort to treat chemical compounds from the extreme ionic viewpoint. Using the concepts of J. J. van Laar and of W. Kossel on the shielding of central atoms, van Arkel was able to go relatively far in the interpretation of some properties; e.g., the volatility of compounds.

Apparently unaware of the work of K. Fajans and his school, van Arkel overlooked certain important features. Instead of considering the core of the atom he uses the oxidation number of an element as an indication of the nature of the building units of the molecule. It is customary to describe the sulfur atom in SO_2 as having an oxidation number of four, but one has to assume that this element participates in the molecule SO_2 as the core S^{6+} plus a pair of electrons which acts in the same capacity as the O^{2-} ions. Treating SO_2 as the molecule $S^{4+}(O^{2-})_2$ produces an insurmountable obstacle in van Arkel's approach. He cannot understand why SO_2 is not linear like CO_2 and the writes: "Thus none of the molecules, H_2O, H_2S, Cl_2O, SO_2, ClO_2, and NO_2 is linear, while NH_3, PH_3, PF_3, PCl_3, AsF_3 and $AsCl_3$ have the shape of the trigonal pyramid, so that the positive ion is not in the same plane as the negative."

Treating his ions as rigid spheres, van Arkel (12) comments: "This simple theory of shielding them can only partly explain the phenomenon of volatility. It is difficult, for example, to see how the two O ions can shield the C ion completely and the fact that CO and NO are gaseous completely contradicts the simple theory."

Probably the concept of the screening of cations as a major principle in inorganic chemistry would have been developed much earlier if scientists had paid more attention to the polarization properties of the ions. The early ideas of J. J. van Laar and of W. Kossel and, in particular, this recent approach of A. E. van Arkel to the volatility of shielded molecules, all suffer from having too many exceptions.

There is only one rigorous approach to chemistry, the quantum mechanical treatment, but this is too complicated because it has to be based on the interaction between nuclei and all electrons rather than between atoms or ions. Such a rigorous treatment is possible only for the very simplest compounds, e.g., the molecules H_2 and Li^+H^-.

2. Origin of the Solid State

In order to explain the reason for the formation of solids, one has to formulate a plausible hypothesis for the fact that under normal conditions only a very few elements seem to be stable as individual atoms: the noble gases. No other element at room temperature and atmospheric pressure forms a gas which consists of single atoms. Either the atoms interact among themselves, reshuffle some of their electrons and form molecules (Cl_2, O_2, P_2, P_4, S_8, etc.), or they react with the atoms of other elements and form compounds. One needs a hypothesis that can account for the fact that individual sulfur atoms at room temperature are not stable but have a higher potential energy than puckered rings which contain eight sulfur atoms each. Crystalline sulfur as well as a solution of sulfur in carbon disulfide contain molecules; i.e., rings which consist of eight atoms each.

In order to have a physical picture for the cause of this regrouping of electrons with respect to nuclei, we assume that in the present environment the positive cores of most atoms require a more intense shielding by electrons than can be supplied by the number of electrons that neutralize the excess charge of the nucleus.

The formation of a metal seems to be an efficient method by which the atoms can improve the screening of their cores. The mobility of the electrons and their high symmetry around the cores seem to be very important factors. The efficiency of this type of screening is revealed through the fact that most elements are metals or, like selenium, form a metallic modification and that many nonmetallic compounds, e.g., VO and UO_2, imitate "metallicity" by having mobile electrons in their structures.

As far as the structures of glasses are concerned, we are primarily interested in the formation of solids from cations and anions.

When a group of atoms, such as the sodium and chlorine atoms, interact chemically, single molecules are formed only if the cation is the proton or if the number of anions required for neutralizing the charge of the cation at the particular temperature is sufficiently great so that proper screening is provided. The first case is exemplified by NH_3, the second by SF_6. Unless both conditions, electroneutrality and adequate screening, are met, the interaction of atoms does not lead to molecules but to an infinitely extending array of ions; i.e., a solid.

In order to screen a Na^+ ion at ordinary temperature and pressure six Cl^- ions are required. Each Cl^- ion, therefore, has to screen six Na^+ ions, a condition which can be expressed by the following formula:

$$Na^+ (Cl^-/6)_6$$

The formula NaCl which has been used widely in chemical equations applies strictly only to the vapor state of this substance but not to the crystal. Neither a quartz crystal nor silica glass contains SiO_2 molecules. Silica in its known crystalline modifications and in the vitreous state is better described by the following formula:

$$Si^{4+} (O^{2-}/2)_4$$

This expression indicates that the cation Si^{4+} is screened by four O^{2-} ions. Because of the composition being SiO_2 each O^{2-} ion belongs to two Si^{4+} ions and can, therefore, be counted only as $O^{2-}/2$ for each Si^{4+} ion. This type of formula brings out the screening of the coordination requirements of the cations and the nature of the building units.

One of the best known principles that govern the formation of the condensed state, in particular solids, is the principle of electroneutrality in the smallest volume. This principle has been applied as a useful tool for understanding crystal structures by L. Pauling (10) who referred to it as the "electrostatic valence rule."

The screening of the Si^{4+} ion requires at least four O^{2-} ions. However, the SiO_4 tetrahedra could be linked in different ways; e.g., some O^{2-} ions may form the corner of only one tetrahedron and others may be shared by three adjacent tetrahedra. Such a structure, however, would be less stable than the known structures of silica. In a stable ionic structure the valence of each anion is equal to the sum of the strengths of the electrostatic bonds extending toward it from the adjacent cations. This rule is obeyed in silica because the valency or charge of the anion O^{2-} is compensated for exactly by two-fourths the charges of silicon. We can write the formula of silica also as follows:

$$O^{2-}\ (Si^{4+}/4)_2$$

This expression means that each oxygen ion belongs to two silicon ions and each silicon belongs to four oxygens.

In addition to the screening concept we have to use the electrostatic valence rule in our speculations concerning the atomic structures of glasses or the structural changes which take place on heating and cooling. It is unlikely that silica glass or any form of crystalline silica will have the hypothetical structure previously mentioned: one half of the O^{2-} ions nonbridging and the other half forming the corner of three adjacent tetrahedra. However, if the temperature is sufficiently high, the energy for producing such a structure becomes available and as a result one should expect this constellation to occur in fused silica. The higher the temperature the greater becomes the influence that the entropy, the disorder, has on the stability of the system. This means that a system will violate the rules of maximum screening and of establishing electroneutrality in the smallest possible volume if the temperature is sufficiently high. This feature is important for the constitution and the chemistry of glasses because many glasses form at 1400 to 1500°C.

The number of anions which is required for proper screening depends not only on the sizes but also on the deforming power of the cations. The small size and relatively high charge of the carbon core produce a strong electrical field which can deform two anions, say O^{2-} or S^{2-} ions, to such an extent that it is completely screened. Under ordinary pressure neither CS_2 nor CO_2 has a tendency to polymerize. At low temperature these substances form solids which consist of single molecules which are held together by van der Waals' forces.

Elements other than carbon can form individual molecules only if the general formula is AX_3 or AX_4. The gaseous molecules NO_2 and SO_2 are considered to have the formula AX_3 rather than AX_2. Their quanticule formulas are $N^{5+}(O^{2-})_2(e^-)$ and $S_6{}^+(O^{2-})_2(e_2^-)$.

Somewhere in between single molecules and polymerized infinitely-extending structures such as NaCl and SiO_2, we find that the screening demand leads to polymers of low molecular weight; e.g., P_4O_{10} or Al_2Cl_6.

The concept of the coordination number of a cation A^+ with respect to an anion X^- has been developed on a purely geometrical basis. In order to produce the most stable crystal of the composition A^+X^- or $A^{2+}X^{2-}$, etc., equal numbers of these two ions have to be packed closely so that electroneutrality is established within the smallest possible volume. In those cases in which the anion X^- is larger than the cation A^+ and both ions can be treated as rigid spheres, the most stable lattice is obtained when the maximum number of X^- is packed around A^+ ions which permits the formation of an infinitely-extending three-dimensional pattern.

In 1922, A. Magnus calculated the arrangements of anions around a cation as a function of the ratio of their sizes, assuming that the ions are rigid spheres. The number of anions determines the geometry of the group because the mutual repulsive forces cause anions to assume positions in which they are as far away as possible from the other anion. The arrangements shown in Table I result from the coulombic interactions between cations and anions when the ratio of their sizes, r_{cation}/r_{anion}, increases. The relation given in Table I was verified when Goldschmidt (4) and his school determined experimentally the radii of a large number of ions. The ratio of the sizes of the ions is one of the most important factors which determine the structure of a simple compound because it determines the coordination number of the cation.

TABLE I

Arrangements Resulting from Coulombic Interactions

Number of anions	Arrangement	Limit radius ratio
3	Equilateral triangle	0.15
4	Tetrahedron	0.22
4	Square	0.41
6	Octahedron	0.41
8	Cube	0.73

3. Types of Screening of Positive Cores

The concept that atoms interact by forming cations and anions and that the cations have to be screened by an environment of anions provides a useful picture for the formation of ionic solids, crystals and glasses. The screening concept, however, is not limited to ionic structures but is equally applicable to molecules such as nitrogen. For these molecules the screening concept provides a picture that illustrates the high stability of the molecule N_2. The conventional treatment of N_2 molecules as triple bonded nitrogen atoms $N \equiv N$ cannot account for its inertness because molecules such as acetylene $CH \equiv CH$, which contain triple bonds, are very reactive.

We found it useful to divide the ways in which a cation or a positive core can be screened into five groups which we shall review briefly.

A. Noble Gases

The only elements that form atoms under normal conditions are the noble gases. According to our concept, these elements are the only ones in which at ordinary temperature the positive cores are sufficiently screened by the number of electrons which neutralizes the excess charges of their cores. The octet configuration of neon, argon, etc., seems to play an important role because many atoms imitate this configuration either by forming charged particles (Cl^-) or by forming molecular orbitals.

B. Metals

The formation of metals requires the cooperation of a large number of atoms. The concept of "metallicity," cannot be applied to a small number of atoms because it is based on the presence of an "electron gas" and in order for the electrons to display metallic properties sufficient space is a prerequisite. The formation of mobile electrons seems to be one of the most efficient ways to improve the screening of cores so that many solids utilize this type of screening (semiconductors).

One can describe the formation of the ruby color in a gold ruby glass on reheating as a process in which the gold atoms aggregate because they can improve the screening of their cores by developing "metallicity."

C. Formation of Molecules with Molecular Orbitals

In our approach to the chemistry of solids we attribute the chemical inertness of neon and the fact that this element forms single atoms to the satisfactory screening of the neon core Ne^{10+} by the 2 + 8 electrons. Fajans (7) explains the inertness of the N_2 molecule on the same basis. He postulates that the nitrogen molecule contains two positive cores N^{5+} which take the place of the one core Ne^{10+}. In the nitrogen molecule the ten electrons move in orbitals which are quantized with respect to both N^{5+} cores (molecular orbitals).

The formation of molecules is not restricted to the interaction of only two atoms. Phosphorus, for example, forms P_2 and P_4 molecules. Sulfur and selenium can form molecules consisting of a much larger number of atoms (S_8), and even infinitely-extending chains. In these molecules, in contrast to the metals, the binding electrons are quantized with respect to a small number of nuclei.

When discussing the formation of vitreous sulfur we will take advantage of the electronic formula in order to demonstrate the mechanism of polymerization and crystallization.

D. Formation of Cations and Anions

A group of atoms can improve the screening of their cores by the formation of a compound. The first step consists of transferring electrons from one atom to another. This process leads to charged particles. In the second step, the cations (those atoms which donated one or more electrons) surround themselves with those atoms (anions) which have accepted the electrons. The binding forces between cations and anions can be treated as electrostatic or coulombic forces between ions, the electron clouds of which are more or less deformed. In order to screen all cations, an infinitely extending three-dimensional network may be formed (NaCl).

E. Screening of the Proton

The interactions between atoms which we subdivided into the formation of metals, molecules, and ions are not restricted to atoms of one element but are also observed between atoms of different elements. Alloys are metals which contain two or more elements. The molecule CO, according to Fajans, has a structure analogous to that of N_2 only it contains two different positive cores and its quanticule formula is $C^{4+}e_{10}^{-}O^{6+}$ as compared with $N^{5+}e_{10}^{-}N^{5+}$. This formula accounts for the inertness of CO and for the fact that N_2 and CO have the same van der Waals' constant (boiling points N_2, -195°C.; CO, -190°C.). There is one element, however, which has to be treated differently: hydrogen.

Hydrogen compounds which contain the H^- ion resemble the halides. KH and KCl have certain characteristics in common;

both are white salts which can be electrolyzed. Hydrogen compounds which contain the H^+ ion, however, differ drastically from corresponding compounds containing other cations. The melting points of NaF, KF, RbF, and CsF, when plotted against the radii of the cations, lie on a straight line. LiF has a lower melting point than expected from a linear relationship. The melting point of hydrogen fluoride (−85°C.), however, falls way out of line from an expected extrapolated value. Hydrogen compounds which contain protons can melt or vaporize at much lower temperatures than the corresponding compounds containing Na^+ or K^+ ions instead of protons. The proton, because of its lack of electrons, can enter the electron cloud of a polarizable anion.

Among cations the proton is unique, because it can be screened in two basically different ways. Like the other cations, it can coordinate with anions—in which case it usually has the coordination number 2 or, in rare cases (H_3BO_3), 3—or it can enter the electron cloud of a single anion. This dual role of the proton with respect to its screening is responsible for some of the unique features which are characteristic for hydrogen compounds (hydrogen bonding, polymerization of HF, condensation difficulty of water vapor, catalysis by protons, etc.).

K. Fajans and N. Bauer (13) derived the structures of hydrogen halide molecules on the basis that a proton, having no electrons, is not repelled by an electron cloud but may enter the electron cloud of the anion to a depth where the repulsive force between the proton and the nucleus of the anion balances the attractive force between the proton and the electron cloud. Thus, its lack of electrons provides the proton with a unique way of being screened. This process tightens the electron cloud of the anion because the proton, so to speak, adds its charge to that of the nucleus of the anion. An anion has to be fairly polarizable in order to permit this interpenetration.

Hydrogen fluoride has some unique properties as compared with the other hydrogen halides because the low polarizability of the F^- ion favors a screening of the proton by coordination with two F^- ions rather than by an interpenetration. As a result, HF molecules polymerize. A number of HF molecules aggregate and make it possible for their protons to coordinate with two F^- ions each. This polymerization of the HF molecules takes place even in the vapor phase.

Water molecules exist as monomers in the vapor phase because an O^{2-} ion can screen two protons by accepting them into its electron cloud. In the condensed state, however, the protons of water are screened in a fashion similar to that in HF; namely, by an environment of two anions. In contrast to the condensation of hydrogen fluoride or hydrogen sulfide, water has to undergo a structural change during the gas-liquid or gas-solid transition. The regrouping of electrons represents the energy barrier which separates the supersaturated water vapor from the liquid or from ice. This feature accounts for the paradoxical situation that water condenses on a glass surface even if the ambient atmosphere is not saturated with water vapor. Even a quartz crystal becomes coated with a multilayer of H_2O molecules when brought from a vacuum into a normal atmosphere.

The low boiling point of NH_3 shows that this molecule has less tendency to polymerize than water because the N^{3-} ion is sufficiently polarizable to screen three protons. The existence of the NH_4^+ ion proves that the N^{3-} ion may accommodate and screen as many as four protons.

This method of screening the proton, by permitting it to enter the electron cloud of an anion, is unique and distinguishes the hydrogen compounds from other compounds. In hundreds of molecules, such as CO_2, SO_3, SiF_4, PF_5, one finds that a central positive core is surrounded by that number of anions which neutralize its excess charge. These compounds can exist as molecules in the vapor state. The reverse combination; namely, a molecule in the vapor state, consisting of a central anion such as a N^{3-} or a C^{4-} ion neutralized by an environment of three or four singly charged cations, is rare because it is limited to those cases in which the cation is the proton. Why do molecules such as $S^{2-}Na_2^+$, or $N^{3-}Na_3^+$ have to polymerize and form solids? The cation Na^+, has to be surrounded by anions in order to be screened because its own electrons make it impossible for it to enter the electron cloud of an anion, even if the anion were sufficiently large.

The cations Be^{2+} and Li^+ possess properties that reveal an interaction with anions between that of the proton and the other "normal" cations because their deformation in an electrical field leaves their nuclei unscreened toward the negative field.

CHAPTER II

PROPERTIES OF CATIONS AND ANIONS

Our knowledge of the properties of ions is primarily knowledge of the hydrated ions gained from analytical chemistry. From the chemistry of aqueous solutions, we are accustomed to attribute to a cation or an anion certain characteristic properties. The blue color of the Cu^{2+} ion and the green color of the Ni^{2+} ion are characteristic for solutions that contain Cu^{2+} and Ni^{2+} ions in a state of maximum hydration. Ni^{2+} ions, however, need not always be green: they are responsible for the blue color of the spinel $NiAl_2O_4$ and can produce yellow and purple colors in glasses depending upon the composition of the base glass.

Solid $CuCl_2$ is yellow, $CrBr_2$ is dark brown, basic cupric carbonate (malachite) is green. This also means that in solids, the Cu^{2+} ion does not necessarily have the blue color of its aqueous solution. PbO is yellow, but the Pb^{2+} ion is colorless in both aqueous solutions and glasses.

One of the chief difficulties in understanding the chemistry of condensed systems is the variation of all properties of the ions; not just in their light absorption. An ion in aqueous solution is surrounded more or less symmetrically by water and occupies a position in which the electrical field is zero over a time average. This condition is not always met in crystals. The electrical fields to which ions are exposed in solids may reach the order of ten million volts per centimeter.

The term "ion," as we use it, does not necessarily refer to a particle which is stable either in the gaseous state or in the hydrated state. When we refer to a S^{6+} ion as a constituent of SO_4^{2-}, SF_6, or SO_3 we refer to the quantum state of the sulfur atom. The number of cations is considerably greater than the number of anions. A difference exists also with respect to the magnitude of the excess charge. Cations with excess charges of 6 (S^{6+}, W^{6+}, U^{6+}) are very common and those with a charge of 7 participate in the molecules $KClO_4$ and $KMnO_4$. Osmic acid is described as $Os^{8+}O_4^{2-}$ containing a central cation with an excess charge of 8.

Anions with excess charges of more than 2 are rare and they are not stable in the free state. Even the O^{2-} ion is not known in its free state; it does not exist in aqueous solution as a hydrated particle. Fajans pointed out that it is the proximity of positive cores that stabilizes anions such as O^{2-}, N^{3-}, and C^{4-}. All anions have the electronic structure of a noble gas atom, the H^- ion has the structure of the He atom and F^-, O^{2-}, and N^{3-} ions have the structure of the Ne atom.

The simple C^{4-} ion exists in compounds containing cations with high field strengths; e.g., Be_2C, Al_4C_3, SiC, TiC, ZrC, and HfC. Carbides containing cations of weaker fields may stabilize the $(C_2)^{2-}$ ion, e.g., CaC_2, Ag_2C_2, or the $(C_3)^{4-}$ ion, e.g., Mg_2C_3. The structure of the anion determines the reaction products: the carbides of beryllium and aluminum give methane when hydrolyzed, calcium carbide gives acetylene, and a magnesium carbide of the formula Mg_2C_3 gives methylacetylene. The O^{2-} ion forms when metallic Li is oxidized, but the corresponding reaction with Cs metal does not lead to $Cs_2^+O^{2-}$. The field of the large Cs^+ ion is not sufficiently strong for stabilizing an O^{2-} ion. As a result, more complex ions such as $(O_2)^{2-}$ are formed. Cs_2O can be prepared by an indirect method (oxidation of Cs dissolved in liquid NH_3) but it decomposes into the peroxide Cs_2O_2 and metallic cesium at 200°C.

This stabilization of anions with a charge greater than 1 by an environment of cations is of importance for the understanding of surface chemical phenomena and of certain electronic properties of solids.

Later, in our discussion of the sulfide and related glasses we will see that vitreous selenides, tellurides, etc., have a certain electronic conductivity. This conductivity is the result of the inherent instability of a particle such as Se^{2-} that has a twofold negative charge. This type of anion has a tendency to dissociate according to

$$Se^{2-} \rightarrow Se^- + e^-$$

thus providing electrons that can carry a current when an external electrical field is applied.

Spectroscopy has supplied us with detailed information concerning the electronic structure of atoms. We have to be cautious when applying this information to the structure of the atoms in the solid state because one can never know how much it is changed by the environment. The Stark effect reveals the distortion of the electronic orbits in an external electrical field which must be considered weak when compared with the fields to which the ions are exposed in single molecules or in solids.

1. Electronic Structures of Ions

For many of our purposes it will be sufficient to discuss the structure of atoms on the basis of the classical model which was developed by N. Bohr and Lord Rutherford. The atom can be pictured as a solar system with the positive nucleus as the sun and the electrons as the planets. The latter are then treated as negatively-charged particles moving in spherical or elliptical orbits. Each orbit can be described by its major and minor axis. Groups of electrons which are characterized by similar binding energy are thought to move in orbits which have the same principal quantum number; i.e., the same length of the major axis. As the size of the minor axis approaches that of the major axis the orbit becomes more spherical and the electron does not come as close to the nucleus as in those orbits that have a high ellipticity. This model is sufficient for explaining the basic facts of excitation, fluorescence, and ionization, but refinements are needed in order to account for the structures of the spectra and for the magnetic properties of atoms and ions.

The modern wave mechanical approach replaces the picture of particles moving in orbits by statistical concepts. The Bohr orbits are described as regions in which the probability of finding an electron is high. In gaseous atoms these energy levels in which the "electron occupancy" is high are discrete in character, as can be seen from their line spectra. The relative positions of the spectral lines make it possible to derive the distribution and the energy levels of the electrons in an atom. The energy levels are designated K, L, M, etc. as they become farther removed from the nucleus.

The application of the Pauli exclusion principle to the electronic structure of atoms reveals that the number of electrons participating in the K, L, M, etc., levels cannot exceed 2, 8, 18, 32, etc.

Using the Pauli exclusion principle and the possible electron distribution in the different shells (maximum numbers), one can build up the atoms of the various elements by starting with the hydrogen atom having a nuclear charge Z equal to 1 and adding both nuclear charges and electrons. The hydrogen atom has one electron in the K shell: $1s^1$. Increasing the nuclear charge by one and adding one electron to the lowest available level we obtain the helium atom with two electrons in the K shell: $1s^2$. Two is the maximum number of electrons that can participate in the lowest energy level. As a result, the increase of the nuclear charge from two to three and the addition of a third electron leads to the configuration: Li, $Z = 3$, $1s^2 2s^1$. In this configuration the new electron occupies the L shell. In this fashion we can continue to build up the elements until we reach argon $Z = 18$ which has the configuration: Ar, $Z = 18$, $1s^2$, $2s^2$, $2p^6$, $3s^2$, $3p^6$. Potassium, $Z = 19$, and calcium, $Z = 20$, have the argon configuration and, in addition, one and two electrons, respectively, in the N shell: $4s^1$ and $4s^2$.

The next elements, beginning with scandium, $Z = 21$, however, do not follow this simple pattern. Instead of increasing the number of electrons in the N shell, they fill up the M shell as can be seen from the electron configuration of the atoms, scandium, titanium and vanadium.

Ca,	$Z = 20$	$1s^2$	$2s^2$	$2p^6$	$3s^2$	$3p^6$	—	$4s^2$
Sc,	$Z = 21$	$1s^2$	$2s^2$	$2p^6$	$3s^2$	$3p^6$	$3d^1$	$4s^2$
Ti,	$Z = 22$	$1s^2$	$2s^2$	$2p^6$	$3s^2$	$3p^6$	$3d^2$	$4s^2$
V,	$Z = 23$	$1s^2$	$2s^2$	$2p^6$	$3s^2$	$3p^6$	$3d^3$	$4s^2$

Elements with incomplete inner shells are of particular interest to the glass technologist because they are the ones used for producing colored glasses. The atoms $Z = 21$–28, i.e., from scandium to nickel, called "transition elements", fill up the M shell until it has reached its maximum number, 18, for copper. Four such series of transition elements with incomplete levels are known, the first beginning with scandium, the second with yttrium, the third with lanthanum, and the fourth with actinium. All transition elements are metals.

Our present knowledge of the electronic structures of atoms and of ions is derived primarily from spectroscopic data and from magnetic measurements.

With the exception of the helium atom, the atoms of the rare or noble gases, namely, neon, argon, krypton, xenon, and radon, have an outer electronic configuration of 8. G. N. Lewis and W. Kossel pointed out the tendency of the neighboring elements to assume this electron configuration by either accepting additional electrons or by donating some of their own electrons. The following ions have the electronic structures of the neon atom: ten electrons, two in the *K* and eight in the *L* shell:

Ion	O^{2-}	F^-	Ne	Na^+	Mg^{2+}	Al^{3+}	Si^{4+}	P^{5+}	S^{6+}	Cl^{7+}
Atomic number	8	9	10	11	12	13	14	15	16	17

Their excess charges represent the difference between their nuclear charges (atomic number) and the tenfold negative charge of the electron cloud of the neon atom.

Chlorine and sulfur atoms may assume neon structure by donating seven and six electrons, respectively. However, they also may assume the electronic structure of the argon atom (2,8,8) by accepting one and two electrons, respectively, and forming the anions Cl^- and S^{2-}.

The ions which have eight outer electrons are particularly stable. The composition of terrestrial matter such as water, sand, limestone, clay minerals, consists largely of ions which have the electronic configuration of He, Ne, Ar, and Kr. These ions are called "ions of the noble gas-type." In contrast to the ions of the transition elements, which can produce colored glasses, the noble gas-type ions in glasses as well as in their hydrated state are colorless. The "colorless" ions, the noble gases and their electron groups are listed in Table II.

Another group of ions, which also forms colorless hydrates, can form colored compounds. This group has eighteen electrons in the outermost shell:

Electron groups	Cations			
2,8,18	Cu^+	Zn^{2+}	Ga^{3+}	Ge^{4+}
2,8,18,18	Ag^+	Cd^{2+}	In^{3+}	Sn^{4+}
2,8,18,32,18	Au^+	Hg^{2+}	Tl^{3+}	Pb^{4+}

Silicate glasses containing Cd^{2+} ions are colorless, but if they also contain S^{2-} and Se^{2-} ions, colors can be produced by the preferential interaction of the Cd^{2+} ions with these highly polarizable anions (selenium ruby).

Most of the information concerning the electronic structure of atoms and ions is based on the interaction of energy with matter. The absorption of a quantum of energy leads to an "excited state" of an atom. This energy can be released in the form of radiation when the atom goes from its excited state back to its ground state.

TABLE II

Noble Gases and Their Electron Groups

Electron groups	Anions				Atoms	Cations			
2				H^-	He	Li^+	Be^{2+}	B^{3+}	C^{4+}
2,8	C^{4-}	N^{3-}	O^{2-}	F^-	Ne	Na^+	Mg^{2+}	Al^{3+}	Si^{4+}
2,8,8	Si^{4-}	P^{3-}	S^{2-}	Cl^-	A	K^+	Ca^{2+}	Sc^{3+}	Ti^{4+}
2,8,18,8	Ge^{4-}	As^{3-}	Se^{2-}	Br^-	Kr	Rb^+	Sr^{2+}	Y^{3+}	Zr^{4+}
2,8,18,18,8	Sn^{4-}	Sb^{3-}	Te^{2-}	I^-	Xe	Cs^+	Ba^{2+}	La^{3+}	
2,8,18,32,18,8	Pb^{4-}	Bi^{3-}			Rn		Ra^{2+}	Ac^{3+}	Th^{4+}

However, if the energy which is absorbed by an atom or molecule surpasses a certain critical value, an electron, the one which is most weakly bound, is completely removed from the sphere of influence of the nucleus. The energy which is necessary to accomplish the removal of an electron from an atom in its ground state is called the "first ionization potential" of this element. Further absorption of energy may remove a second electron and in this case one speaks of the "second ionization potential," etc.

These ionization potentials can be measured with great accuracy. They are characteristic for the element, but, as they refer to the free gaseous atoms and ions, their quantitative interpretation with respect to their meaning in solid state chemistry is difficult. Nevertheless, we will refer to these values because in a semiquantitative fashion they indicate the tendency of an ion to attract electrons.

The fact that a silver ion, as compared with a sodium ion, exerts a stronger deforming influence upon the electron clouds of surrounding anions is the result of the different electronic structures of these two ions. This difference expresses itself in the ionization potential of the two elements. The energy of 7.5 e.v. (electron volts) is required for removing the most loosely bound electron from a silver atom, but a considerably lower energy, namely, 5.1 e.v., is sufficient to accomplish the same with a sodium atom. In the same way, 16.6 e.v. are sufficient to remove the first two electrons from a Sr atom, but 22.3 e.v. are required to accomplish the same for Pb atoms. In Table III the total ionization potentials of some elements are given in electron volts. For more complete information a textbook of inorganic chemistry should be consulted.

Whereas energy has to be supplied to an atom to remove an electron, energy is released when a single electron is added to a neutral, gaseous atom in its ground state. This energy is called the "electron affinity" of the element. The electron affinities of some elements are listed in Table IV. These values cannot be obtained with the same precision as the ionization potentials, but they have to be derived from thermodynamic data by means of Born-Haber cycle processes. The values for the electron affinities show that energy is released when the first electron is added to an

TABLE III

Total Ionization Potentials of Some Elements

Element	Ion	Ionization potential, e.v.
H	H^{+}	13.59
Li	Li^{+}	5.39
Na	Na^{+}	5.13
K	K^{+}	4.33
Rb	Rb^{+}	4.17
Cs	Cs^{+}	3.89
Cu	Cu^{+}	7.72
Ag	Ag^{+}	7.57
Au	Au^{+}	9.22
Hg	Hg^{+}	10.43
Be	Be^{2+}	27.52
Mg	Mg^{2+}	22.67
Ca	Ca^{2+}	17.98
Sr	Sr^{2+}	16.67
Ba	Ba^{2+}	15.16
Mn	Mn^{2+}	23.13
Fe	Fe^{2+}	24.05
Co	Co^{2+}	25.16
Ni	Ni^{2+}	25.83
Cu	Cu^{2+}	28.06
Zn	Zn^{2+}	27.28
Cd	Cd^{2+}	25.83
Hg	Hg^{2+}	29.08
Pb	Pb^{2+}	22.37
B	B^{3+}	71.36
Al	Al^{3+}	53.24
Ga	Ga^{3+}	57.03
C	C^{4+}	147.98
Si	Si^{4+}	103.08
Ge	Ge^{4+}	103.56

TABLE IV

Electron Affinities of Some Elements

Element	Addition of electrons	Electron affinity	
		kcal.	e.v.
F	1	98.5	4.27
Cl	1	92.5	4.01
Br	1	87.1	3.78
I	1	79.2	3.43
H	1	16.4	0.71
O	2	−168.0	−7.28
S	2	−80.0	−3.44

atom. However, the addition of two electrons as in the formation of the O^{2-} ion or the S^{2-} ion requires a considerable amount of energy, because of the coulomb repulsive forces between an O^- ion and the second electron.

The electron affinities of metals are considerably weaker than those of nonmetals. In many metals the removal of one or more electrons from the atom leads to a stable octet shell as in Na^+, K^+ or Mg^{2+}, Ca^{2+}. In others, like zinc, the removal of electrons leads to an eighteen shell. One cannot expect that the addition of one more electron to an alkali atom which is surrounded by a low electron density area causes a major change of the energy. In contrast to the alkali atom, the addition of an electron to a fluorine or a chlorine atom completes their octet shells and, thus, it is a major contribution to the lowering of the energy of the system and toward a better screening of the core. These relations are expressed in the first ionization potentials which range between 10 and 20 e.v. for nonmetals and between 4 and 10 e.v. for metals.

It should be sufficient to list the energies which are required for removing one electron from atoms, anions, and cations. However, the concept of the atom as the building unit of matter makes it necessary to introduce two parameters; the electron affinity and the ionization potential that designate the energy changes observed if an electron is added to a neutral gaseous atom and if an electron is removed, respectively. Usually we do not deal with single atoms and, like most properties, we must expect that these energies change with the environment of an atom.

Pauling (10) introduced the "electronegativity," a parameter referring to the tendency of an atom within a molecule to attract an electron. R. A. Mulliken (14) suggested that this function should be the average of two energy terms; namely, the energy gained by this atom in adding an electron (electron affinity) and the energy required to remove an electron from the neutral atom (first ionization potential).

We mention "electronegativity" only because some scientists have used it in connection with their search for a criterium of glass formation.

2. Sizes of Ions

The early attempts to correlate the crystallography or, more precisely, the symmetry and the habitus of a compound, with its chemical composition (Mitscherlich) made wide use of the molar volume. The atomic volume of the element (Lothar Meyer) contributed much to the establishment of the periodicity of properties of the elements. Today the concepts of atomic and molar volume have been replaced by the radii of the atoms or ions. Goldschmidt (4) and his school contributed much to the determination of ionic radii and their application in modern crystal chemistry. In contrast to the classical crystal chemistry, the modern version can operate with the sizes and the polarizabilities of the particles and exact information can be had about their arrangement in space. The coordination number of cations has become a major parameter. At the present time, the geometry of the glass structure is being overemphasized because the last few decades have witnessed a rapid development of methods which permit the determination of the geometry of crystals and single molecules with high precision. In addition, it is easier to visualize the geometrical arrangements of atoms in space than to picture their mutual interactions and the resulting chemical binding forces between them.

It is this overemphasis on the geometrical aspects which delayed our progress in the development of a reasonable picture of the constitution of glasses. The argument about the coordination number of boron is a typical example of an undue emphasis on the geometrical aspects at the expense of a true evaluation of the role played by forces.

In spite of the fact that the concept of an ionic size will remain only an approximation, it has become extremely useful. We will use it extensively, always keeping in mind its limitations. The primary difficulty arises from the lack of a method for determining the dimensions of a single atom or ion. Many scienticts who use the ionic description of glasses are not aware of the fact that one depends entirely on the evaluation of internuclear distances in order to obtain the size of an ion. The O^{2-} ion has the same number of electrons as the F^- ion and both have the structure of the neon atom, but their nuclei have lower positive charges than the neon atom. Under these conditions one would expect the volume of the electron cloud to expand as the nuclear charge decreases; i.e., from Ne^0 to F^- and O^{2-}. Consulting the tables of accepted values of atomic and ionic radii we find the following values:

$$Ne^0 = 1.60 \text{ A.} \qquad F^- = 1.33 \text{ A.} \qquad O^{2-} = 1.32 \text{ A.}$$

The neon atom is described as a larger particle than the two anions and even among the F^- and O^{2-} ions the trend is opposite to what one would expect. In measuring the radii of the anions we refer to some internuclear distances and the latter are functions of the attractive and repulsive forces acting between the particles. A given cation will be attracted more strongly by the doubly charged O^{2-} ion than by the singly charged F^- ion. Thus, our measurements of the internuclear distances cation-F^- and cation-O^{2-} will not reflect the electron density distribution around the nuclei of the free ions but will include their deformation during the interaction with the cation. As a result, this interaction is superimposed over the trend of neon gas-like particles to become smaller with increasing nuclear charge and the volume derived from internuclear distances goes through a maximum with the uncharged neon atom.

In using the size of ions we should always be aware of the fact that they vary with the environment. Goldschmidt was fully aware of the shortcomings of the concept of ionic sizes and he suggested corrections for the influence of the environment. The cation-anion distance increases with increasing coordination number and some cations, e.g., Al^{3+} ions, occur both in tetrahedral and octahedral coordination.

Pauling (10) derived a formula which allows one to correct internuclear distances of elements which occur in different valence states. His formula has proved very helpful for elements of which the univalent radius is known, and from which one wants to extrapolate to a more dissociate atom.

A few radii of atoms, cores, and anions of elements with low atomic number are given in Table V. They illustrate the electron density distribution in these elements. The radii of atoms and ions reveal that for the alkali atoms the single valence electron occupies nearly three quarters of the total volume.

As far as noble gas-like ions are concerned, one can assume that in a highly symmetrical lattice they behave approximately like rigid spheres. On this basis, Goldschmidt and his school have determined a number of ionic radii by measuring the shortest distances between ions in a large number of compounds. Pauling, too, calculated a number of ionic radii from interionic distances. There are other ways to calculate the size of a simple ion such as the H^- ion. The theoretical value, however, is much higher than the one determined by measuring the internuclear distance in a metal hydride such as LiH. One must expect that the interaction between singly charged ions, e.g., Na^+F^-, is considerably less than that between doubly charged ions, e.g., $Mg^{2+}O^{2-}$, even if both compounds have the same crystal structure.

The fact that the O^{2-} ion seems to be of the same size or even slightly smaller than the F^- ion is the result of a stronger mutual interaction between the doubly charged Mg^{2+} and O^{2-} ions as compared with that between the singly charged Na^+ and F^- ions. The magnitude of this interaction is not constant for two

TABLE V

Sizes of Some Atoms and Ions (Radii in Angstroms, A.)

Atom		Cation		Anion	
Li	1.22	Li^+	0.78		
Na	1.57	Na^+	0.98		
K	2.02	K^+	1.33		
Be	0.89	Be^{2+}	0.34		
Mg	1.36	Mg^{2+}	0.78		
B	0.80	B^{3+}	0.20		
Al	1.25	Al^{3+}	0.57		
C	0.77	C^{4+}	0.20	C^{4-}	2.6
Si	1.17	Si^{4+}	0.39	Si^{4-}	2.7
P	1.10	P^{5+}	0.34	P^{3-}	2.1
O	0.74	O^{6+}	0.09	O^{2-}	1.3
S	1.04	S^{6+}	0.34	S^{2-}	1.7
F	0.72	F^{7+}	0.07	F^-	1.3
Cl	0.99	Cl^{7+}	0.26	Cl^-	1.8

ions. In the different forms of silica one finds an Si-O distance equal to 1.61 A. Going to sodium silicate, Na_2SiO_3, one finds two Si-O distances; namely, 1.57 A. for Si-O-Na and 1.68 A. for Si-O-Si groups.

In the same way the Al-O distance, which is 1.90 A. in Al_2O_3, decreases to 1.78 A. in barium aluminate and becomes as small as 1.66 A. in potassium aluminate, $K_2Al_2O_4$.

In the TlF crystal, the Tl^+ ion is surrounded by six F^- ions which, in pairs, have the distances, 2.59, 2.75, and 3.04A. The bond energy or field strength derived from the charge alone for this asymmetrical system cannot be considered in the same manner as the noble gas-like Rb^+ in the more symmetrical RbF crystal. Similarly, in PbO, the Pb^{2+} ion is surrounded by eight O^{2-} ions which form the corners of a tetragonal prism, height 4.99 A., width 2.79 A. The cation Pb^{2+} does not occupy the center of this tetragonal prism but is closer to one group of four oxygens (2.30 A.) than to the other group of oxygens (4.30 A.). This asymmetrical position is the result of the deformation of the Pb^{2+} ion, which not only has an excess charge of 2 but, in addition, has a dipole: $[Pb^{4+}(e_2^-)]^{2+}$. Therefore, we cannot expect that the bond energy or field strength of the Pb^{2+} in PbO be comparable with that of Sr^{2+} in the symmetrical SrO, although the ions are of similar size and have identical charge. In aqueous systems and in glasses the two ions resemble one another more closely: Sr^{2+} and Pb^{2+} ions have the same entropy of hydration and both are colorless. Replacing Sr^{2+} ions by Pb^{2+} ions in a sodium strontium silicate glass does not change its expansivity at ordinary temperature.

Quantum mechanics teaches that no line that will include all the electrons of an atom can be drawn around the nucleus of the atom. No methods are available which will permit us to measure the radii of single ions. The values are derived from internuclear distances of compounds and one has to realize their limitations.

The fallacy of the constancy of the ionic size will be illustrated by comparing the internuclear distances of the thallous halides with those of the alkali halides.

The high temperature forms of $TlClO_4$ and $RbClO_4$ have identical unit cell edge lengths; i.e., 7.7 A. This agrees with Goldschmidt's statement (4) that the Tl^+ ion has the size of the Rb^+ ion but it is more polarizable (molar refractivity (R_M) = 9.5 cc.) than the Rb^+ ion (R_M = 6.0 cc.).

At −190°C both RbCl and TlCl have the crystal structure of CsCl, and measurements show that the Rb^+ to Cl^- distance and the Tl^+ to Cl^- distance are equal (3.24 A.). Similar measurements carried out on the vapor phase of each of these substances indicate that the Tl^+ to Cl^- distance is now 2.55 A. while the Rb^+ to Cl^- distance is 2.89 A. Internuclear distances were measured (A.) also for NaCl (vapor), TlI (vapor) and NaI (vapor) and a comparison of these values is as follows:

TlCl, 2.55	RbCl, 2.89	NaCl, 2.51
TlI, 2.87		NaI, 2.90

These data indicate that the Tl^+ in TlI vapor is slightly smaller than the Na^+ in the NaI vapor because of the mutual deformation which the ions undergo in single molecules of the substances. It is important to realize that this deformation is due to the asymmetry of the grouping, a condition applying to the surface of crystals and glasses as well.

3. Charges of Ions

By using the ionic description for glasses and for crystalline solids we emphasize that chemical binding forces are essentially electrical in nature. Especially when dealing with the constitution of glasses, we need not consider magnetic interactions as contributing to the binding forces.

Our treatment of glasses as arrays of ions focuses interest upon their charges because they determine the intensity of their interactions, the strengths of their fields and with it the strength of the binding forces. We learned that cations exist with charges ranging from 1 in Na^+ to 8 in Os^{8+}. We want to emphasize, however, that the highly charged particles do not exist in aqueous solutions as hydrated ions. As soon as their charges are greater than 2 their description as hydrated particles becomes highly problematic. An aqueous solution of thorium nitrate or aluminum chloride cannot be properly described as containing Th^{4+} and Al^{3+} ions in their hydrated form, e.g., as $[Th^{4+}(H_2O)_8]^{4+}$ and $[Al^{3+}(H_2O)_6]^{3+}$ complexes. The interaction of these ions with water goes beyond a mere solvation process.

An Si^{4+} ion in water will repel protons from its environment and form neutral orthosilicic acid molecules $Si(OH)_4$ or charged particles such as $Si(OH_6)^{2-}$ anions. We will discuss this important aspect of the charges of cations in more detail in a later chapter dealing with the acidity-basicity concept.

We mentioned earlier that a single atom can combine with only one electron in an exothermic reaction. Hence, no anion with a charge greater than one is stable in the gaseous state. In connection with the constitution of glasses we have no opportunity to extend our treatment to anions with a charge greater than 2 because anions with a charge greater than 2 do not participate in glasses.

The charge of an ion is usually characterized by the expression "ze" in which e is the elementary charge ($e = 4.80 \times 20^{-10}$ electrostatic units), and z is numerically identical with the valence of an element. The tetravalent silicon atom is described in our structures as the Si^{4+} ion or the core of silicon that has the electron configuration of the neon but a fourfold positive excess charge. In some cases we will have to deviate from this description. We mentioned earlier that the shape of the SO_2 molecule would be linear if it would contain the S^{4+} ion as the cation. The O-S-O bond angle reveals that we have to describe the molecule SO_2 as an S^{6+} core which is screened by two O^{2-} ions and one pair of electrons. The molecules SO_3 and SO_2 have the same O-S-O bond angle.

O^{2-} $(e^-)_2$

S^{6+} S^{6+}

O^{2-} O^{2-} O^{2-} O^{2-}

For this reason, we give the sulfur atom in SO_2 a charge of plus 6, which gives it the electronic structure of the neon atom, and combine it with an electron pair rather than describe the "tetravalent" sulfur as an S^{4+} ion. We can describe the constitution of a lead silicate glass as containing Pb^{2+} ions in an environment of O^{2-} ions but we prefer to speak of $[Pb^{4+}(e^-)_2]^{2+}$ groups if we refer to surface properties of lead glasses or to their "solvent power" for noble metals.

Goldschmidt emphasized the importance of the absolute charge of the ions for the reactivity of compounds after van't Hoff had found that the rates of chemical reactions depended upon the valencies of the elements involved. The high solubility and chemical reactivity of the halides of the alkalies stands in striking contrast to the insolubility and the inertness of the oxides of silicon, titanium and zirconium. This relation between valence and solubility and reactivity was used by Goldschmidt for making "model structures," i.e., chemical compounds which have different "valence sums" but the same anion to cation ratios. Their ions have the same sizes and similar electron configurations but different charges. CaF_2 and ThO_2 have the same structures, but the "weak model" CaF_2 with a valence sum of $(1 \times 2) + (2 \times 1) = 4$ has a much lower melting point and a greater chemical reactivity than ThO_2, the valence sum of which is $(1 \times 4) + (2 \times 2) = 8$. Beryllium fluoride, BeF_2, is the weak model of SiO_2. We will return to this interesting subject when we discuss fluoride glasses. BeF_2 not only forms a low melting glass itself but, like SiO_2, it can be used as a basis for complex fluoride glasses analogous to complex silicate glasses.

The valence, z, of an element multiplied with the elementary charge, e, has been used widely by Goldschmidt for interpreting the electrostatic interaction of ions. The coulombic energy of a pair of ions having the "valencies" z_1 and z_2 separated by the distance, a, is given by the following expression:

$$\frac{(z_1 e)(z_2 e)}{a}$$

The charge, ze, of an ion is frequently combined with its radius, r, and expressions such as ze/r (electrical potential of the ion) and ze/r^2 (field strength of the ion) have been used for correlating properties of compounds with the electrical interaction of their component ions.

The effect which the electrical field of an ion has upon its mobility in aqueous solutions, upon its hydration, and upon its interaction with neutral molecules is well appreciated. When W. A. Weyl (15) approached the structure of glasses on the basis of solutions (solvation theory) he pointed out that the strong catalytic effect of the lithium oxide upon crystallization or phase transformations of silicates might be connected with its small size and relatively strong electrical field that is the highest among all alkalies. When K. Endell and H. Hellbrügge(16) studied the effect of the different alkalies upon the viscosity of silicates they were guided in their interpretation of the viscosity by this comment on the field strength of the alkalies.

The electrical potential and the field strength of ions were the first parameters used in order to convert the molecular approach to the constitution of glasses, which was based on the dissociation and association of molecules, into one that considered electrical forces between the ultimate particles. When Weyl referred to the field strength of the Li^+ ion in silicates he used this factor in the same way as he used the dipole moment or organic compounds in order to explain analogous catalytic effects in organic melts. In his studies of nucleation rates G. Tammann (1*a*) found that the presence of certain molecules, e.g., benzamide, catalyzed nucleation rates in supercooled melts or organic substances.

Not only the alkalies but also the alkaline earth oxides behave very differently in silica systems. When B. E. Warren and A. G. Pincus (17) explained the liquid immiscibility in the system CaO–SiO_2 on geometrical grounds they had to account for the drastic differences between the alkaline earth oxides. MgO and CaO show large gaps in their miscibilities with silica, whereas BaO seemed to be completely miscible. In order to correlate these differences with the nature of the alkaline earth oxides, Warren and Pincus used the electrical potentials of the ions. With increasing value of ze/r from the Ba^{2+} ion to the Mg^{2+} ion the width of the miscibility gap increased.

A. Dietzel (18) used the electrical fields of cations extensively, and he made the first systematic effort to use the field strength of cations in order to explain the fundamental relations in oxide systems. He asked himself such questions as: Which oxides will combine chemically and form a stable compound? Which oxides form a homogeneous liquid which can be supercooled to a glass? What determines the number of stable compounds that occur in a certain binary or ternary system which is of interest to the glass technologist?

It was not possible at this time to give satisfactory answers to all of these questions, but Dietzel was the first one to ask them and he deserves credit for his efforts to bring order into the phase relations between oxides. His thinking was centered around the field strength of the cations, but he realized that parameters such as z/r or z/r^2 needed refinements. Rather than using a factor that would characterize the electrical field of a free gaseous ion, Dietzel turned to the interaction between cations and the anions of their first coordination spheres. This interaction depended upon the cation to anion distance and the latter increases with increasing coordination number of the cation. In order to take this variable into consideration Dietzel selected the parameter z/a^2, i.e., the field strength of a cation with the charge, z, at the distance, a, in which a was defined as the internuclear distance between cation and anion. (See Table VI.) The use of the field strength of the cation at the distance of the anion made it possible for Dietzel to compare Al^{3+} ions in different states of coordination or compare the behavior of series of cations in oxide systems with those in halide systems.

Comparing the field strengths of different cations, Dietzel discovered that their ability to react chemically depended largely on the value $\Delta z/a^2$, the difference between their respective field strengths.

If the value of $\Delta z/a^2$ was large, as for example for the couple SiO_2 and K_2O or the couple SiO_2 and BaO, the number of compounds that are formed in these two binary systems is considerably greater than for a system characterized by a small $\Delta z/a^2$ value, e.g., SiO_2–Li_2O and SiO_2–BeO.

In order to apply this relation to cations of the non-noble gas type Dietzel (18) had to introduce an empirical factor that would

TABLE VI

Arrangement of Cations According to Their Field Strength (18)

Ion	Radius, A.	Coordination number	Cation-oxygen distance, a	Electron potential, z/r	Field strength, z/a^2
P^{5+}	0.34	4	1.55	15.0	2.10
Si^{4+}	0.39	4	1.60	10.0	1.57
B^{3+}	0.20	3	1.36	15.0	1.63
		4	1.50	15.0	1.34
Ti^{4+}	0.64	6	1.96	6.3	1.04
Al^{3+}	0.57	4	1.77	5.3	0.96
		6	1.89	5.3	0.84
Be^{2+}	0.34	4	1.53	5.9	0.86
Zr^{4+}	0.87	8	2.28	4.6	0.77
Mg^{2+}	0.78	6	2.10	2.6	0.45
Ca^{2+}	1.06	6	2.38	1.8	0.33
S^{92+}	1.27	6	2.59	1.6	0.28
Ba^{2+}	1.43	6	2.75	1.4	0.24
Li^{+}	0.78	6	2.10	1.3	0.23
Na^{+}	0.98	6	2.30	1.0	0.19
K^{+}	1.33	6	2.65	0.7	0.13

increase this apparent interaction beyond that value which was derived on purely geometrical grounds.

4. Polarization Properties of Ions

Quantum mechanics teaches that atoms and ions which have an octet shell, or an 18-shell, have a charge distribution with spherical symmetry. Electrostatic principles reveal that the electrical field of a charged sphere is the same as that of a point located in the center of the sphere in which the charge of the sphere is located. It should be possible, therefore, to calculate the interactions of ions; e.g., the lattice energies of simple crystals on the basis of a lattice consisting of points with excess charges. We know that this is not the case and that identical geometrical structures containing singly charged ions, e.g., NaCl and AgCl, have very different lattice energies; namely, 214 kcal. for AgCl and 180 kcal. for NaCl.

This must mean that ions with spherical electrical symmetry in the gaseous state change their charge distribution in condensed systems, even in very symmetrical structural systems such as NaCl and AgCl.

If ions were rigid spheres which could be characterized by their sizes and charges, all crystalline compounds of the composition A^+B^- would have a highly symmetrical structure which would depend only upon the radius ratio. A compound of this type would have either the structure of ZnS (fourfold coordination), of NaCl (sixfold coordination), or of CsCl (eightfold coordination). We know that this is not the case: Tl^+F^-, for example, has a lower symmetry.

This raises an important question: Why and how much do the shapes of ions deviate from those of spheres?

The first part of the question is easily answered. In compounds the ions are exposed to the electrical fields of other ions and an electrical field induces a dipole in an atom, ion, or molecule regardless of whether the particle as a whole has an electrical excess charge. As all atoms contain a positive core and a negative shell of electrons, all atoms develop a dipole when brought into an electrical field. The dipole interaction modifies the electron distribution and causes deviations from spherical symmetry.

The second part of the question is much more difficult and there is no simple answer to it. Theoretical approaches to this problem are restricted to systems which are oversimplified with respect to the behavior of the atoms and the symmetry of the electrical field so that they cannot give us much information on the actual conditions in a crystal. For this reason, we depend upon measuring and interpreting the effects.

For a capacitor consisting of two parallel plates separated by a certain distance and placed in a vacuum the capacitance, C_o, is given by the geometry of the system; i.e., the sizes of the plates and their distance apart. Bringing matter between the plates causes the capacitance to increase by a factor, D, which depends upon the nature of the substance which now fills the space between the plates. This increase of the capacitance is the result of a displacement of the positive charges with respect to the negative charges. The displacement may be the result of an orientation of polar molecules. The liquid or the solid which increases the capacitance by the factor D

$$C = C_o \cdot D$$

is called a "dielectric" and the constant D is called the dielectric constant of the medium. As one can visualize there are many ways in which a complex system such as glass or an organic liquid can lower the original electrical field E_o between the two plates by a displacement of charges. The field is reduced to E and

$$E = E_o/D$$

In order to lower the electrical field the dielectric has to be polarized and one can describe its state of polarization by the dipole moment which is induced per unit volume. The induced dipole moment, m, of an atom or a molecule is proportional to the local field, F, that surrounds the particle:

$$m = \alpha \cdot F$$

and one refers to the proportionality constant, α, as the polarizability of the particle.

Let us assume the particle is a simple atom. In order to simplify matter further we describe the atom as consisting of a nucleus which has the positive excess charge, ze, surrounded by a sphere of the radius, r, which has the same charge as the nucleus only with opposite sign and the charge is equally distributed over the volume of the sphere. Exposing this atom to the electrical field, F, causes a displacement of the positive nucleus from the center of the sphere by a distance, x. This means that now the neutral atom has developed a dipole moment, m, because the positive and the negative charges are displaced, they are separated by the distance, x. The distance x is the result of the external field F and the restoring force exercised by the homogeneous spherical cloud of electrons with the charge ze. Equilibrium is reached when the system meets the condition

$$ze \cdot F = (ze)^2 x / r^3$$

The atom is still electrically neutral but it has developed a dipole, m, which is proportional to the external field, F.

$$m = zex = r^3 F$$

According to the equation

$$m = \alpha F$$

we find that for our oversimplified atom the polarizability assumes the dimensions of a volume. The polarizability of the atom is proportional to its size.

The atomic radii are of the order of 10^{-8} cm. which means that the polarizability is of the order of 10^{-24} cm^3.

An electrical field of the order of 100–1000 v./cm. produces a displacement, x, of the nucleus which is very small, approximately 10^{-15} to 10^{-16} cm., when compared with the dimensions of the atom, 10^{-8} cm.

Going beyond this first approximation becomes exceedingly difficult. Firstly, the electron cloud is not homogeneous and does not remain spherical in an electrical field. Secondly, the mutual interaction of atoms or ions involves asymmetrical electrical fields. It is very difficult to estimate the value of F, the local field to which the atom is exposed. Finally, the contribution of the electrons to the polarizability depends upon the electronic structure of the atom, the outer electrons being by far the most important contributors.

For obtaining values of the polarizabilities of ions we cannot depend upon calculations but we have to measure the polarizability. Instead of bringing the ion or atom into a uniform electrical field we measure its response to light. The interaction of light and matter can be treated as the exposure of a molecule or a solid to an oscillating electrical field. The high frequency of its oscillation makes it impossible for the molecules to follow the electrical vector of light and to orient themselves. The inertia of the molecules is too great for their orientation so that only the electronic polarization, i.e., the displacement of electrons with respect to the positive cores, is responsible for the polarization produced by light. Clausius and Mosotti, in 1879, showed that the expression,

$$(D - 1)/(D + 2)$$

is a constant for a dielectric that is rather independent of its density and its temperature. Lorentz and Lorenz, in 1880, combined this expression with one found by Maxwell, namely, that the dielectric constant (D) of a substance equals the square of the index of refraction (n) (for long wavelength) and thus obtained an expression for the molar refractivity R_M of a substance

$$R_M = \frac{n^2 - 1}{n^2 + 2} \cdot \frac{M}{d} = \frac{4}{3} \pi N \alpha$$

The Lorentz-Lorenz equation establishes a relationship between the refractive index (n) of a substance for long wavelengths, the number of particles per mole (N = Avogadro's number), the molecular weight (M) and the density (d) of this substance. This relation is independent of its state of aggregation. The Lorentz-Lorenz equation gives us the polarizability, i.e., the magnitude of the response of the electrons to an electrical field. The molar refractivity R_M has the dimension of a volume (cm^3).

CHAPTER III

MUTUAL INTERACTION OF IONS

Our description of the structure of solids is based on those concepts of the chemical binding forces which were developed by Fajans and his school. The work of Fajans (7) which led to his "quanticule theory" started as early as 1920 when he and H. Grimm proved that ions do not possess a constant sphere of action but that their "sizes" must be influenced by their environment. In 1920, in collaboration with K. F. Herzfeld, Fajans reached the conclusion that the deviations of interionic distances from additivity for the crystalline alkali halides depended upon the ratio of the sizes of anion:cation.

In 1923 the concept of the mutual interaction of ions and the deformation of their electron clouds was used for explaining lattice distances and lattice energies, as well as volatility, solubility, and color of simple inorganic substances. In the following year, 1924, Fajans (7) published a series of papers with G. Joos in which the deviations from additivity of the Lorentz-Lorenz refraction, i.e., the loosening and tightening of the electron clouds of ions, was interpreted as a change in chemical binding forces. In many cases these changes in the chemical binding forces were found to be continuous, for example, when a less polarizable anion was replaced by a more polarizable one; e.g., the color deepens for the cupric halides in the following order:

$$Cu^{2+}\,F_2^- \rightarrow Cu^{2+}\,Cl_2^- \rightarrow Cu^{2+}\,Br_2^-$$

In some cases the mutual interaction led to a discontinuous change of the quantum state, e.g., the compound $Cu^{2+}I_2^-$ decomposes into Cu^+I^- and elemental iodine.

In the years following, this concept of the nature of chemical binding forces was supported by measurements of the refractivity of gases and solutions. New fundamental data were obtained that form the basis of our present concept of the mutual interactions of ions. For example, the addition of one electron to an iodine atom

$$I + e^- = I^-$$

increases the refraction from 12.4 cm^3 to 18.1 cm^3. This means that the eighth valence electron, so to speak, contributes one third of the refraction of all electrons of the I^- ion. This type of information provides valuable insight into the happenings during chemical reactions and leads to a better understanding of chemistry.

On this basis the phenomenon of hydrogen bonding was explored. It has been found that the molar refractivity of acetic acid increases by 1.5% when the dimers dissociate into monomer molecules. In our terminology this means that the protons are better screened in acetic acid molecules when they can surround themselves by two O^{2-} ions rather than remain within the electron cloud of a single O^{2-} ion, that of one COOH group.

A necessary conclusion of the Fajans concept of chemical binding was introduced in 1941: one-sided polarization. This concept was proven by comparing internuclear distances in the vapor molecules of alkali and thallous halides. This phenomenon is particularly important for surface chemistry because the asymmetry of the environment is a feature typical for all surfaces. The understanding of surface chemistry requires the consideration of "one-sided polarization."

Fajans and N. Bauer (13) proved in 1942 that in contrast to other cations the protons can penetrate into the electronic systems of anions. On this basis they explained the polarizabilities and the charge distribution of the hydrogen halide molecules. They also gave a simple and logical explanation for the nonexistence of the FO_4^- and the BrO_4^- anion as compared with the relatively stable ClO_4^- and IO_4^- groups. Cores of very small size and high field strength (F^{7+}) and cores which are larger but have an 18 shell (Br^{7+}) cause the deformation of the O^{2-} ions to become so strong that a change in quantization results.

The years 1941 and 1942 also mark the beginning of a systematic exploration of the nature of the covalent bond. Particularly in collaboration with T. Berlin, Fajans (7) corrected some deep-rooted misconceptions concerning the chemical bonding of the simplest of molecules; namely, the molecules O_2, N_2, and H_2. Not only could he provide a clear picture of the chemical binding forces within these molecules, but he showed why the conventional treatment of the N_2 molecule as having a triple bond and of the O_2 molecule as consisting of two O atoms which have completed an octet shell are definitely wrong.

Fajans and his associates showed that the regularities of many properties of the alkali halides break down when a large anion is polarized by a small cation or vice versa. In these compounds, one can no longer neglect the polarization energy which has to be added to the coulombic energy. In calculating the lattice energy one first considers the coulombic energy U_c of a pair of point charges z_1e and z_2e separated by the distance, a.

$$U_c = \frac{(z_1 e)(z_2 e)}{a}$$

To this energy the polarization energy has to be added if the ions are highly polarizable. Despite the distances between the ions being identical for AgCl and NaCl, the lattice energy of AgCl (214 kcal.) is greater than that of NaCl (180 kcal.).

The polarization is responsible for the deviation of ions from behaving as if they were rigid spheres. If an alkali halide molecule consisted of two rigid spheres, its dipole moment (m) could be calculated from the internuclear distance (a) which for NaCl is 2.36×10^{-8} cm. In this case one would obtain the following:

$$m_{\text{NaCl}} = e \cdot a_{\text{NaCl}} = (4.80 \times 10^{-10}) \times (2.36 \times 10^{-8} \text{ cm.}) = 11.33 \text{ Debyes}$$

The measured values of m, however, are smaller than the calculated ones. This difference is due to the mutual polarization of the ions in the vapor molecule. The ratio $m_{\text{exp.}}/m_{\text{calc.}}$ has been called the "degree of polarity" (p). The mutual polarization of the ions lowers the dipole moment of the molecule. This mutual deformation among the hydrogen halide molecules is a minimum for HF (p = 0.44) and a maximum for HI (p = 0.04). Due to the penetration of the proton deep into the electron cloud of the highly polarizable I^- ion the HI molecule has an extremely low polarity.

The value of p of the alkali halide molecules (19) varies between 0.85 and 0.54 as can be seen from the following data:

Molecule	p Value	Molecule	p Value
NaF	0.85	CsF	0.69
NaCl	0.75	CsCl	0.75
LiBr	0.59	KBr	0.76
LiI	0.54	CsI	0.76

The low value of p for LiI can be attributed to the strong polarizing effect that the small Li^+ ion (high polarizing power) exerts upon the large I^- ion.

It has become customary to deal with the complex phenomenon of mutual polarization by dividing it into two parts, the first, we may call the active part and the second, a passive part. Polarization phenomena, as a rule, are the result of mutual interactions. The only exception is the interaction of anions with protons because the proton has zero polarizability. In many cases the effect of the anions upon the cations are negligibly small so that one attributes the active part to the cations and describes their activity by their "polarizing power." The anions are then considered to play a passive role: they are "deformed" and "polarized" and the magnitude of their responses are described by their "polarizability."

This terminology is based on the fact that the proximity of a cation interferes with the spherical charge distribution of an anion by inducing a dipole moment. Sometimes it becomes advantageous to refer to the mutual polarization of two ions as their mutual "deformation." One can easily understand that the small Si^{4+} ions can deform the large O^{2-} ions but that the reverse process must be insignificant. Anions are usually larger than the cations so that it became customary to attribute the active part of the mutual polarization and deformation to the cation. This assumption, however, is not correct. Even when dealing with noble gas-type cations the anion may cause the deformation; e.g., the interaction between Cs^+ and F^- ions consists essentially of the deformation of the large Cs^+ ion by the F^- ion. When referring to systems that contain cations of the non-noble gas-type, e.g., PbF_2, the properties of the deformed cation (Pb^{2+}) may become very important, particularly for surface chemical reactions.

The polarities of the alkali halides reveal that only in extreme cases, e.g., for crystalline NaF but not for the vapor molecule, can the interaction between ions be described as due to coulombic forces or rigid particles which carry an excess electrical charge. For single molecules and for most crystals one has to take into consideration the fact that in close proximity the electron clouds of the ions become deformed and that their response to an external electrical field (light) will be altered. A proton, for example, has zero molar refractivity because it does not have electrons that can follow the alternating electrical field of light. An iodine ion has the ionic refraction of 19.2 cm^3. However, the molar refractivity of the combination of both, i.e., the neutral HI molecule, does not equal the sum of the refractivities but has a lower molecular refractivity; namely, only 13.7 cm^3. The penetration of a proton into an I^- ion tightens its electron cloud and makes it less responsive to light. The complex interaction between ions can be treated mathematically only for the simplest cases. Fajans (7) evaluated the ionic refractivities, particularly the deviations from additivity, and arrived at certain rules that describe the interactions between ions. We summarize the ideas of Fajans on this subject by presenting them in the form of rules.

1. K. Fajans' Rules

RULE I. The size of an ion is determined by its electron cloud. The electrons repel each other but they are strongly attracted by the nucleus or the positive core. For a given group of electrons, for example two K electrons and eight L electrons, the size of the particle decreases with increasing nuclear charge. As the electrons are pulled closer to the highly charged nucleus, they become "tightened," i.e., they become less responsive to an outer electrical field, as can be seen from the following particles, all of which have the configuration of the neon atom.

	O^{2-}	F^-	Ne	Na^+	Mg^{2+}	Al^{3+}	Si^{4+}	P^{5+}
Nuclear charge	8	9	10	11	12	13	14	15
Radius (A.)	1.32	1.33	1.60	0.98	0.78	0.57	0.39	0.36
Polarizability (in arbitrary units)	3.1	0.99	—	0.21	0.12	0.065	0.04	—

The polarizabilities (according to M. Born and W. Heisenberg (20)) are given in arbitrary units. They decrease from the O^{2-} ion to the Si^{4+} ion. We can treat small cores, e.g., Al^{3+}, Si^{4+}, and P^{5+}, as nonpolarizable because these cores do not contribute much to the molar refractivity of a molecule. The relative polarizabilities of these ions with neon structure reveal that the response of alkali silicate glasses to light (molar refractivities) is dominated by the polarizability of the O^{2-} ions.

RULE II. The penetration of a proton into an anion has an effect analogous to that of an increase in the nuclear charge; it tightens the electron cloud. Thus, the polarizability decreases in the following order:

$$O^{2-} > OH^- > H_2O > H_3O^+$$

The degree to which one or more protons tighten the electron cloud of an anion depends upon its polarizability; thus, it is greater for the transition of I^- into HI than for F^- into HF.

	F^-	Cl^-	Br^-	I^-
Radius of X^- (A.)	1.3	1.81	1.96	2.20
Ionic refraction (R_I) of X^- (cm.^{3})	2.5	9.0	12.6	19.2
Molar refraction (R_M) of HX (cm.^{3})	2.0	6.7	9.1	13.7
Tightening ($R_I - R_M$)	0.5	2.3	3.5	5.5

The penetration of a proton into the electron cloud of an O^{2-} ion decreases its polarizability to a similar extent as the addition of a positive charge to the nucleus. The latter would change an O^{2-} ion into an F^- ion. In many complex crystal structures OH^- ions and F^- ions can replace one another (mica, apatite, topaz). There is, however, one major difference between an F^- ion and an OH^- ion, namely, the (OH^-) ion has a permanent dipole moment and the F^- ion has not. Thus, $Ca(OH)_2$ in contrast to CaF_2 crystallizes in a layer lattice.

RULE III. The electron cloud of an anion is tightened by an increase of the nuclear charge (Rule I), by the penetration of one or more protons (Rule II), and by adjacent cations. This effect, too, is most pronounced if the anion has a high polarizability. Thus, we find that the refractivity of the free gaseous I^- ion (19.2 cm.^{3}) is reduced to 15.9 cm.^{3} in crystalline LiI. The polarizing power of cations increases with decreasing size and with increasing charge, e.g.,

Polarizing power:

$$Cs^+ < Rb^+ < K^+ < Na^+ < Li^+$$

or

$$Ba^{2+} < Sr^{2+} < Ca^{2+} < Mg^{2+} < Be^{2+}$$

and

$$Na^+ < Mg^{2+} < Al^{3+} < Si^{4+} < P^{5+} < S^{6+} < Cl^{7+}$$

For a given electronic system the molecular refractivity is increased if the nuclear charge is split or the distribution of positive charges around the system becomes less symmetrical.

Splitting of a single core into two or more cores weakens the binding of the electrons and increases the molar refractivity. (The number of cores increases from one (Ne) to four (NH_3) in direction indicated by arrows.)

$$He = 0.5 \text{ cm}^3 \qquad H_2 = 2.2 \text{ cm}^3$$

$$Ne = 1.0 \rightarrow HF = 2.0 \rightarrow H_2O = 3.7 \rightarrow NH_3 = 5.6 \text{ cm}^3$$

In the neon atom all ten electrons are neutralized and tightened by one positive core. In ammonia the same number of electrons are neutralized by four cores—that of nitrogen and three protons:

$$[N^{7+} (e_2^-)(H^+)_3]^{8+} (e^-)_8$$

This formula of NH_3 indicates the state of quantization of the electrons. Two electrons are quantized with respect to the core of nitrogen only.

RULE IV. The electron cloud of a cation is deformed by adjacent anions. However, this effect is weaker than is the reverse in most cases. For anions and cations with the same electronic structure, e.g., O^{2-} and Mg^{2+}, the anion is larger, more polarizable and, therefore, more affected than the cation. In some cations, e.g., Tl^+ and Pb^{2+}, electron pairs are not as close to the nucleus as the octet shell of the noble gas cations. In this case an anion, especially a small one, may exert a considerable influence upon the cation. The properties of CsF also reveal the polarizing effect of the F^- ion upon the large and polarizable Cs^+ ion.

RULE V. The mutual deformation of ions is minimal for ions of the noble gas-type, it is greater for cations with a complete 18 shell, and reaches its highest value for cations with an incomplete outer shell. The Sr^{2+} ion (1.27 A.) is less polarizable than the Pb^{2+} ion which has approximately the same size (1.32 A.). These two ions differ basically in crystal structures, because the Pb^{2+} ion can develop a strong dipole and should be described by the formula $[Pb^{4+}(e_2^-)]$. The vapor molecule $PbBr_2$ is not linear, like $BeCl_2$, but has a bond angle Br-Pb-Br of 86 degrees.

RULE VI. The mutual deformation for a given anion and cation is a minimum in a highly symmetrical crystal and reaches its maximum for the isolated molecule in the vapor phase.

The internuclear distances of the ions of the alkali halide molecules in the vapor phase are much smaller (15 to 28%) than those in the crystals. For KCl the distance is 2.66 A. in the vapor molecule, but 3.14 A. for the crystal. If one assumes that the ions retain in KCl the same electron density distribution as in the free state, then the electronic systems interpenetrate each other in the single molecule to a larger extent than in the crystal. If one assumes that the interpenetration is negligible and that the ions have a definite radius, then at least one of the ions in the vapor molecule must have undergone a considerable contraction of its electron cloud and must have lost its spherical symmetry. Fajans assumes that both phenomena, interpenetration and deformation, take place in the vapor molecules.

Rule VII. Rules II and III refer to the tightening effects which protons or an environment of strongly deforming cations exert upon the electron clouds of anions. The same conditions are essential for stabilizing anions with a charge greater than 1. The addition of an electron to a neutral atom is an exothermic process in which the core of the atom improves its screening. For example:

$$F + e^- = F^- + 98.5 \text{ kcal.}$$

$$Cl + e^- = Cl^- + 92.5 \text{ kcal.}$$

However, an O^{2-} ion or a S^{2-} ion is not stable in spite of its octet shell. The corresponding reactions are strongly endothermic:

$$O + 2\,e^- = O^{2-} - 168 \text{ kcal.}$$

$$S + 2\,e^- = S^{2-} - 80 \text{ kcal.}$$

The neon-like O^{2-}, N^{3-}, and C^{4-} ions are not stable in the gaseous state; they cannot be found as hydrates in aqueous solutions. Their stabilization requires either the penetration of protons into their electron clouds or an environment of fairly strong cations. This relation is of considerable importance in chemistry and some of its manifestations are as follows.

1. The oxidation of metallic lithium and sodium leads to $Li_2^+O^{2-}$and $Na_2^+O^{2-}$, respectively. The direct oxidation of potassium and cesium metal leads to peroxides because the fields of K^+ and Cs^+ are not sufficiently strong for stabilizing the O^{2-} ions. $Cs_2^+O^{2-}$, prepared by the oxidation of a solution of metallic cesium in anhydrous liquid ammonia, decomposes on heating, according to:

$$2Cs_2O \rightarrow Cs_2O_2 + 2Cs$$

into the peroxide and metallic cesium.

2. Heating BaO in air leads to the formation of BaO_2, but CaO and MgO do not give a peroxide under similar conditions.

3. Very few carbides contain the simple C^{4-} ions because the latter is stabilized only by a cation with a strong field, Al^{3+}, Si^{4+}, B^{3+}, Be^{2+}. The carbides of magnesium or calcium contain complex anions; e.g., the $(C_2)^{2-}$ ion.

4. In solids, anions with a charge greater than 1 are stabilized by an environment of cations. In SiO_2, for example, each O^{2-} ion is tightened and stabilized by two Si^{4+} ions. This, however, does not apply to surfaces and, as a result, freshly formed surfaces (by fracture, or dehydration) may give rise to some unusual chemical reactions and may show electronic conductivity.

5. As mentioned earlier, the electronic conductivities of some selenide and telluride glasses is the result of the dissociation of doubly charged anions, e.g., Se^{2-} ions, into singly charged anions and "available" electrons.

2. Effect of Temperature and Pressure

The deformation of the electron cloud of an anion by an adjacent cation increases strongly with decreasing internuclear distance. The internuclear distance depends upon the symmetry of the polyhedra and upon the coordination number. The wide variety of colors which one can obtain by introducing Ni^{2+} ions into different parent glasses is primarily the result of the coordination number of the Ni^{2+} ions which can be either 4 or 6. The coordination number in turn decreases with increasing polarizability (screening power) of the oxygens so that it decreases if Li_2O in a silicate glass is replaced by Na_2O and K_2O. The color change from yellow to grey and purple is the result of the variation of the polarizability and screening power of the O^{2-} ions, which results from this substitution.

The polarizability of an anion can be decreased by bringing the system under a hydrostatic pressure. Pressure forces the electron clouds closer to their nuclei and as a result their responses to external fields decreases and so does their screening power. Indeed, the color change from purple toward yellow can be achieved not only by the substitution of Li_2O for K_2O but also by exposing a potassium silicate glass to hydrostatic pressure and allowing it to cool under pressure from a temperature above its softening range.

Temperature has an effect opposite to that of pressure. Raising the temperature of a sodium silicate glass which contains Ni^{2+} ions as a color indicator changes the color from grey to purple which means that it affects the Ni-O interaction in the same way as the replacement of Na_2O by K_2O. Thermal expansion causes the nternuclear distances to increase: the O^{2-} ions of the glass become more polarizable.

The polarizability of the O^{2-} ions in a glass is the chief factor controling its chemical reactivity with water and acids. The volume of a glass, and with it the polarizability of the O^{2-} ions, depends upon pressure, temperature, and the past thermal treatment.

Our interest in the constitution of glasses covers a wide temperature region. The secular drift of the icepoint of a thermometer indicates a structural change that involves a low energy barrier so that it can occur at ordinary temperature. The dependence of a property upon the melting history of a glass reveals structural changes that have such a high energy barrier that they occur only in the molten glass and are slowed down noticeably if the temperature is lowered to the working range. How does the mutual interaction of ions change if the temperature is varied over a wide range? What happens to the polarizing effect which the cation exerts upon its environment and how will the polarizabilities of the anions be affected?

In order to answer these questions we begin with a crystal of MgO which has a high symmetry (NaCl-structure) and which can be heated up to its melting point without undergoing a structural change. As the crystal expands on heating, the binding forces decrease uniformly. Below the Tammann temperature we can ignore the effect of the formation of new vacancies as the temperature increases. The lattice of MgO expands and with increasing internuclear distances the mutual interaction of the ions should decrease when averaged over long times.

We can describe this change in the MgO crystal in several ways, for example:

1. On heating, the binding forces between the Mg^{2+} ions and the surrounding O^{2-} ions decrease more than one would expect from the application of Coulomb's law to the change of the Mg-O distance as derived from the thermal expansion.

2. Considering the Mg^{2+} ions as rigid spheres and only the O^{2-} ions as deformed or polarized we can say that the electron density distribution of the O^{2-} ions averaged over long times ap-

proaches spherical symmetry as the temperature increases. This change in the state of polarization decreases the Mg^{2+} to O^{2-} attractive forces and increases the O^{2-} to O^{2-} repulsive forces.

3. The tightening of the O^{2-} ions by the six Mg^{2+} ions decreases with increasing temperature. The polarizability of the O^{2-} ions or the molar refractivity of the MgO crystal increases with increasing temperature. Indeed, it has been found that in spite of its relatively high thermal expansion the refractive index of MgO increases with increasing temperature.

The fact that the increase of the internuclear distances on heating causes the electron clouds of the anions to assume a higher or more spherical symmetry manifests itself occasionally in changes of the crystal symmetry. Many substances occur in several modifications and, as a rule, those modifications that are stable at the highest temperature have also the highest symmetry.

Looking at the structure and at its change with temperature tells us only a part of what happens on heating, because structures are the result of the interactions of ions averaged over long times. Structures are described by the average positions of the ions. The mutual interaction of ions, however, must also change with the thermal vibrations even if their equilibrium positions would remain the same. Crystals expand on heating and the average internuclear distances increase, but the amplitudes of the thermal vibrations increase also. As a result, the mutual interactions between ions can become even more intense in spite of the increased equilibrium distance.

It is important to realize that structural changes are the result of changes in the mutual interactions of ions averaged over long times but that chemical reactivity and light absorption are governed by the extreme instantaneous interactions.

This may lead to an apparently paradoxical situation as can be seen from the behavior of a cadmium sulfide glass on heating and cooling. On heating such a glass we observe that its yellow color changes into orange and red. This color change is instantaneous and reversible. It is the result of a more intense instantaneous interaction between the Cd^{2+} and S^{2-} ions that occurs when the amplitude of the thermal vibrations increase. The same color change can be produced by replacing some of the S^{2-} ions by the more polarizable Se^{2-} ions (selenium ruby). Light absorption and other electronic responses (electron transfer) are instantaneous and are controlled by the maximum mutual deformation of the ions. The maximum mutual deformation of ions increases with increasing temperature in spite of the increase of the equilibrium distance (volume) which decreases the average deformation.

In order to produce a cadmium sulfide glass one has to cool it slowly or reheat it. Why does a CdS- glass strike? At high temperature the mutual interaction between Cd^{2+} and S^{2-} ions is not sufficient to cause a preferential grouping of S^{2-} ions around the Cd^{2+} ions. The structure of the hot glass is more random and gives the impression that the Cd-S interaction decreases with increasing temperature; i.e., just the opposite of that revealed by the color change.

CHAPTER IV

DISPROPORTIONATION OF THE BINDING FORCES

Our description of the structures of substances, crystals and glasses will be based on Fajans' concept of chemical binding discussed in the preceding chapters. This concept brings out the electrical nature of chemical binding, it does not require the hybridization of structures which have no reality, or the mixing of two incompatible descriptions of chemical binding, such as the ionic and the covalent bond.

It was not merely a matter of terminology and of a better pictorial interpretation of the binding forces that made us select this approach but we found that it can open new avenues to the solution of problems that could not be tackled in the past.

This chapter deals with the disproportionation of binding forces or the change of the average bond strength of a solid into two groups of forces, some weaker and other stronger than the average binding forces. This phenomenon is a natural consequence of the mutual polarization of ions which could not be anticipated on the basis of conventional concepts.

The conventional concepts of the bond strengths in solids are not adequate for explaining the behavior of simple crystals, for example the mechanical strength or the melting of sodium chloride. The actual strength of a sodium chloride crystal is only $1/1000$ of that value which one derives on the basis of its lattice energy.

The conventional approaches cannot explain why sodium chloride at its melting point changes abruptly from a solid into a liquid with a low viscosity in spite of the fact that the volume change which accompanies the melting process amounts to only a few per cent. Within the last few years the authors (21) have demonstrated that the binding forces in a solid under mechanical stresses, in surfaces and around vacant lattice sites, i.e., under conditions which introduce an asymmetry, disproportionate into some weaker and some stronger forces. A sodium chloride crystal, when brought under uniaxial tension, undergoes a change that can be described as follows: The binding forces in the direction of the stress axis are weakened to a greater extent than one would expect from the application of Coulomb's law to the slight increase of the interionic distances. Due to the deformation of the electron clouds of all ions, in particular the anions, Coulomb's law is not applicable to the strained lattice. Even as a first approximation the ions can no longer be treated as rigid spheres or excess point charges. Prior to the deformation, the crystal could be described as having an average Na-Cl bond strength and its value could be obtained by dividing the lattice energy by the number of bonds. For the crystal under stress, this concept has lost its physical reality. The change of the electron density distribution in all ions is such as to weaken the binding forces in the direction of the tensile stress but to strengthen the binding forces in all directions perpendicular to this stress axis. This change of the electrical interaction among all ions reveals itself in the birefringence of cubic crystals and glasses under stress and in Poisson's ratio.

The reverse phenomenon occurs if a solid is brought under uniaxial compression. It is the weakening of the binding forces in the direction perpendicular to a uniaxial compressional stress that makes it possible for a glass to flow under shear stresses. This disproportionation of the binding forces into some stronger and some weaker forces is the result of an asymmetry introduced into the arrangement of the ions by mechanical forces.

The phenomenon is of a fundamental nature and does not depend upon the application of stresses. Asymmetry may result from many causes. The fact that every crystal has surfaces is sufficient, in itself, to introduce asymmetries. A foreign atom, a flaw or a vacant lattice site is the seat of an asymmetry.

Before discussing the effects of flaws and surfaces we shall briefly examine what happens if the symmetry of an array of ions is disturbed. More specifically, we want to see how the forces between ions deviate from those of point charges if their arrangement bebecomes asymmetrical. For this purpose a three-dimensional model is not needed: the essential features can be demonstrated in a plane.

As a good approximation, a sodium chloride crystal can be treated as consisting of electrically-charged rigid spheres. The forces acting between the ions can be derived on the basis of the electrostatic forces acting between point charges. In other words, the bond strength can be calculated on the basis of Coulomb's law. The electron density distribution, especially those of the anions, are not strictly spherical; however, they are highly symmetrical over a time average. For a Cl^- ion the probability of finding an electron within a certain distance from its nucleus is greatest in the direction toward the Na^+ ions and least in the direction toward the adjacent Cl^- ions. The Cl^- ions are polarized by the surrounding six Na^+ ions. The Na^+ ions attract the electron density of the Cl^- ions, whereas the Cl^- ions repel the electrons and thus lower the electron density. As long as the octahedral symmetry is not disturbed, the Cl^- ions can be treated as negative particles which are spherical with respect to the distribution of the electrons around their nuclei.

The interaction of only two ions, one anion and one cation, within the NaCl vapor molecule is very different from that in the crystal. The symmetry of the electron density distribution is lowered so that the ions, in particular the anions, can no longer be treated as rigid spheres. Some of the electron density that was used in the crystal for binding a Cl^- ion to its six surrounding Na^+ ions has now become available for binding the Cl^- ion to a single Na^+ ion. Fajans (7) describes the chemical binding forces as follows: "The physical nature of binding forces acting in all states of aggregation of atoms or ions consists in the overcoming of the electrical repulsion between the atomic nuclei almost exclusively by the electrical attraction on them by the electrons." It is important here to recall this description of the chemical bond because it reveals that our concept of the disproportionation of binding forces applies to all solids and is not restricted to the typical ionic crystals which we use as examples.

In comparing the crystal with a single molecule of NaCl we find that the electron density between the nuclei of chlorine and of sodium is higher in the molecule than in the crystal. This means that the binding forces between Na^+ and Cl^- ions are greater in the single molecule than in the solid state. We are interested primarily in the qualitative aspect of this change of bond strength but it also lends itself to a more quantitative treatment. The internuclear distance and the dipole moment of a NaCl molecule can be measured experimentally and the values compared with those derived from calculations based on the idealized ions.

The experimental value of the Na-Cl distance for the vapor

molecule NaCl is smaller (2.51 A.) than that for the crystal (2.81 A.). The dipole moment of the NaCl molecule (8.5 Debyes) is smaller than the value one obtains from calculating it on the basis of two rigid ions (11.3 Debyes). These differences are the result of the more intense interaction of the ions in the vapor molecule.

The formation of a NaCl vapor molecule from a crystal is a process in which the chemical binding forces between one sodium and one chlorine ion become much stronger than they were in the crystal, but all other binding forces become zero.

In principle, similar changes occur if some ions are removed from the lattice and vacancies are formed. Any vacant lattice site is the seat of an asymmetry and must affect the distribution of binding forces in its environment. The same applies to the surface of a crystal. The lower coordination of surface ions causes some binding forces within the surface film to become stronger.

Chemists use the word "disproportionation" for describing the change of an element from one state of valence into a higher and a lower state of valence. It is a characteristic feature of many systems involving elements of variable valence that they can lower their free energy by an electron transfer that causes the formation of some particles with a higher and others with a lower charge than the original ones, e.g.,

$$2Sn^{2+} \rightarrow Sn^{0} + Sn^{4+}$$

Stannous ions can disproportionate into stannic ions and tin atoms. We apply the same expression to those changes within a system which produce simultaneously stronger and weaker binding forces. Because of this phenomenon it becomes advisable to avoid the terms "chemical bond" and "bond strengths" in discussions of solids because these terms convey the meaning of a defined mechanism which holds the atoms together with a certain strength.

We will use this concept of the disproportionation of the binding forces when we discuss the kinetic aspects of melting, the mechanical strength of glasses and their surface structures, in particular, the origin of the "Griffith flaws."

CHAPTER V

CHEMICAL ASPECTS OF THE STATE OF POLARIZATION OF IONS

So far our treatment of ions and their interactions has been based strictly on electrostatic concepts. The screening concept is a picture of the energy relations in the electrostatic interaction of ions. The state of polarization of an ion has been described as the introduction of a dipole or a multipole into a charged particle. The same approach has been used for the interaction of a large number of ions in a crystal that contains defects. The disproportionation of distances and forces does not involve chemical aspects: it is applicable to salts as well as to metals.

In contrast to the colorless solution of lead salts or of glasses containing lead oxide as a major constituent, lead oxide itself is strongly colored. We attribute its light absorption to the strong polarization of the Pb^{2+} ion in the asymmetrical environment of the PbO crystal in which it is surrounded by eight O^{2-} ions. Four of these anions are closed to the Pb^{2+} ion (2.30 A.) and the other four are in more remote positions (4.30 A.).

Conventional chemistry does not operate with these concepts and even structural crystal chemistry places no major emphasis on the polarizability of ions. Oxides which contain noble gas-type ions, e.g., MgO, can form solid solutions with those containing ions of the transition elements, e.g., CoO and NiO. Most structural considerations are centered around the volume of ions or their radii. The charges are important but differences in charges can be compensated for. $AlPO_4$ and SiO_2 are isostructural because the couple $Al^{3+}P^{5+}$ can take the place of two Si^{4+} ions in a lattice that corresponds to that of quartz without producing a major disturbance of the lattice. The field strengths of Al^{3+} and P^{5+} ions, however, are very different. (See Table VI.) Apparently the polarizing powers of cations and the polarizabilities of anions are not of major importance as long as one is interested primarily in the geometry of compounds. The reader may ask, therefore, why we give so much space to the polarization properties and place so much emphasis on the mutual deformation of ions. There are two reasons for this emphasis. Firstly, we have to find a method for translating conventional chemical descriptions of glasses into structural or atomistic descriptions. Secondly, we have to go beyond the geometrical description of structures and develop a dynamic picture in order to lay the ground for an understanding of reaction rates on an atomistic basis.

It is the object of this chapter to point out how these targets can be reached. Technical glasses are based on silica, boric oxide, and to a lesser extent on phosphorus pentoxide. These compounds are acidic oxides from a chemical point of view. It is important for us to learn the connection between the properties of ions and the conventional concepts of acidity-basicity.

Our description of the Pb^{2+} ion as being strongly polarized in PbO suggests that such an ion must have different chemical properties in different directions. In glasses, one finds cations in strongly asymmetrical environments in the surface. Cations in asymmetrical positions are also found in the interior if a glass contains metal atoms such as gold or copper. We shall attempt, therefore, to correlate the state of polarization of ions with their chemical properties.

$AlPO_4$ and SiO_2 show surprising similarity in their different crystalline modifications. From a dynamic point of view, however, they are very different. The melting point of $AlPO_4$ is more than 300°C. higher than that of SiO_2 and, in contrast to silica, $AlPO_4$ does not form a glass. As far as the geometry is concerned a difference in charges can be compensated for, but as far as the kinetics is concerned this is not so. One of the major reasons for our choosing the Fajans approach to chemical binding has been its suitability for understanding rate phenomena. In this chapter an attempt will be made to advance the treatment of reaction rates above the conventional descriptions to a level at which it can be understood on an atomistic basis and can be correlated with the fundamental properties of the constituents of the system.

1. Acidity-Basicity Concept in Condensed Systems

La definition de l'acide est à
vrai dire la clef de la chimie.
Guyton de Morveau (1786)

These words of de Morveau fit present day chemistry just as much as they did at the time when chemistry became a science.

The history of the acid-base concept shows the struggle of scientists to penetrate into nature's secrets.

Most of us will agree with de Morveau that an understanding of acidity and basicity should provide a key to the understanding of chemistry. At the time when the constitution of glasses was treated on the basis of chemical compounds it appeared that the "acidity" of the melt was an important parameter. Technical glasses at the beginning of this century were grouped primarily around silicic acid and to a lesser extent, boric acid. The glass-forming oxides were acidic compounds but no explanation could be offered for the fact that the only oxides which would form glasses were acidic and that no basic oxide by itself could form a glass.

The concept that acidic oxides are essential to glass formation was deeply rooted in the minds of glass technologists when W. H. Zachariasen (3*a*) introduced the concept of "network-forming cations" and "network-modifying cations." As a result, these names were used synonymously with acidic and basic constituents. The "amphoteric" oxides which in aqueous chemistry were known to form salts with both acids as well as bases, e.g., ZnO forms zinc sulfate $ZnO \cdot SO_3$ and potassium zincate $K_2O \cdot ZnO$, were called "intermediates." Whenever a nonacidic compound was found to form a glass, e.g., lead orthosilicate or zinc orthosilicate, it was believed necessary to provide a special explanation for this "anomalous" glass. When J. M. Stevels (22) extended the fields of glass formation beyond the metasilicates he thought it necessary to coin a new word for them and called these "basic" glasses "invert-glasses."

The simplest way to deal with the presently confused situation would be to point out that the acidity-basicity concept in glasses is of historical interest only because it marks the beginning of scientific thinking about the conditions of glass formation. One could easily defend the attitude that from a scientific point of view it is now obsolete to talk about acidities in silicate melts and glasses. This would mean, however, that a large body of empirical information which was gathered by glass technologists would be deprived of a common basis for understanding.

As far as the constitution of glasses is concerned, there can be no need for the acidity-basicity concept because there are many glasses such as the alkali-magnesium nitrates, elemental sulfur and selenium, as well as vitreous As_2S_3, in which the concept is not applicable or its application would be artificial. A large part of the chemistry of silicate glasses and related boro-silicates and alumino-silicates, however, has been treated from the acid-base point of view so that it becomes important to establish the relations between acidity and atomic structure. We can use this approach also for describing the interaction between glasses and refractory oxides.

In teaching chemistry, one usually introduces the acid-base concept by presenting its historical development. The different interpretations of acidity, basicity, and salt formation are given to the student side by side and most textbooks avoid expressing a preference for one particular concept.

The first concise definition of an acid as a hydrogen compound which produces hydrogen ions in water (Arrhenius) is still sufficient for most purposes; e.g., the titration of acids and bases in aqueous solutions.

For a quantitative treatment, the extension of the Arrhenius concept by J. N. Broensted and T. M. Lowry offers a decided advantage. An acid is defined as a molecule that is capable of donating one or more protons to another molecule (base) that can accept the proton. Acid-base reactions are treated as competitions for protons. Water is no longer an essential factor in this concept. Salt formation, e.g.:

$$NH_3 + HCl = NH_4Cl$$

can take place in any liquid as well as in the gas phase.

Abandoning water as a reference is important if one wants to extend the acid-base concept to nonaqueous solvents. Furthermore, it becomes evident that in those reactions in which water participates, the water plays a role beyond that of a solvent. Water can behave as an acid or as a base depending on the molecular species with which it interacts. Thus, water is an acid with respect to molecules that can accept protons, e.g., NH_3:

$$NH_3 + H_2O = NH_4^+ + OH^-$$

but it becomes a base with respect to molecules that have a tendency to release a proton:

$$HCl + H_2O = Cl^- + H_3O^+$$

The hydrolysis of "neutral" salts, e.g., $AlCl_3$ to form an acidic solution and Na_2CO_3 to form a basic solution, becomes understandable when one realizes that water is a potential acid rather than a liquid which ionizes these compounds and solvates the ions.

The interaction of a silicate glass with water is essentially a reaction of a base (glass) and an acid (water). In principle there is no difference between the corrosive effect of water and that of a solution of hydrochloric acid. The reaction is initiated by the penetration of protons from the water into the oxygen ions of the silicate glass. The more polarizable the O^{2-} ions of the glass the faster is the rate of proton penetration and with it the attack.

Glasses can also react as acids; e.g., with an aqueous solution of sodium hydroxide. This reaction, however, is based on a very different mechanism. Its description requires an extension of the acidity concept because it does not proceed by the process of the donation of protons to the solution by the glass.

The leveling effect of water upon strong acids and upon strong bases which could not be understood on the basis of the Arrhenius concept became understandable on the basis of the Broensted-Lowry concept. The chief limitation of this concept is its dependence upon the proton, a limitation that becomes very serious if one wants to extend the concepts into solid state chemistry. For the chemistry of glasses and fused salts one cannot use a concept which is centered around the proton.

The G. N. Lewis concept of acid-base reactions which involves the formation of a covalent coordinate bond between two atoms cannot be applied to systems which are ionic. The Lewis concept defines acids as molecules that contain atoms with incomplete electron shells and bases as molecules which contain atoms which can donate electron pairs. This concept makes it difficult to emphasize one of the main features of the acid-base concept; namely, that it is only relative. Even a strong acid, e.g., HNO_3, can become a base with respect to a stronger acid; namely, perchloric acid. Silica is an acid with respect to BaO but it is a base when it reacts with P_2O_5 and forms silicylphosphate. Furthermore, the concept of the completion of an electron shell and the formation of a covalent bond cannot take into consideration electrostatic interactions of ions and, as a result, it cannot lead to an energy term which can be interpreted as "acid strength."

As far as the usefulness of the different concepts is concerned, the authors share the opinion of L. F. Audrieth (23) who concluded his Priestley Lecture, in 1949, with the words: "The solvent system concept, the protonic theory, and the Lewis definition are all useful word pictures. Each of them will continue for some time to serve as useful guides to further advance chemical science and to stimulate academic and industrial research activities."

It is important, indeed, that we realize that these definitions are word pictures but not explanations. In 1953, this was expressed by J. A. A. Ketelaar (24) when he referred to acidity in the introduction of his book *Chemical Constitution.* He uses the decreasing acidity of the molecules H_2SO_4, C_6H_5OH, C_2H_5OH, etc., as an example for the present difficulty in attempting to give an atomistic explanation for the widely different dissociation constants of these and similar molecules. He writes: "The first step in the right direction is made when it is realized that the question as to the essential 'why' of chemical properties and reactions is significant, even though the complete answer may hardly ever be obtained."

A. Development of an Acidity-Basicity Concept Based upon the Nature of the Cation

In our approach to chemical binding we describe matter as consisting of ions and we characterize the ions by their electronic structures, their sizes, and their charges. These parameters can be linked to the acidity-basicity of aqueous solutions as well as to glasses.

Starting out with water $(H_2^+O^{2-})_n$ we replace an equivalent number of protons by a cation and determine whether the resulting system deviates from "neutrality," i.e., whether it has become an acid or a base. We retain electroneutrality of the system by removing as many protons from the water as the excess positive charge of the cation which we introduce.

In order to find out the role which the charges of the cations play in determining the acidity of an aqueous system we replace protons by a series of cations which have different charges but the same electronic configurations, namely, that of the neon atom (Table VII).

As we see from Table VII, the replacement of one proton by the singly charged Na^+ ion produces a basic solution, and the replacement of seven protons by the Cl^{7+} ion produces a very strong acid. We see that the acidity increases with increasing charge of the neon-like cations progressing from the basic NaOH to the

TABLE VII

Change of the Acidity of Water by Cations of Increasing Charge and Identical Electronic Configuration (Ne-Type)

Compound	Cation			Solution
H_2O	H^+_{2n}		O^{2-}_n	Neutral
NaOH	H^+_{2n-1}	Na^+	O^{2-}_n	Strong base
$Mg(OH)_2$	H^+_{2n-2}	Mg^{2+}	O^{2-}_n	Weak base
$Al(OH)_3$	H^+_{2n-3}	Al^{3+}	O^{2-}_n	Amphoteric
$Si(OH)_4$	H^+_{2n-4}	Si^{4+}	O^{2-}_n	Weak acid
H_3PO_4	H^+_{2n-5}	P^{5+}	O^{2-}_n	Stronger acid
H_2SO_4	H^+_{2n-6}	S^{6+}	O^{2-}_n	Strong acid
$HClO_4$	H^+_{2n-7}	Cl^{7+}	O^{2-}_n	Strongest acid

amphoteric $Al(OH)_3$, to the weakly acidic $Si(OH)_4$ and, finally, to the strong acids.

We also observe that this substitution series produces substances with widely different solubilities in water. The end members NaOH and $HClO_4$ are extremely soluble and those in the middle of the series are insoluble in water.

Keeping the charge of the cation constant and increasing its size has an effect upon the acidity which is similar to that produced by decreasing its charge. CsOH is considered a stronger base than NaOH and LiOH is considered a weaker base. $Ba(OH)_2$ is more basic than $Mg(OH)_2$ and $Be(OH)_2$ is the least basic in this series of hydroxides.

The same applies to the acidic members of this group. $HClO_4$ is a stronger acid than HIO_4. Hence, we may say that the acidity of a system increases with increasing field strength (Table VII) and decreasing size of the cation. Vice versa, the basicity increases with decreasing charge and increasing size of the cation. There seems to be little doubt that this concept can be directly used in nonaqueous systems.

As far as the electronic configuration is concerned we have no simple parameter which could be used for characterizing a cation of the non-noble gas-type. As long as we restrict ourselves to ions of the noble gas-type we can operate with their charges and sizes or we can combine these two parameters and use the field strength of the cation as a measure of its acidity.

The size of the non-noble Zn^{2+} ion (0.83 A.) ranges between that of the noble ions Mg^{2+} (0.78 A.) and Ca^{2+} (1.06). If the field strengths of these ions alone would determine the basicity of their hydroxides, $Zn(OH)_2$ should have acid-base properties similar to $Mg(OH)_2$ and $Ca(OH)_2$. However, the latter hydroxides do not dissolve in KOH, but $Zn(OH)_2$ forms potassium zincate. This means that zinc hydroxide is more acidic than $Mg(OH)_2$. In order to understand the influence of the electron configuration upon acidity, we consult the first and second ionization potentials of the elements.

Element	Ionization I	Ionization II	Potential I + II
Calcium	6.1	11.8	17.9 e.v.
Magnesium	7.6	15.0	22.6 e.v.
Zinc	9.4	17.9	27.3 e.v.

In order to remove two electrons from a zinc atom 27.3 e.v. are required, whereas 22.6 e.v. are sufficient to produce a Mg^{2+} ion from the atom and 17.9 e.v. for producing a Ca^{2+} ion. These values indicate that the screening demand of the non-noble gas-type Zn^{2+} is considerably greater than even that of the smaller noble gas-type Mg^{2+} ion.

With respect to an anionic environment, i.e., either electrons or O^{2-} ions, the Zn^{2+} ion behaves as if it had a higher charge or a smaller size than the Mg^{2+} ion. The greater acidity of cations of the non-noble gas-type fits well into our previous concept which links acidity with field strength.

This relation seems to hold true in a rather general way. Noble gas-like cations are better screened by their electrons than non-noble gas-like cations which have the same charge and size. For this reason $Mg(OH)_2$ is more basic than $Zn(OH)_2$ or $Cu(OH)_2$. $Ba(OH)_2$ is more basic than $Pb(OH)_2$.

There seems to be no serious obstacle encountered in applying this acidity-basicity concept of aqueous solutions to oxide glasses. We can link acidity with the energy of the interaction between cations and anions. The need for screening a cation corresponds to its acidity, and this energy term increases with increasing charge, decreasing size, and increasing ionization potential.

We can easily eliminate the acid-base relation and replace it by a terminology which does not need a neutral point. This is essentially what A. Dietzel (18) did when he correlated acid-base reactions with the differences among the field strengths of cations as we shall see later.

B. Development of an Acidity-Basicity Concept Based upon the Nature of the Anion

When we discussed the properties of ions we emphasized that O^{2-} ions are not stable as free gaseous particles but that they require stabilization by an environment of cations. The process of surrounding an anion by cations lowers its energy by tightening its electron cloud.

In our approach to the constitution of glasses we follow the practice of crystal chemistry where attention is focused upon the coordination number of the cation. The fact that NaCl vapor molecules interact on cooling and form a crystal has been attributed to the screening demand of the Na^+ ions. This concept provides a simple physical picture of polymerization and condensation reactions which could be used for explaining the formation of the solid state. However, this is not the only way to describe the formation of solids. One may also assume that NaCl molecules can lower their free energy by tightening the Cl^- ions: a process which can be accomplished by surrounding the anions by as many cations as geometrically possible. The interaction between cations and anions is a mutual one and, therefore, no difference exists between the two descriptions as far as the energy relations are concerned. In the one description the screening of the cation and, in the other, the stabilization and tightening of the anion is emphasized. In the same way one can look upon the acidity-basicity concept from two points of view; namely, by focusing one's attention upon the cations and speaking about their screening by the anions or by focusing upon the anions and examining the degree to which they are tightened by the cations.

From the anionic point of view, one can explain the greater acidity of non-noble gas-like cations, e.g., Cu^{2+} and Zn^{2+}, as compared with noble gas-like cations of the same charge and similar size, e.g., Mg^{2+} and Ca^{2+}, on the basis of the different polarizabilities of the O^{2-} ions. The polarizability of an O^{2-} ion is decreased when it is exposed to the field of a stronger cation. The tightening increases with the field strength of the cations to which it is exposed and cations with an incomplete shell (Zn^{2+} and Cu^{2+}) have a stronger tightening effect than less penetrable cations of the noble gas-type (Mg^{2+} and Ca^{2+}).

In fused salts and glasses we cannot use the proton as a common ion, therefore, it becomes advantageous to shift emphasis from the cations to a common anion. Acidity is inversely proportional to the polarizabilities of the anions which means that it corresponds to the degree to which the anions are tightened by the fields of the cations. When we replace O^{2-} ions by F^- ions we frequently find that the acidity of the system is increased. Thus, H_2SiF_6 is a stronger acid than H_2SiO_3. The same is true for fluoroborates as compared with borates.

H. Flood and T. Förland (25) made systematic experiments to determine acidity-basicity relations in fused salts. They based their work upon the polarizability of the O^{2-} ions. According to Flood and Förland, the characteristic process of acid-base reactions is the transfer of an O^{2-} ion from one state of polarization to another.

In silicates, the acid-base transition consists of the breaking of an oxygen bridge (strongly polarized O^{2-} ion) and the formation of a pair of more polarizable nonbridging O^{2-} ions:

$$\left(\frac{O^{2-}}{2}\right)_3 Si^{4+}\,O^{2-}\,Si^{4+}\left(\frac{O^{2-}}{2}\right)_3 + O^{2-} = 2\left[\left(\frac{O^{2-}}{2}\right)_3 Si^{4+}\,O^{2-}\right]^-$$

This process connects acid-base reactions with the disintegration of macromolecules by the change of some bridging O^{2-} ions into nonbridging O^{2-} ions. The bridging O^{2-} ions which are exposed to two Si^{4+} ions are more tightened and, therefore, they are less polarizable than the nonbridging ones.

Experiments concerning the stability of the pyrosulfate ion $(S_2O_7)^{2-}$

$$\begin{matrix} & O^{2-} & & O^{2-} & \\ O^{2-} & S^{6+} & O^{2-} & S^{6+} & O^{2-} \\ & O^{2-} & & O^{2-} & \end{matrix}$$

in fused salts reveal that the bridges are broken through the polarizing action of the cations. K^+ ions are less effective than Na^+ ions. The small Li^+ ions are the most effective alkali ions with respect to their ability to change pyrosulfate into sulfate and sulfur trioxide, according to

$$(S_2O_7)^{2-} = (SO_4)^{2-} + SO_3$$

Just as the "acidity" increases with increasing field strength, i.e., from K^+ to Li^+, it also increases when going from a noble gas-type ion to one which has a greater polarizing power. Potassium pyrosulfate was found to be more stable than thallous pyrosulfate and sodium pyrosulfate is more stable than silver pyrosulfate.

H. Flood and T. Förland's measurements of the breaking of oxygen bridges in pyrosulfate, borate, and titanate systems reveal that in fused oxide systems acidity-basicity can be linked to the state of polarization of the O^{2-} ions or, what is the same, to the polarizing action of the cations which surround and stabilize the O^{2-} ion.

The stability of the O^{2-} ions in a fused salt or a glass can be measured by a galvanic cell and compared with the stability of O^{2-} ions in other systems at the same temperature.

C. Molar Refractivity of O^{2-} Ions and the Acidity of Solids

A direct approach to the interaction of ions in a glass can be based upon the determination of the apparent molar refractions of the O^{2-} ions. Fajans (7) and his associates used the Lorentz-Lorenz molar refraction of ions as a measure of the "looseness" of the electrons in a system. The Lorentz-Lorenz equation gives the molar refraction R as a function of quantities which can be accurately measured.

$$R = \frac{n^2 - 1}{n^2 + 2} \cdot \frac{M}{d} = \frac{n^2 - 1}{n^2 + 2} \cdot V$$

In this statement, n = refractive index, usually n_D, the refractive index measured for the D-line; M = molecular weight, taken from the formula; d = density; and V = molar volume.

By introducing the Avogadro number, N, the molar refractivity R can also be expressed as a function of the polarizability α of a molecule

$$R = 4/3\pi\alpha N$$

The value of n_D can be directly measured for glasses but it has to be computed for nonisotropic crystals.

As an example we shall follow the work of K. Fajans and N. J. Kreidl (26) and see how they determined the refractivity of O^{2-} ions for magnesium metasilicate in the crystalline and glassy states.

The molecular weight M for magnesium metasilicate is 100.38.

The density of the glass, d_{Gl} is 2.758 and that of the enstatite crystal d_{Cr} is 3.175. These values give the molar volumes $V = M/d$ as follows:

$$V_{Gl} = 36.40$$

and

$$V_{Cr} = 31.61$$

The refractive index n_D is 1.580 for the glass. For the biaxial enstatite crystal the n_D value has to be computed as an average value as follows

$$n_D = (\alpha \cdot \beta \cdot \gamma)^{\frac{1}{3}} = (1.640 \times 1.646 \times 1.652)^{\frac{1}{3}}$$

From these values the molar refraction of magnesium metasilicate can be calculated and one obtains

$$R_{Gl} = 12.11 \text{ cm.}^3$$

and

$$R_{Cr} = 11.48 \text{ cm.}^3$$

Subtracting from the molar refraction of the glass R_{Gl} and from that of the crystal R_{Cr} the refractivities of one Mg^{2+} ion (0.26 cm.^{3}) and one Si^{4+} ion (0.12 cm.^{3}) gives us the apparent refraction of the three O^{2-} ions in the $MgSiO_3$ molecule. For one O^{2-} ion one obtains

For the magnesium metasilicate glass: $R_{O^{2-}} = 3.91$ cm.^{3}
For the enstatite crystal: $R_{O^{2-}} = 3.70$ cm.^{3}

The values reveal a greater tightening of the electron clouds of the O^{2-} ions in the crystal as compared with the glass.

When we discussed the acidity-basicity concept as applied to nonaqueous oxide systems such as glasses we learned that Flood and Förland (25) used the polarizability of the O^{2-} ion as a measure of the basicity of an oxide.

A comparison of the ionic refractivities of the O^{2-} ions in different crystalline barium silicates reveals that indeed the basicity as measured by the refractivity of the O^{2-} ions increases with increasing BaO to SiO_2 ratio or with increasing O to Si ratio (Table VIII).

A comparison of the refractivities of O^{2-} ions of different orthosilicates (Table IX) is most revealing. Writing silica proper as $SiSiO_4$ one can compare it with an orthosilicate such as Be_2SiO_4 and one finds that the combined effect of the two Be^{2+} ions is to make the O^{2-} ions less polarizable. The O^{2-} ions are tightened

TABLE VIII

Ionic Refractivity of Oxygen in Barium Silicate Crystals (26)

Composition	O:Si ratio	$R_{O^{2-}}$
SiO_2	2.0	3.52
$BaO \cdot 2SiO_2$	2.5	4.09
$2\ BaO \cdot 3SiO_2$	2.66	4.28
$BaO \cdot SiO_2$	3.0	4.46
$2BaO \cdot SiO_2$	4.0	4.97

TABLE IX

Ionic Refractivity of Oxygen in Some Silicates (26)

Cation	Field strength	Metasilicate		Orthosilicate crystal
		Glass	Crystal	
Be	0.84	—	—	3.35
Si	1.57	—	—	3.52
Al	0.84 (C.N. = 6)	—	—	3.75
Mg	0.45	3.73	3.91	3.83
Li	0.23	3.97	3.97	4.50
Ca	0.33	4.19	4.21	4.53
Na	0.17	—	4.45	4.50
Sr	0.27	4.29	4.60	4.67
Ba	0.24	4.46	—	4.97

more strongly if one replaces one Si^{4+} core (neon-configuration) by two Be^{2+} cores which have the same electronic configuration as the helium atom (two outer electrons). This means that beryllium orthosilicate is a more "acidic" compound than silica. These apparent discrepancies are unavoidable if one tries to combine the traditional and conventional concepts of acidity and salt formation with modern structural considerations. We must look upon Be_2SiO_4 as a solid which bears no more relation to a "salt" than an $AlPO_4$ crystal bears to the "phosphate of aluminum."

The molar refractivity reveals the relation which exists between the tightening of the O^{2-} ions and the field strengths of the cations. Let us be aware of the fact, however, that these values are average values, that they are summations over the responses of the electrons of all O^{2-} ions to an electrical field. Hence, we cannot correlate the molar refractivity of the O^{2-} ions with the chemical reactions of crystals or glasses which involve the penetration of protons into some of its O^{2-} ions. Later, in our discussion of the constitution of alkali phosphate glasses, we will learn that these glasses contain some O^{2-} ions which are easily penetrated by protons and others which resist proton penetration and hydrolysis. The molar refractivity cannot help us in structural problems that make it necessary to differentiate between the polarizabilities of individual O^{2-} ions. We can lower the molar refractivity of a sodium silicate glass by adding either silica or alumina. The effects of the two additions upon the chemical resistivities of the resulting glasses are very different and do not parallel the molar refractivities.

We see from Table IX that the introduction of BeO into a silicate system produces a strong tightening of the electron clouds. Indeed BeO is a most efficient addition to glasses for producing a high modulus of elasticity. Beryllium oxide is the only ingredient which can substantially increase the hardness of a silicate glass.

The molar refractivity of the O^{2-} ions can be very useful in certain structural problems but, contrary to some authors, we do not consider it an additive property which can be used in increment relations. Due to the depth action of chemical binding, the introduction of K_2O into silica glass not only introduces some highly polarizable nonbridging O^{2-} ions but it also increases the polarizability of all O^{2-} ions.

E. Kordes (27) used the molar refractivity of glasses extensively in his research on the constitution of binary phosphate, borate, and silicate glasses and he developed and used increments for bridging and others for nonbridging O^{2-} ions. We must look upon such a subdivision as a first approximation to the actual conditions.

2. Field Strengths of Cations and Compound Formation in Oxide Systems: Dietzel's Rules

The value of z/a^2, the field strength of a cation at the distance a, of an adjacent O^{2-} ion, can be used for estimating the interaction between these ions and with it the acidity or basicity of the oxide. A. Dietzel (18) derived rules for the formation of compounds, in particular from oxides. By using the term z/a^2 instead of the conventional z/r^2 he was able to distinguish between the interactions of Al^{3+} and O^{2-} ions in fourfold and in sixfold coordination.

The aluminum ion has a threefold charge ($z = 3$) and a radius of 0.57 A. When surrounded by four O^{2-} ions the average

$Al^{3+} - O^{2-}$ distance, *a*, is 1.76 A. Using this distance, Dietzel arrived at the value of

$$z/a^2 = 3/(1.76)^2 = 0.97$$

for the field strength of the Al^{3+} ion at the distance of the O^{2-} ions in tetrahedral coordination.

An Al^{3+} ion in octahedral coordination is not as closely surrounded by its O^{2-} ions, the average $Al^{3+} - O^{2-}$ distance being 1.89 A. The electrical field to which the six O^{2-} ions are exposed is therefore lowered to the value of

$$z/a^2 = 3/(1.89)^2 = 0.84$$

In octahedral coordination a cation exerts a weaker electrical field upon its surrounding anions than the same cation in fourfold coordination. The state of polarization of the anion or the field strength of the cation can be used for describing the acidity of a complex.

Dietzel used this relation for deriving a number of rules which govern the interaction of oxides.

Rule I: Two oxides may be expected to form a stable compound if the field strengths of their cations differ by more than 0.3. (See Table VI, Chapter II, 3).

The difference, Δ, represents a measure of the difference in the relative acidity-basicity of the two oxides. As far as the field strengths for SiO_2 (1.57) and CaO (0.33) are concerned, this difference is large

$$\Delta = 1.57 - 0.33 = 1.24$$

so that the two oxides behave as acid and base. P_2O_5 contains a cation which has a very high field strength (2.08) so that this oxide is an acid not only with respect to CaO but even with respect to SiO_2.

$$\Delta = 2.08 - 1.57 = 0.51$$

As the value of Δ for the couple P_2O_5-SiO_2 exceeds 0.3 it is to be expected that the two oxides will form a stable compound: this is indeed the case: silicyl phosphate SiP_2O_7.

Rule II: The more two cations differ in their field strengths,

TABLE X

Compound Formation and Field Strength of Cations (18)

System	Δ	Number of compounds
PbO-P_2O_5	1.74	5
CaO-P_2O_5	1.73	5
K_2O-SiO_2	1.44	4
Na_2O-SiO_2	1.38	4
Li_2O-SiO_2	1.34	2.5[a]
BaO-SiO_2	1.33	3.5
SrO-SiO_2	1.30	2
CaO-SiO_2	1.24	2.5
Fe_2O_3-P_2O_5	1.17	2.5
MgO-SiO_2	1.12	1.5
Al_2O_3-P_2O_5	1.11	0.5
ZnO-SiO_2	0.98	1
ZrO_2-SiO_2	0.79	1
Al_2O_3-SiO_2	0.73	1
BeO-SiO_2	0.70	0.5
B_2O_3-P_2O_5	0.63	1
TiO_2-SiO_2	0.32	—
SO_3-P_2O_5	0.10	—

[a] Compounds such as $AlPO_4$, which decompose and which have no congruent melting point, are counted as one half (0.5).

i.e., the greater the value of Δ, the more probable becomes multiple compound formation between the two oxides.

In Table X the number of compounds for several oxide systems are listed. The fraction 0.5 is used for indicating compounds which have no congruent melting points. One can see that the number of compounds which occur in a binary oxide system increases with increasing value of Δ.

In pronouncing these rules Dietzel (18) made a decisive step in the direction of a better understanding of solid state chemistry. The first rule was more or less obvious because one expects an acid to react with a base to form a salt. With the second rule, however, Dietzel answered a question which could not be answered up to that time. He was able to correlate the number of compounds in the alkali-silica and the alkaline earth-silica systems with the sizes and the charges of the cations which are involved.

In Table XI the types of silicates which exist are correlated with the value Δ, the difference in the field strength of Si^{4+} and that of the other cations.

TABLE XI
Compound Formation in Silicate Systems (18)

Oxide	z/a^2	Δ	Stable silicates			
			Ortho-	Meta-	Di-	Tetra-
Cs_2O	0.10	1.47	+	+	+	+
Rb_2O	0.12	1.45	+	+	+	+
K_2O	0.13	1.44	+	+	+	+
Na_2O	0.17	1.40	+	+	+	−
Li_2O	0.23	1.34	+	+	+	−
BaO	0.24	1.33	+	+	+	−
SrO	0.27	1.30	+	+	−	−
CaO	0.33	1.24	+	+	−	−
MgO	0.45	1.12	+	+	−	−
BeO	0.87	0.70	+	−	−	−

Further rules refer to the maximum amount of silica which can react with an oxide of the general formula R_mO_n and with the existence of ternary compounds among oxides. For details the original work of Dietzel should be consulted.

3. Change of Chemical Properties of Cations Through One-Sided Polarization in Surfaces

The polarized Pb^{2+} ion as it participates in a PbO crystal can be described as the core Pb^{4+}, having an 18-shell, and a pair of electrons quantized with respect to this core in an asymmetrical fashion $[Pb^{4+}(e_2^-)]^{2+}$. From a chemical point of view we may describe the polarized ion as a particle one half of which resembles a Pb^{4+} core and the other half of which looks like a neutral lead atom:

$$\tfrac{1}{2}\,Pb^{4+} - \tfrac{1}{2}\,Pb^0$$

This description relates the electrical dipole or the asymmetrical electron density distribution to the directional chemical properties which polarizable cations may assume in surfaces. A crystal of lead fluoride must contain in its surface film lead ions which are strongly polarized. The electrical field of the practically nonpolarizable F^- ion must repel the electrons of the Pb^{2+} ion and one may anticipate that such a crystal has surface properties which are the result of a strong one-sided polarization:

$$\text{crystal–}F^-\text{–}[Pb^{4+}(e_2^-)]^{2+}\text{–atmosphere}$$

or

$$\text{crystal–}F^{-}\text{–}\tfrac{1}{2}\,Pb^{4+}\text{–}\tfrac{1}{2}\,Pb^{0}\text{–atmosphere}$$

This chemical description is a relatively crude picture but it can account for the chemistry of surfaces which cannot be derived from descriptions based on electrical double layers or on surface ions which have a dipole moment in addition to their excess charges.

Metal surfaces catalyze the decomposition of hydrogen peroxide. Neither an aqueous solution of lead nitrate nor solid lead chloride are catalysts for this reaction. D. P. Enright, P. A. Marshall and W. A. Weyl (28) found that, indeed, PbF_2 was a positive catalyst for the decomposition of hydrogen peroxide. Only the combination of the lead ion with the least polarizable anion (F^-) can produce this effect. Other lead compounds such as $PbCl_2$ do not show this extreme polarization and catalytic activity.

Silver ions like lead ions do not catalyze the decomposition of H_2O_2. Glass surfaces by themselves are not catalysts for this reaction but they become activated in the presence of Ag^+ ions. Such a surface has the following structure:

$$\text{glass–}O^{2-}\text{–}\tfrac{1}{2}\,Ag^{2+}\text{–}\tfrac{1}{2}\,Ag^{0}\text{–solution of }H_2O_2$$

We can describe this reaction as the result of the formation of atomic silver in the glass surface. The asymmetrical electron density distribution of the chemisorbed Ag^+ ion may encourage an electron transfer from the H_2O_2 to the absorbed Ag^+ ion. It is immaterial for our purpose how we describe the reaction but it is important that we realize that cations in an asymmetrical environment can assume chemical reactivities which are very different from those of the hydrated ions.

For glass technologists this feature is of considerable interest. It explains the empirical observation that rinsing a glass surface with a stannous chloride solution increases its adhesive forces for a silver mirror. Writing the Sn^{2+} ion as $[Sn^{4+}(e_2^-)]^{2+}$ shows its dipole nature. Describing the polarized Sn^{2+} ion as consisting of one-half Sn^{4+} and one-half Sn^0 brings out its "metallophilic" properties:

$$\text{glass–}O^{2}\text{–}\tfrac{1}{2}\,Sn^{4+}\text{–}\tfrac{1}{2}\,Sn^{0}\text{–silver metal}$$

W. A. Weyl (29) utilizes this concept for explaining the solvent power of glasses which contain "metallophilic" ions for gold, copper and silver. In order to make a good gold ruby glass one either uses a lead crystal glass or one adds tin oxide to a soda lime silicate glass. This measure prevents gold particles from precipitating too rapidly during cooling and enables the glass technologist to control the color by proper heat treatment. A gold particle is very mobile in a glass unless it is bound to its environment. This can be achieved by Sn^{2+} ions:

$$\text{glass–}O^{2-}\text{–}\tfrac{1}{2}\,Sn^{4+}\text{–}\tfrac{1}{2}\,Sn^{0}\text{–Au–}\tfrac{1}{2}\,Sn^{0}\text{–}\tfrac{1}{2}\,Sn^{4+}\text{–}O^{2-}\text{–glass}$$

We may describe this interaction by saying that the high electron density part of the polarized stannous ion "alloys" with the gold particle whereas the low electron density part interacts strongly with an O^{2-} ion of the glass.

4. Atomistic Approach to the Rates of Chemical Reactions

A. Conventional Descriptions of Rate Phenomena

The conventional approach to the rate of homogeneous reactions as affected by the concentration of the reactants is based on the determination of the "rate law" or the "order of the reaction." One speaks of a reaction of the "first order" if the velocity of the reaction is proportional to the concentration of the reactant:

$$\text{velocity} = k[A]$$

In this equation k is a constant which is characteristic for the reaction and the symbol $[A]$ means the concentration of the species A (atoms, ions, molecules) in the system.

A reaction of the "second order" is one in which the velocity is proportional to the square of the concentration of one reactant $[A]^2$ or to the product of two concentrations, e.g., $[A]\cdot[B]$.

$$v = k[A]^2$$

$$v = k[A][B]$$

One might be inclined to associate the order of a reaction to the number of molecular species which have to collide and interact in order to make possible the chemical change. Reactions of the type

$$A \rightarrow B + C$$

or

$$A_2 \rightarrow A + A$$

may thus be called reactions of the first order, whereas reactions of the type

$$A + B \rightarrow C + D$$

or

$$2\,A \rightarrow A_2$$

would be of the second order. A reaction which involves three molecules of ions such as

$$A + B + C \rightarrow D + E, \text{ etc.}$$

would be called a reaction of the "third order." This, however, is not necessarily so.

The rate law is an observed law and cannot be predicted from the chemical equation which describes the net change in the system. Most likely a reaction proceeds by following several reaction paths simultaneously and each path may have its own concentration dependence. As all paths contribute to the rate of the reaction, their terms have to be added and the order of a reaction must not necessarily be an integer, it can be zero or fractional.

However because of the usual predominance of one reaction path, one finds that many rate equations reveal that the rate is a simple function of the concentration of the substances involved.

For this reason we must look upon the order of a reaction as merely an empirical expression of the concentration dependence of its rate.

If a physical chemist wants to call attention to the fact that a certain reaction does not take place unless three species of molecules or ions can interact simultaneously as in

$$A + B + C \rightarrow D + E +, \text{ etc.}$$

he calls this reaction "trimolecular." Trimolecular reactions are very rare and tetramolecular reactions are practically unknown. Nevertheless, we know many reactions which are of a high order.

The formation of hydrogen molecules from the single atoms should be a "dimolecular" reaction

$$H + H \rightarrow H_2$$

The kinetics of this reaction however reveals that three particles have to collide because one particle, X, is needed to absorb the energy which is released when two H atoms combine to the H_2 molecule. This makes the formation of H_2 from the atoms behave as a "trimolecular" reaction.

$$H + H + X \rightarrow H_2 + X$$

Measuring the effect of the temperature upon the rate of a chemical reaction is perhaps the most powerful single tool which enables one to derive a better understanding of the reaction. As early as 1889, Arrhenius theorized on the observation that the rate of the inversion of cane sugar is accelerated by raising the temperature and that the effect of the temperature can be described by an equation such as

$$k = Ae^{-E/RT}$$

in which k is the rate of inversion, R and T the gas constant and the absolute temperature respectively. A and E are constants which are characteristic for the system.

The Arrhenius equation is not a law, it is an approximation but one which proved to be extremely useful. The constant A has been called the frequency factor because this constant is thought to be connected somehow with the frequency of collisions between the reactants.

According to the concepts of Arrhenius this equation expresses the fact that the reacting molecules must acquire a certain critical energy before they can react on colliding. According to Boltzmann the factor $e^{-E/RT}$ represents the fraction of molecules whose energy exceeds the average energy of the molecules by the amount of E and consequently the fraction of molecules which has the energy necessary for reacting. The energy E is called the activation energy of the reaction.

If one measures the rate of a chemical reaction (k) as a function of the temperature and plots its natural logarithm, $\ln k$, against $1/T$ one obtains a straight line, the slope of which is proportional to the activation energy of the reaction.

Soda lime silicates are stable as glasses because the activation energy of nucleation and crystallization is not available at ordinary temperature. Some natural silicates, obsidian, remained glassy over geological times.

The phenomenon that many low melting substances, e.g., a

mixture of some fused nitrates, or glycerol, fail to crystallize on cooling and form glasses is the result of the low thermal energy which is available at their freezing point. On the other hand many substances, e.g., nitrides and carbides, cannot be obtained as glasses because their melting points are very high. At high temperatures, the available thermal energy kT can overcome even a high energy barrier of nucleation and crystallization.

The concept of reactions having a certain activation energy and the descriptions of their rates by the Arrhenius equation are very useful and convenient tools but the constants which enter the equation have to be determined experimentally for each individual reaction. It would be desirable to go beyond an empirical approach and to understand the reasons for the variation of the activation energy. To be specific we would like to know why SiO_2 but not TiO_2 forms a glass and why a glass of the composition 85% SiO_2, 15% Na_2O deteriorates rapidly when exposed to water whereas a glass containing 70% SiO_2, 15% CaO, and 15% Na_2O is resistant. The conventional approach to rate phenomena cannot explain why the chemical resistivity of a sodium silicate can be improved if some of the insoluble SiO_2 is replaced by a much more soluble oxide; e.g., CaO or B_2O_3. In order to answer these questions we have to go beyond the conventional descriptions of reactions. In addition to determining the order of the reaction and its activation energy, we need a model of the mechanism of the hydration reaction.

The physical chemistry of reaction rates is still in the stage where scientists are confined to descriptions. In those fields of physical chemistry where scientists are engaged in correlating physical properties with the composition and the structure of substances we find continuous efforts to refine the concepts of chemical binding forces.

The difficulty of understanding rate phenomena and the fact that conventional physical chemistry offers no clue for how to approach them on an atomistic basis accounts for the fact that many scientists engaged in the theoretical treatment of rate phenomena, such as the viscous flow of glasses, bypass modern developments on the nature of chemical binding and use mechanistic concepts which date back to the times when chemistry became a science.

Statistical approaches to rate phenomena are based on very primitive mechanistic concepts. The system is assumed to consist of particles which are held together by a mechanism called "bond." Whether the particles are molecules, or neutral atoms, or electrically charged ions is irrelevant for this treatment. The particles are assumed to be in constant thermal motion and this motion causes each particle to break its bonds with the adjacent particles and to reform them. Atoms which vibrate with a frequency of approximately 10^{13} vibrations per second break their bonds at this rate and reform them. For a system in equilibrium which is not subject to any external forces the rate of bond breaking and the rate of reformation of bonds are equal and no change takes place macroscopically.

When a mechanical force is applied to the system this equilibrium is upset and the rates of breaking and forming bonds are no longer equal in all directions. Viscous flow is treated formally as if it were a chemical reaction that does not involve any change in the chemical nature of the system.

Statistical approaches to rate phenomena have become very popular during the last 20 years because they provide a theory without requiring a more precise knowledge of the constitution of the glass. Statistical theories have been developed for rate phenomena such as the ionic conductivity, nucleation, and diffusion processes, and in particular for viscous flow.

The statistical approach is convenient because it does not require an assumption concerning the nature of the particle that diffuses or flows. The particle must not be an atom or a molecule, it can be a structural unit such as an SiO_4 tetrahedron. Regardless of the nature of the flow unit it is treated as if it were an atom in a monoatomic liquid. If one prefers to assume a mixture of units, the statistical methods are ideally suited for introducing a distribution function.

The same treatment is applied to the height of the energy barrier. If one energy barrier or activation energy does not fit the data one introduces a distribution of activation energies.

D. A. Stuart and O. L. Anderson (30) used the statistical mechanical approach for describing the ionic conductivity of glasses as a function of the temperature. They made a special effort to connect the activation energy of this process with structural parameters of the glass. In a similar way R. W. Douglas (31) made efforts to connect the statistical model of viscous flow with the geometry of the glass. There can be no question that some scientists who apply the statistical mechanical concepts to the glassy state are fully aware of the gap that exists between the mathematical treatment on one side and the structure and the chemical composition of the glass on the other.

In a review paper "Statistical Theories as Applied to the Glassy State," O. L. Anderson and D. A. Stuart (32) discuss the different approaches which have been made in the last 20 years in attempting to develop a basis for the understanding of various rate phenomena, in particular of the viscosity of glass. They describe several equations suitable for describing the change of the viscosity of a glass with temperature. All of these equations, however, contain four arbitrary constants. The remarks which Anderson and Stuart made concerning the value and the future of the mechanical statistical approach are most revealing; they wrote:

"In spite of the fact that these theories of viscosity are in good qualitative agreement with experiment, it must be candidly admitted that many types of equations with so many arbitrary parameters can be fitted to a set of experimental points with a fair degree of accuracy. It would seem that no further progress can be made with statistical theories of viscosity until the arbitrariness of such theories is reduced."

Our main criticism of the statistical approach to rate phenomena is the lack of a connection between the constants which have to be derived empirically and the chemical composition of the system which is described by the equation.

B. Partial Temporary Unscreening of Cations as an Energy Barrier in Chemical Reactions

When we develop an atomistic explanation of the viscosity of glasses (33) as a function of the composition we attributed the activation energy of viscous flow to the need for a partial temporary unscreening of cations during flow. The same concept applies to many solid state reactions. The Mg^{2+} ions in MgO are well screened by six O^{2-} ions. The same applies to the Al^{3+} ions in Al_2O_3. The fact that a mixture of MgO and Al_2O_3 in the ratio 1:1 does not react at ordinary temperature in spite of having a higher free energy than spinel, $MgAl_2O_4$, can be explained as follows. In order to reshuffle the Mg^{2+} and Al^{3+} ions and make them form a new lattice, that of the spinel, they have to be partly unscreened. Their coordination number may have to be lowered temporarily below the value of 6 and the cation-anion distances must be temporarily increased. In order to accomplish this the system has to be raised to a high temperature. The mixture of MgO and Al_2O_3 requires an activation energy for reacting and forming spinel. The mixture goes through an "activated state" before it assumes the state of greatest stability or lowest free energy.

G. F. Hüttig (34) to whom we owe much for elucidating the kinetics of solid state reactions talks about "aktive Zwischenzustände," i.e., active intermediate states, which can be frozen in. If the mixture of MgO and Al_2O_3 is allowed to react but the reaction has not yet gone to completion the system assumes properties that are foreign to both the reactants and the reaction product as well. The partially unscreened cations in the intermediate active state impart acidity to the solid. Such a partly reacted mixture is a strong adsorbent for basic dyes dissolved in benzene. Neither a mixture of MgO with Al_2O_3 nor the spinel has acidic properties that can compare with this intermediate state. The concept of an "active state" in chemical reactions is widely used but only in solid state reactions can this intermediate active state be isolated and examined.

The concept of the partial temporary unscreening of cations as being the energy barrier for reactions can explain why gases which can screen a cation, e.g., H_2O vapor, will accelerate this type of reaction. We shall use this picture for explaining the influence of catalysts upon rates of crystallization and solid state reactions such as the change of vitreous silica into cristobalite. We will use the same concept for the viscous flow of glasses and the diffusion of ions through a rigid glass.

Our treatment of reaction rates and viscous flow is very different from the conventional treatment which is based on the artificial concept of the "breaking of bonds." This treatment of a bond as a mechanism holding together two atoms and as a force that must be "broken" in order to permit reaction or flow is a heritance from the eighteenth century. It dates back to times when chemists thought in terms of mechanical rather than electrical forces.

The danger of using such a mechanistic model lies in the fact that the average bond strength between atoms can be estimated and that numerical values for different bond energies are listed in our textbooks. It is unavoidable that one is tempted to correlate rate phenomena with these bond energies. Scientists working on the modern aspects of the constitution of glasses have become victims of this fallacy.

We find this fallacy of connecting viscosity and glass formation with bond strength in papers in which the author bases the bond strength on the electrical interaction between cations and anions, as well as in those that are based on thermochemical data which give the energy required for dissociating a substance into its free atoms.

The concept that the bond strength between atoms is a decisive factor in determining the rates of reactions and the viscous flow of a glass is characteristic for the statistical-mechanical approach to rate phenomena.

In this approach, each individual bond is given a finite probability of being broken. It is assumed that this probability depends upon the strength of the bond, Q, and upon the energy of the vibration. The latter increases with the absolute temperature, T. The probability of breaking a bond is treated as being proportional to the expression $\exp - Q/kT$ in which k is the Boltzmann constant. This treatment suggests that the activation energy of a rate process is related to the chemical binding force Q.

In spite of all the advances which have been made in quantum mechanics, the concept that a mechanism exists which holds together two atoms with one finite force (the bond strength) is still deeply rooted in the minds of some scientists who continue to think in terms of "breaking of existing bonds" and "forming of new bonds" as the basic mechanism of chemical reactions and of viscous flow.

J. D. MacKenzie (35) calculated the energy of the B—O bond to be ~100 kcal./mole. This value is very much the same as the energy of the Si—O bond (106 kcal./mole). The following sentences are quoted as examples for the failure of the mechanistic picture which is used for linking the bond strength to the flow behavior of B_2O_3 and SiO_2 glasses:

"Viscous flow can, therefore, occur only by the rupture of B—O bonds, the most probable unit to flow being B_2O_3. However, the energy of activation for viscous flow for SiO_2 is about 130 kcal., almost four times greater than that for B_2O_3.

"Thus for flow to occur, energy approximating to half of four B—O bonds is involved. As the same number of Si—O bonds must be broken when viscous flow takes place in SiO_2 it would appear that the energy of the Si—O bond is much greater than that of the B—O bond."

The time has come for scientists to free themselves from these obsolete concepts and realize that the viscous flow of fused B_2O_3 and of SiO_2 involves a motion of the nuclei of boron, silicon, and oxygen which must be accompanied by major changes in the electron density distribution within the system.

For some purposes the description of B_2O_3 or SiO_2 as consisting of boron and oxygen or silicon and oxygen atoms can be satisfactory. For other purposes their description as an array of B^{3+} and O^{2-} or Si^{4+} and O^{2-} ions provides a better approximation. During viscous flow the system goes through "active states" for which none of the two approximations is completely satisfactory because the ions undergo major deformations. No bonds are "broken" so do not have to be "reformed": the nuclei move through positions which are so far from their equilibrium positions that any description of the system based on rigid particles, atoms or ions which can be applied to its equilibrium state loses its usefulness.

A more widespread use of the dynamic models built by A. Dietzel and E. Deeg (36) would help to overcome the mechanistic description of reactions. In these models the electrical forces between ions are replaced by equivalent magnetic forces and not by mechanical devices such as wires. Those who study these dynamic models would never think of describing crystallization or a flow process as involving breakage of magnetic forces or bending of existing bonds.

The application of bond energies to flow processes has been very misleading. We pointed out earlier that in many systems the disproportionation of the binding forces makes it impossible to use the average bond strength as a parameter with a physical reality. The melting point of AgCl (455°C.) is considerably lower than that of NaCl (800°C.). Both crystals have the same structure but the bond strength Na—Cl as expressed by the lattice energy of NaCl (180 kcal./mole) is considerably lower than the corresponding value for AgCl (214 kcal./mole). These substances melt by a disproportionation of all binding forces into stronger and weaker forces (21) forming liquids for which the average bond strength has no physical meaning as far as flow is concerned. Even though the average bond strength for AgCl is greater than for NaCl, the melting point of AgCl is much lower than that of NaCl.

In the case of a polyatomic molecule such as an S_8 molecule thermochemical data provide a value for the total heat of dissociation of the molecule into single atoms. It is important that we realize that experimental methods provide data for the sum of the bond energies but not for the individual bond energies.

L. Pauling (10) emphasizes that the bond energy values which he lists represent not the amount of energy required to break one bond in the molecule, but instead an average of the amount required to break all the bonds.

Let us take a look at some of these values for the bond energy (kcal./mole) of single bonds (10).

C—H	87.3 kcal./mole
C—C	58.6 kcal./mole
S—S	63.8 kcal./mole
Se—Se	57.6 kcal./mole

The higher value for the C—H bond as compared with that for the C—C bond does not mean that heating a mixture of deuterium D_2 with ethane $CH_3 \cdot CH_3$ will produce deutero-methane

$$D_2 + CH_3 \cdot CH_3 = CH_3D + CH_3D$$

at a lower temperature than that required for the formation of deuteroethane according to:

$$D_2 + CH_3 \cdot CH_3 = CH_3 \cdot CH_2D + HD$$

As a matter of fact, the second reaction takes place at a lower temperature than the first, because these reactions do not involve the breakage of C—C and C—H bonds.

The same applies to viscous flow, nucleation and crystallization of sulfur and selenium glasses. Because of their chemical simplicity these two systems which are also similar as far as the geometry is concerned have always been favorites of physical chemists. Both glasses contain chainlike molecules of different lengths. The molecular weight varies with the heat treatment and must be represented by a distribution function. The two elemental glasses resemble in their structures a linear organic polymer.

Selenium glasses have been studied by Tammann (1) and his

school because of their greater stability as compared with amorphous sulfur. Sulfur in the glassy state is very unstable. J. A. Prins (37) who has given much time and thought to the exploration of amorphous sulfur describes the plastic sulfur obtained from chilling viscous sulfur as follows: Initially the plastic sulfur is roughly identical with viscous sulfur solidified in small quantities but soon it becomes contaminated with rhombic sulfur. The usual product is possibly stabilized by atmospheric nitrogen, it turns brittle after a few hours. With phosphorus it may stay elastic for a month. In liquid air its lifetime, of course, is infinite.

This description of vitreous sulfur reveals that there is a tremendous difference between a pure sulfur glass which can be obtained only in small quantities and a pure selenium glass. The S—S bond strength is approximately 10% greater than the Se—Se bond strength. Nevertheless, S_8 rings form at ordinary temperature within hours, probably within minutes and it takes liquid air temperature to prevent a sulfur glass from crystallizing.

This difference can be understood only on the basis of the electronic formula.

We write the electronic formula of the sulfur chains as follows:

$$\begin{array}{ccccccccc} & & (e_2^-) & & (e_2^-) & & (e_2^-) & & \\ \cdots & (e_2^-) & S^{6+} & (e_2^-) & S^{6+} & (e_2^-) & S^{6+} & \cdots \\ & & (e_2^-) & & (e_2^-) & & (e_2^-) & & \end{array}$$

Each sulfur core S^{6+} is screened by four electron pairs (e_2^-) two of which are shared with two other S^{6+} cores and the other two are quantized with respect to one core only. The mutual repulsive forces between the (e_2^-) quanticules accounts for the helical shapes of these chains. This description applies to the infinitely extending chains. The chains must have two end groups which originally may have contained unpaired electrons but which have reacted in the course of preparation with constituents of the atmosphere.

Our description of the activation energy of reshuffiing such an array of atoms does not involve the breakage of bonds but the partial temporary unscreening of cores. The small S^{6+} cores are well screened in an environment of four (e_2^-) quanticules and can reshuffle easily even at ordinary temperature. We may say that the isomerization of sulfur has a much lower activation energy than the isomerization of selenium because the Se^{6+} core is larger than the S^{6+} core. For corresponding compounds the screening demand of cores increases with their sizes. The melting points of the compounds XO_2 increases rapidly in the series:

Compound	CO_2	SiO_2	TiO_2	ZrO_2	ThO_2
Radius of cation, A.	0.20	0.39	0.64	0.87	1.10
Melting point, °C.	Gas	1713	1830	2700	3050

These oxides are arranged in the order of increasing size of the cation.

The higher activation energy of isomerization for hydrocarbons is the result of the lower screening power of the hydrogen. We write the electronic formula of a chain molecule of a hydrocarbon as follows:

$$\begin{array}{ccccccc} & & H^+ & & H^+ & & \\ & & (e_2^-) & & (e_2^-) & & \\ \cdots & (e_2^-) & C^{4+} & (e_2^-) & C^{4+} & (e_2^-) & \cdots \\ & & (e_2^-) & & (e_2^-) & & \\ & & H^+ & & H^+ & & \end{array}$$

The carbon cores in this hydrocarbon are screened by four (e_2^-) quanticules each. Two of the (e_2^-) quanticules are shared with other carbon cores in exactly the same way as in the sulfur and selenium chains. However, the difference between the hydrocarbon and the sulfur chains lies in the fact that the other two electron pairs are not quantized with respect to only one carbon core but that each of them have to screen a proton. These H^- quanticules or electron pairs containing a proton are much poorer screeners than those that are quantized with respect to S^{6+} cores only.

The weaker C—C bond strength (58.6 kcal./mole) as compared with the S—S bond strength (63.8 kcal./mole) is the result of the lower charge of the carbon core (C^{4+}) as compared with the sulfur core (S^{6+}). The fact that the Se—Se bond energy (57.6 kcal./mole) is smaller than the S—S bond energy is the result of the larger size of the Se^{6+} core as compared with the S^{6+} core. If the isomerization of the chainlike molecules would involve a breakage of bonds or an overcoming of the bond energies by thermal energy either sulfur should not recrystallize at ordinary temperature or it should be impossible to separate hydrocarbons by distillation without their changing into the thermodynamically more stable mixture of isomers.

C. State of Polarization of Anions as a Rate-Determining Factor in Hydrolysis

The inversion of sucrose is a classical reaction in several respects. It was the first chemical reaction which was timed and which was used for studying the relation between temperature and the rate of a reaction. This reaction has attracted the attention of hundreds of investigators and over one thousand publications dealing with its kinetics have appeared since the days of Wilhelmy (1850). That we are still very far from understanding its mechanism is an illuminating comment on the difficulties attending the problem in general (38).

E. A. Moelwyn-Hughes (1947)

The rate of hydrolysis of a glass determines its chemical resistivity with respect to atmospheric corrosion. The fact that antique glasses, several thousand years old, have chemical compositions which are not far removed from our modern window glass seems rather surprising, but the reason for it is very simple. Raising the silica content would make the glass more difficult to melt. Raising the lime content would cause the glass to devitrify. Raising the alkali content would cause the glass to hydrolyze and disintegrate. The rate of hydrolysis is one of the three main factors that determines the field of useful glasses. From a chemical point of view hydrolysis is a very simple reaction consisting of the addition of water to a neutral molecule.

Conventional descriptions of molecules offer no clue to their widely different chemical reactivities with water. In order to introduce this chapter on hydrolysis rates the authors have chosen the words of a scientist who has devoted a lifetime to the exploration of rate phenomena. There is no better way to characterize the present situation. Moelwyn-Hughes (38), in the introduction to his book on *The Kinetics of Chemical Reactions*, makes a very strong statement: ". . . we are still *very far* from understanding" the inversion of cane sugar, i.e., the hydrolysis of an oxygen bridge between the two parts of a disaccharide molecule.

Moelwyn-Hughes points out the difficulties of understanding the *mechanism* of the reaction. This is extremely important because some scientists are satisfied when a reaction can be described by an equation. We distinguish between such a description of its rate, namely, the kinetics of the reaction, and an understanding of a reaction; the latter involves a picture of its mechanism; i.e., the path of the reaction.

The rate of hydrolysis of a glass is of fundamental significance because it determines its usefulness primarily with respect to its corrosion or weathering but also with respect to its mechanical performance. Fracture of a glass is a mechano-chemical process that is aided by hydrolysis. Unlike the solubility of NaCl in water, the hydrolysis of a glass affects different parts of its structure at different rates. The Vycor process is based on the fast hydrolysis of sodium borate and the greater resistance to hydrolysis of the matrix. Before we go into the details of hydrolysis reactions we shall take a look at some of the problems which one faces in this field.

1. Many hydrated compounds, e.g., the hydrates of aluminum sulfate, ferric sulfate, and chromic chloride, are quite soluble in water and dissolve rapidly. The corresponding anhydrous compounds, however, dissolve very sluggishly; some of them are not even wet by water. For example, anhydrous, sublimed, chromic chloride can float on water for hours. The rate of solution of the anhydrous substances can be accelerated by the addition of an acid. Why does anhydrous aluminum sulfate dissolve faster in diluted sulfuric acid than in water?

2. No hydroxide or carbonate is stable in contact with acetic or hydrochloric acid. However, $Be(OH)_2$ is not attacked by acetic acid at ordinary temperature and mineralogists use diluted HCl as a reagent for distinguishing between the mineral calcite, $CaCO_3$ which effervesces, and dolomite $MgCa(CO_3)_2$, which does not. The magnesium-calcium carbonate is not noticeably attacked by diluted HCl at ordinary temperature. How can we account for this drastic difference in the reaction rates of two closely related carbonates?

3. The rate of hydrolysis of a potassium silicate glass at room temperature is very fast, that of a sodium silicate glass is considerably slower, and a lithium silicate glass of the same molecular composition hydrolyzes least when exposed to the atmosphere.

A pure sodium silicate glass even if it contains as much as 85% SiO_2 and 15% Na_2O hydrolyzes too rapidly to be useful as a window pane. However, a glass containing 15% Na_2O, 15% CaO, and 70% SiO_2 resists weathering and is satisfactory for this purpose. Why should the replacement of 15% of the insoluble SiO_2 by the more soluble calcium oxide reduce the rate of hydration so as to produce a satisfactory glass?

4. Many esters do not hydrolyze at a measurable rate in pure

water or in an aqueous-alcoholic solution. Their hydrolysis, however, can be strongly catalyzed by the addition of acids as well as of bases. How can two antagonistic changes in such a system, namely, increasing as well as decreasing its pH, have the same effect upon the rate of the reaction?

5. The inversion of cane sugar is a reaction in which a molecule of water is added to a molecule of sugar. Hydrolysis leads to two molecules, one of glucose and one of fructose:

$$\text{sucrose} + \text{water} = \text{fructose} + \text{glucose}$$

This reaction takes place at a noticeable rate only in the presence of a catalyst. Acids have an accelerating effect upon this reaction. How does the presence of H^+ ions affect the rate of the addition of a molecule of water to one of sugar?

6. Textbooks of inorganic chemistry rarely fail to mention the striking similarity between crystallized phosphates and arsenates with respect to compound formation, crystal structures, habitus, and their solubilities. Classical crystal chemistry was developed from Mitscherlich's discovery of the isomorphism of phosphates and arsenates. However, in aqueous solution, these groups show a drastic difference. Metaarsenates and pyroarsenates dissolved in water change into orthoarsenates immediately. The stability of the corresponding phosphates in aqueous solutions is well known and has been used for studying the constitution of phosphate glasses. What accounts for the drastic difference between these compounds with respect to their rates of hydration?

All of these problems involve rate phenomena. The science dealing with the speed of chemical reactions, reaction kinetics, involves time as a variable. The effect of time upon reactions between gaseous molecules can be treated on the basis of molecular collisions. One can assume that a reaction occurs only when the molecules have an energy which exceeds a certain critical value. Moelwyn-Hughes in his "collision theory" has extended this approach to the kinetics of some reactions in solution. In aqueous systems the concept of a collision between a water molecule and, say a molecule of sucrose, is somewhat artificial because we know that the water interacts with the sucrose through hydrogen bonds.

When asked how two substances, for example, carbon tetrachloride and silicon tetrachloride, will react with water, one can assume a possible and plausible reaction and calculate the change of the free energy, provided the necessary thermodynamic data are available. In our example one finds that for both compounds

$$CCl_4 + 2H_2O = CO_2 + 4HCl \ (\Delta F = 31.8 \text{ kcal.})$$

$$SiCl_4 + 2H_2O = SiO_2 + 4HCl \ (\Delta F = 14.8 \text{ kcal.})$$

hydrolysis can lower the free energy of the system which means that neither of the two chlorides is stable in contact with water. The value ΔF, the driving force for the hydrolysis of CCl_4 is greater than that for the hydrolysis of $SiCl_4$. However, the facts that CCl_4 at ordinary temperature does not hydrolyze at a noticeable rate and that $SiCl_4$ reacts very fast have to be learned from experiments.

The statement that the hydrolysis of CCl_4 has a higher activation energy than that of $SiCl_4$ is only a description of the experimental findings. In order to give an explanation, we have to link the activation energies or the energy barriers of the two reactions to the structures of the molecules. The reaction of a substance with water may proceed in several ways. As far as the hydrolysis of glasses is concerned we are primarily interested in those cases where the reaction is initiated by a proton of a water molecule or of an acid entering an anion of the substance. This happens when that anion is sufficiently polarizable to provide better screening for the proton than the water. The rate of proton penetration increases with temperature and with increasing polarizability of the anions of the reactant. This statement may require an amplification. A proton in its thermal vibration explores, so to speak, its environment. If such a proton approaches a highly polarizable anion it deforms the electron cloud thus producing in this anion a spot of high electron density. The electrostatic attractive forces between this spot of high electron density and the proton may then become so high that the proton does not return to its original position. The first part of this path of the reaction, therefore, can be described as follows: A proton moves from one electron cloud into another electron cloud and remains there if the latter offers better screening. The rate of this proton penetration into a more polarizable, better screening or more basic anion increases with increasing temperature. Larger amplitudes of the vibrations of the proton increase the probability of its finding a new location which is preferred energetically. The rate of this "proton jump" increases with increasing acidity of the water. The protons in an acidic solution are "less screened" than in pure water.

For a given temperature and acidity of the solution we assume that the rate of hydration as initiated by the proton penetration increases with increasing polarizability of the anion of the reactant. Neutral water can hydrolyze BaS but in order to send a proton into ZnS a diluted acid is required because S^{2-} ions polarized by non-noble gas-like cations (Zn^{2+}) do not offer better screening than neutral water. The sulfides of nickel and cobalt resist even fairly strong mineral acids.

Besides the penetration of a proton into an anion of a reactant, hydrolysis can be initiated also by the addition of an OH^- ion to the molecule. This step requires that the reactant contain a cation that can increase its coordination. The rate of solution of the quartz-like modification of GeO_2 in water is greater than that of the rutile-like modification. In the rutile form each Ge^{4+} ion is screened by six O^{2-} ions so that OH^- addition is not likely to occur. The quartz-like form contains Ge^{4+} ions surrounded by only four O^{2-} ions so that the Ge^{4+} ions can expand their coordination by adding OH^- ions. This first step is then followed by the penetration of a proton into a neighboring O^{2+} ion.

On the basis of these two factors we can explain the failure of CCl_4 to hydrolyze at ordinary temperature and the rapid hydrolysis of $SiCl_4$. Firstly, the carbon core is not likely to expand its coordination above 4; therefore, hydrolysis is unlikely to be initiated by the addition of an OH^- ion. Secondly, the Cl^- ions in CCl_4 are tightened by the carbon core to such an extent that proton penetration is not likely to initiate the hydrolysis of carbon tetrachloride. The hydrolysis of $SiCl_4$ and of CCl_4 are reactions which are not microscopically reversible so that no relation exists between the rates of the reactions and the changes of the free energies. In spite of the smaller change of the free energy, $SiCl_4$ hydrolyzes fast because both processes can take place. First, the Si^{4+} ion can expand its coordination number above 4 and add an OH^- ion. Second, the Cl^- ions attached to a Si^{4+} ion are more polarizable than those under the influence of a carbon core. This makes proton penetration more likely to occur in $SiCl_4$ than in CCl_4.

From these examples we see that hydrolysis can be initiated by either one of two mechanisms:

1. Addition of OH^- ion followed by proton penetration into an anion. This reaction is likely to take place if the reactant contains cations which can expand their coordination.

2. Penetration of a proton into an anion followed by the addition of an OH^- ion. This reaction requires that the reactant contain polarizable anions.

For reactions of solids with water, the second mechanism is the most important because in the surface of a solid the anions predominate. This mechanism of hydration focuses attention upon the polarizability of surface ions.

It is customary to describe the hydration of aluminum sulfate, etc., by equations such as

$$Al_2(SO_4)_3 + 12H_2O = [Al(H_2O)_6]_2(SO_4)_3$$

The solution process, however, must not necessarily involve the addition of H_2O molecules. It is very likely that the rate-determining step for this process consists of the penetration of a proton of the water into a sulfate ion. For this reason, we will examine the factors which influence the addition of OH^- ions to cations and the penetration of protons into anions.

(*1.*) *Addition of* OH^- *Ions to Cations*

For an atomistic interpretation of the viscosity of silicate glasses we developed the concept of a "temporary partial unscreening" of the Si^{4+} ions as the major energy barrier which opposes viscous flow (33).

The same concept can be used for explaining the hydrolysis of phosphates. The orthophosphates contain isolated PO_4 tetrahedra. In the polyphosphates PO_4 tetrahedra share O^{2-} ions. The P^{5+} core can neither expand easily its coordination from 4 to 5 nor can it be screened easily by three anions. For this reason metaphosphoric acid, $PO_2(OH)$, does not exist as a monomer.

The change of coordination can be a very important factor in determining the rate of hydration of inorganic substances, especially in those cases where proton penetration is unlikely to initiate the process. The bridging oxygen ions polarized by two P^{5+} cores in a polyphosphate have a low polarizability so that protons from water are not likely to penetrate into their electron clouds.

The kinetic stability of anions of different phosphoric acids in aqueous solution shows the importance of the flexibility of the coordination number. The nonexistence of the monomer of metaphosphoric acid, $PO_2(OH)$, or the hydrated $(PO_3)^-$ ion indicates that phosphorus has the minimum coordination number of 4 with respect to oxygen or OH^- ions. Unlike S^{6+}, its neighbor in the periodic table, the field of the P^{5+} core is not sufficiently strong to deform three O^{2-} ions to such an extent that it becomes well screened. The molecule SO_3, but not the anion of the metaphosphoric acid, $(PO_3)^-$, can be obtained as a monomer. Unlike Si^{4+}, the other neighbor in the periodic chart, the P^{5+} core cannot easily expand its coordination and accommodate more than four oxygens, even if they contain protons. As a result, the molecule

$$\begin{matrix} O^{2-} & & O^{2-} \\ & P^{5+} & \\ & (OH)^- & \end{matrix}$$

has to polymerize and share O^{2-} ions. This lack of flexibility of the coordination number with respect to O^{2-} or OH^- ions is responsible for the unique aqueous chemistry of phosphorus which distinguishes it not only from As^{5+}, Sb^{5+}, and V^{5+} compounds but also from related borates and silicates.

The As^{5+}, Sb^{5+}, and V^{5+} cores can expand their coordination number above 4; P^{5+} cores cannot. Boron occurs in threefold and fourfold coordination. Silicon occurs in fourfold and sixfold coordination. As a result, hydration and dehydration reactions of arsenates, antimonates, vanadates, borates, and silicates in aqueous solutions are fast as compared with those of pyro- and metaphosphates in which the structural unit does not permit addition of OH^- ions. The change of pyrophosphate in water into the stable orthophosphate is slow but can be catalyzed by acids. In the presence of acids, proton penetration becomes the rate determining mechanism.

The hydrolysis of an ester does not occur via the simple addition of H_2O molecules; it has to proceed via two steps. One step consists of a proton penetrating a polarizable anion which provides better screening than the water molecule or the acid which causes hydrolysis. The other step is the addition of OH^- ions to cores which can expand their coordination number. Which of these two steps is the first or which determines the rate of hydrolysis depends on the nature of the reactants. Rates of hydrolysis have been studied primarily for organic compounds. It has been found that the hydrolysis of esters, e.g., ethyl acetate, can be catalyzed by acids as well as by bases. The carbon of the carboxyl group marked by an asterisk C*:

$$CH_3—C^*(=O)—O^*—C_2H_5$$

has the coordination number 3; it is linked to one CH_3, one O, and one OC_2H_5 group. Carbon can expand its coordination to 4 and, as a result, OH^- ions will be attracted to this carbon core. The addition of an OH^- ion to the C* carbon gives the molecule a negative charge which helps to attract H^+ ions and leads to the penetration of a proton into the oxygen that has been marked with an asterisk. The O* in this compound can improve the screening of a proton of an acidified aqueous solution. Hence, both acids and bases can catalyze the hydrolysis of this ester to acetic acid and ethyl alcohol.

(2.) *Proton Penetration into Anions*

The main parameter which determines the rate of penetration of a proton into an anion is its polarizability. We will briefly discuss the effects of the major variables upon the polarizability of an anion, e.g., the field strengths of adjacent cations, the coordination number of the anion, the internuclear distances, and the electronic structure of the cation.

A classical example for the influence of the field strength of the cation on the rate of the solubility is the couple calcite, $CaCO_3$, and dolomite, $CaMg(CO_3)_2$. Mineralogists identify these minerals by their different reactivities with diluted HCl. Only calcite effervesces; dolomite does not. Thermodynamically, neither of the two minerals is in equilibrium with hydrochloric acid, but kinetically their reactions differ so strongly that dilute HCl can be used for their identification.

A. Ferrari and L. Sessa (39) measured the reaction rates of calcite, dolomite and magnesite in diluted acids and found the following relative rates:

calcite: 100,000 dolomite: 650 magnesite: 9

Magnesium ions, due to their small size, exert a stronger tightening effect upon the $(CO_3)^{2-}$ ions than the larger Ca^{2+} ions so that proton penetration becomes more difficult.

On the same basis one can explain why crystalline $Al(OH)_3$ and $Be(OH)_2$ are not readily dissolved when treated with acetic acid or dilute HCl, whereas $Ca(OH)_2$ goes into solution practically instantaneously. The small Be^{2+} ion and the triply charged Al^{3+} ion tighten the OH^- ions to such an extent that proton penetration becomes exceedingly slow. In order to dissolve $Be(OH)_2$ a fairly concentrated hydrochloric acid has to be used.

The compound silicon disulfide, SiS_2, contains a large polarizable anion, the S^{2-} ion. The S^{2-} ion is penetrable for a proton because it offers better screening than the O^{2-} of water. Therefore, the SiS_2 hydrolysis easily: it even has a strong H_2S smell in the "dry" solid state.

In alkali silicate glasses we have two types of cations and two types of O^{2-} ions which are described as "bridging" and "nonbridging" oxygens. The "bridging" oxygens are tightened by two Si^{4+} ions and are not very polarizable. The "nonbridging" oxygens have a much greater polarizability because they are exposed to only one Si^{4+} ion. Their added exposure to the much weaker field of the alkali ion has a lesser effect upon their polarizability. An alkali silicate glass hydrolyzes fast because a proton can enter the polarizable "nonbridging" oxygen and then be followed by the addition of an OH^- ion.

Comparing a series of alkali silicate glasses of corresponding alkali content, one finds that the rate of hydrolysis increases drastically with decreasing field strength of the alkali ion. Lithium silicate is fairly stable in an ordinary atmosphere, but cesium disilicate glass becomes plasticized by exposure to water vapor at room temperature. A cesium disilicate glass has O^{2-} ions of the highest polarizability because the large and singly charged Cs^+ ion has the weakest field of all the alkalies. Thus, a proton from the H_2O finds better screening in the O^{2-} of the glass and will initiate hydrolysis.

Thus a glass of the composition 85% SiO_2, 15% Na_2O would be useless as a bottle or window pane. However, replacing 15% of the insoluble SiO_2 by the soluble CaO produces a glass composition suitable for window panes. In order to explain this paradoxical phenomenon some structural considerations must be introduced.

Calcium ions are introduced into the glass in the form of CaO or $CaCO_3$. Each Ca^{2+} ion adds to the melt one polarizable O^{2-} ion but ties up several polarizable O^{2-} ions. Structurally speaking, a

Ca^{2+} ion changes nonbridging O^{2-} ions into O^{2-} ions which are tightened by three cations, one Si^{4+}, one Na^{+}, and one Ca^{2+} ion.

No matter how much we increase the silica content of a sodium silicate glass we do not eliminate the highly polarizable non-bridging O^{2-} ions: we only decrease their concentration. The addition of CaO, however, eliminates the nonbridging O^{2-} ions so that the glass no longer contains anions which are sufficiently polarizable to permit protons to enter.

In gaseous SO_3 the central core is screened by three anions which form the corners of an equilateral triangle:

$$\begin{array}{ccc} O^{2-} & & O^{2-} \\ & S^{6+} & \\ & O^{2-} & \end{array}$$

In order to screen the positive core in space the electron clouds of these three O^{2-} ions are very strongly deformed. The S^{6+} core attracts the electrons of the anions to such an extent that the electron density toward the exterior of the molecule is so low that protons from water cannot enter easily. In the manufacture of sulfuric acid one uses, therefore, a fairly strong sulfuric acid for absorbing SO_3 from the gas phase.

The condensation of SO_3 to a liquid or to a solid consists of a strongly exothermic polymerization process in which the S^{6+} core expands its coordination from 3 to 4, e.g., by forming chains:

$$\begin{array}{cccccccc} & & O & & O & & O & \\ \cdots & O & S & O & S & O & S & \cdots \\ & & O & & O & & O & \end{array} \quad \text{or} \quad [S^{6+}(O^{2-}/2)_2(O^{2-})_2]_n$$

In fourfold coordination the S^{6+} core is better screened and the anions are more polarizable. This leads to the paradoxical phenomenon that solid SO_3 reacts with H_2O with explosive violence, but the gaseous monomer reacts only reluctantly so that for practical purposes its hydration has to be catalyzed by an acid.

Most crystal chemical and structural considerations are centered around the coordination number of the cations because, as a rule, its change involves a major change of electrostatic energy. Due to the high polarizability of anions their coordination is less important from the viewpoint of structure and stability. For the understanding of the rates of penetration of protons into anions it is important to consider the tightening of anions by the surrounding cations. For the understanding of some kinetic phenomena the coordination number of the anions becomes an important parameter.

GeO_2 forms two modifications, one having the structure of quartz, the other that of rutile. In the rutile-like modification each O^{2-} ion is tightened by three Ge^{4+} ions, whereas in the quartz-like modification each O^{2-} ion is exposed to only two cations. This structural difference partly accounts for the much greater solution rate of the quartz-like form of GeO_2 in water. In addition to this feature the Ge^{4+} ions in the quartz structure do not have their most stable coordination but they can easily expand their coordination from 4 to 6, which also facilitates hydration through the addition of OH^- ions.

Also, as we have seen, an increase in the coordination number of some O^{2-} ions in a glass is responsible for the drastic improvement of the chemical resistivity of an alkali silicate glass upon the addition of oxides such as Al_2O_3, MgO, CaO, or B_2O_3.

Bringing cations closer to an anion has very much the same effect as increasing its coordination number or increasing the field strengths of the surrounding cations.

L. Coes (40) synthesized a new modification of silica by oxidizing silicon at 700 to 800°C. under high pressure. Even very small particles of this dense form of silica ($d = 3.0$) are not attacked by HF. The high degree of compacting in this high pressure modification brings the Si^{4+} ions close to the O^{2-} ions so that the polarizability of the O^{2-} ion has been lowered to such an extent that the protons of hydrofluoric acid can no longer enter. In contrast to quartz, cristobalite, tridymite, and vitreous silica, this dense form of silica does not react with HF at a noticeable rate.

An increase in the internuclear distance increases the chemical reactivity because it increases the polarizability of the anions. Another form of silica which was first prepared by A. Weiss and A. Weiss (41) is fibrous and has a low density ($d = 2.0$). In this modification (SiS_2 structure) the Si—O distance is more than 10% greater than that of quartz and, as a result, the polarizability of the O^{2-} ion has reached a value so high that it can react with water rapidly at ordinary temperature. With an aqueous solution of silver nitrate this form of SiO_2 produces a yellow silver silicate.

The internuclear distances can be increased also by mechanical forces. The phenomenon known as stress corrosion is the result of higher chemical reactivity of solids, in particular metals, under tensile stresses.

Temperature also has an effect upon the polarizability of anions. Most solids expand on heating. As the internuclear distances increase, the polarizabilities of the anions also increase. As a result, the refractive index of a crystal or a glass does not decrease to the same extent as one would expect from the decrease of the electron density due to its thermal expansion.

The increase in the polarizability of anions is revealed not only in the refractive index but also in the shift of the light absorption to longer wavelengths. Substances which do not undergo an abrupt structural change but merely expand on heating shift their absorption in the visible or ultraviolet part of the spectrum toward longer wavelengths. The increased polarizability of the anions is partly responsible for the strong increase in the rate of solution of oxides and sulfides in dilute acids. Using the polarizability of an anion and the screening demand of the proton we can use their fluctuations with the thermal vibrations for deriving a picture of their "active states" without involving kinetic energies of collisions.

Also, the polarizing power of cations which have an 18 shell or an incompletely filled inner shell is much greater than one would expect from their sizes and charges. The non-noble gas-type ion prefers an environment of polarizable anions.

The hydroxides of heavy metals exhibit a tendency to cleave off water and to change into oxides or hydrated oxides. The change of two shared OH^- ions into an O^{2-} bridge

$$Fe^{3+} \begin{matrix} (OH)^- \\ \\ (OH)^- \end{matrix} Fe^{3+} \rightarrow Fe^{3+}O^{2-}Fe^{3+} + H_2O$$

improves the screening of the ferric ions more than it would improve that of Al^{3+} ions because it changes anions of low polarizability into the more polarizable O^{2-} ions. The latter can interact more strongly with the penetrable Fe^{3+} ions. This penetration of electrons from the anion into the inner shell of a non-noble gas-like cation can be detected by the decreased paramagnetism. An oxide such as Cr_2O_3 or Fe_2O_3 is less paramagnetic than the hydroxide.

The sulfides of Co^{2+} and Ni^{2+} cannot be precipitated from acid solutions, but once CoS and NiS have formed they resist even fairly strong mineral acids. The S^{2-} ions surrounded and tightened by the penetrable Co^{2+} and Ni^{2+} ions do not permit protons to enter the S^{2-} ions.

An interesting problem to be faced in an attempt to explain

hydration reactions is the hygroscopicity of hydrated substances ($CrCl_3 \cdot 6H_2O$) that are hydrophobic in their anhydrous state (sublimed $CrCl_3$). This situation applies also to glasses, the hydrated glass reacts faster with water than the anhydrous glass. The hydration of a glass is an autocatalytic process because water is not only a reactant but also a catalyst. The sharp transition between obsidian, a natural glass, and perlite, its hydration product, is evidence for this relationship.

The conventional treatment of diffusion reactions often refers to Fick's law because of the simple mathematics involved. Fick's law has been derived for the propagation of heat within a solid and it provides a formula for the temperature gradient which is established. In analogy with the flow of heat one can derive the concentration gradient for the diffusion of a molecular species into a medium as the result of a concentration gradient. Fick's formula is based on the assumption that the diffusion constant of a molecule or ion does not change with its concentration, an assumption which is a gross oversimplification for many systems.

The diffusion of CoO or NiO into a crystal of MgO, for example, causes a disproportionation of the binding forces because the ionization potentials of Co (17.3 e.v.) and Ni (18.2 e.v.) are higher than that of Mg (15.0 e.v.). The early workers in the field of solid state reactions found that the rate of the reaction between MgO and NiO or CoO at a given temperature is much faster than the rate of recrystallization of MgO or its sintering. Because of the higher affinity of Co^{2+} ions for electrons, the Co—O bond is strengthened at the expense of existing Mg—O bonds. For this reason, oxides of the transition elements react at relatively low temperature with MgO or Al_2O_3. For the same reason these ions strongly lower the viscosity of a glass when they are substituted for cations of the same size and charge but of noble gas configuration. The formation of a solid solution of NiO in MgO represents an autocatalytic reaction in which NiO is a reactant as well as a catalyst which weakens the Mg—O bonds.

The same is true for the hydration of some glasses. The importance of this autocatalysis is twofold. Firstly, the diffusion of water into glasses cannot be expected to follow Fick's law; it may produce a steep concentration gradient. Secondly, glasses that are extremely hygroscopic, for example, vitreous P_2O_5, B_2O_3 or the alkali silicates, should become much more resistant toward hydration when they are obtained in an anhydrous state.

CHAPTER VI

IDEAL CRYSTALS

For a compound A^+X^- the radius ratio decides the coordination number of the cation provided that the ions can be treated as rigid spheres. One can calculate the lattice energies for different groupings and find out which one of all possible structures is the most stable. This has been done by M. Born and J. E. Mayer (42). The alkali halides form two groups. At normal temperature and pressure CsCl, CsBr, and CsI crystallize in the CsCl structure in which the cations have the coordination number of eight. All other alkali halides crystallize in the NaCl structure. Using refinements of the original Born-Lande approach, Born and Mayer obtained values for the lattice energies of the alkali halides which are in good agreement with the observed stabilities. They found that the value of the lattice energy of the CsCl structure is not very different from that of the NaCl structure. For a radius ratio, $r_{\text{cation}}/r_{\text{anion}}$, which is larger than 0.73, the CsCl type is the more stable structure; i.e., the one with the highest lattice energy. If the radius ratio becomes smaller than 0.73 the NaCl type is preferred energetically. This structure is characteristic for most alkali halides as well as for the oxides, sulfides, and selenides of the alkaline earth ions. Only in extreme cases, e.g., for the magnesium telluride and the oxide, sulfide, etc., of beryllium, in which the radius ratio is less than 0.4, does a lattice with the coordination number of only 4 (ZnS-type) become stable. This rule holds fairly well if one excludes those combinations of ions which lead to major polarization effects.

The structure of compounds of the general formula AX_2 is also controlled by the radius ratio. For large cations, i.e., values of r_A/r_X greater than 0.73, the fluorite structure is the most stable. In CaF_2 each Ca^{2+} ion is surrounded by eight F^- ions and each F^- ion touches four Ca^{2+} ions. The anions occupy the corners of a cube with a cation in the center and the cations occupy the corners of a regular tetrahedron with the anion in the center. The coordination number of the cations is 8 and that of the anion is 4. BaF_2 and SrF_2 have the structure of fluorite, CaF_2. Oxides of the formula AX_2 also may have fluorite structure if the cation is large, e.g., UO_2, CeO_2, ThO_2.

Another simple structure has the same geometry as CaF_2 but with the positions of anions and cations reversed: antifluorite structure. The oxides of the alkalies, e.g., Li_2O and Na_2O, have the antifluorite structure. In these crystals each alkali ion is surrounded by four O^{2-} ions and each O^{2-} ion, in turn, touches eight alkali ions, e.g.,

$$Li^+ (O^{2-}/8)_4$$

For compounds of the formula AX_2 which contain small cations so that the radius ratio lies between 0.73 and 0.41 the rutile structure is more stable than the fluorite structure. In rutile, TiO_2, the cations have the coordination number of 6 and each anion touches three cations. The fluorides of Mg^{2+}, Mn^{2+}, Co^{2+}, Ni^{2+}, etc., crystallize in the structure of rutile: the same is true for the oxides SnO_2, VO_2, WO_2 or GeO_2. The latter may also form a quartz-like modification in which the cation is surrounded by only four anions. This structure becomes stable for radius ratios smaller than 0.41. In the different modifications of silica and beryllium fluoride the cations are in fourfold coordination.

Looking over the structures of simple chemical compounds, e.g., PbO, $MgCl_2$, TlF, etc., we encounter many more crystal structures of lower symmetry. This raises the questions: Why do not all compounds which have the general formula AX crystallize either in the CsCl, the NaCl, or the ZnS structure? Why do not all compounds which have the general formula AX_2 crystallize in the structure of fluorite, rutile, or cristobalite? Which parameters other than the radius ratio determine the atomic structure of crystal?

Obviously, the purely geometrical approach to the structures of compounds of the formula $A^{n+}X^{n-}$ requires some refinements. It is not possible to treat large and polarizable anions, e.g., S^{2-} or I^- ions, as rigid spheres. The density distribution of their electron clouds may deviate so strongly from that of a rigid sphere that patterns of rather low symmetry, e.g., layer lattices, are energetically preferred over groupings which have a higher symmetry.

The same argument applies to compounds in which the cations are of the non-noble gas-type. The structure of strontium oxide reveals that the electrical field of the Sr^{2+} ion has a spherical symmetry. The structure of lead oxide, however, reveals that the Pb^{2+} ion which in its hydrated state has approximately the same size as the hydrated Sr^{2+} ion does not have a field which is spherically symmetrical. The electron density distribution of the Pb^{2+} ion is such that it interacts more strongly with four of its surrounding eight O^{2-} ions than with the other four. The Pb^{2+} ion in addition to its excess charge of two has a strong dipole and can, therefore, be described as $[Pb^{4+}(e_2^-)]^{2+}$. Some ions, e.g., $(CO_3)^{2-}$ or OH^-, even in their hydrated state are not spheres. One can easily replace in a complicated mica or apatite structure an occasional F^- ion by an OH^- ion, but one must not expect NaOH to have the same structure as NaF, or $Ca(OH)_2$ to have the same structure as CaF_2. The polarity of certain ions is another reason why not all simple compounds crystallize in one of the highly symmetrical structures. Later we will see that there is a considerable difference between glasses based on fluorides and those which contain the OH^- ions as the major anions.

1. Pauling's Rules

L. Pauling (43) derived a number of rules according to which crystals of the complex ionic type are built. In order to exclude major polarization effects, Pauling limits his principles to crystals which contain only small cations (less than 0.8 A.) and which have charges of 3 or 4 but not more. The anions are large as compared with the cations and their charge should be small (F^- or O^{2-} but not N^{3-}). Pauling also excludes crystals which contain highly deformable anions, e.g., Te^{2-} or I^- ions.

RULE I: A coordinated polyhedron of anions forms around each cation. The cation-anion distance is determined by the radius sum. The coordination number is determined by the radius ratio.

We have seen that the "valency" of an element in solid state chemistry has lost its original meaning. Pauling suggests, therefore, that the concept of the valency of atoms be replaced by the "electrostatic valence principle."

RULE II: In a stable coordination structure, the electric charge of each anion tends to compensate for the strength of the electrostatic valence bonds reaching to it from the cations at the centers of the polyhedra of which it forms a corner.

The electrostatic valence principle indicates the number of polyhedra which have a common corner. In rutile, brookite, and anatase each O^{2-} ion is common to three TiO_6 octahedra which means that each Ti^{4+} ion is surrounded by six O^{2-} ions but only one-third of each O^{2-} ion is required for producing electroneutrality.

$$Ti^{4+} (O^{2-}/3)_6$$

The stability of a lattice depends on the number of corners shared by two polyhedra.

RULE III: The presence of shared edges and, particularly, of shared faces in a coordination structure decreases its stability.

The decrease in the stability of the lattice is the result of the cation-cation repulsion which increases with decreasing cation-cation distance. For this reason in the stable modifications of silica the SiO_4 tetrahedra share corners but not edges or faces. The sharing of an edge between two regular tetrahedra decreases the cation-cation distance to 0.58 times and the sharing of a face to 0.33 times its original value. The controlled oxidation of silicon monoxide produces a highly reactive fibrous form of SiO_2 in which the SiO_4 tetrahedra share edges (A. Weiss and A. Weiss (41)). Traces of water are sufficient to convert this form which has the SiS_2 structure into amorphous SiO_2.

The fact that cations with high electric charges tend to be as far apart from each other as possible leads to the next rule governing the nature of contiguous polyhedra.

RULE IV: In a crystal containing different cations, those with high charge and small coordination number tend not to share polyhedron elements with each other.

In silicates, the SiO_4 tetrahedra share corners only if absolutely necessary but not if the O:Si ratio exceeds 4.

The last of Pauling's rules brings out the fact that crystals which contain many different elements are rare.

RULE V: The number of essentially different kinds of constituents in a crystal tends to be small. This rule seems to be obvious for crystals because it guarantees a certain simplicity and makes long range order possible. However the rule seems to be applicable to glasses when long range order is not established. We will see later that certain glass compositions favor the inclusion of Ni^{2+} ions in fourfold, tetrahedral coordination whereas others favor octahedral coordination. Strangely enough, glasses of intermediate composition contain both types of structural units and this raises the question: Why does a glass not contain Ni^{2+} ions in fourfold, fivefold, and sixfold coordination?

2. Isostructural Crystals and Solid Solutions

As compared with inorganic chemistry as a whole, the emphasis in crystal chemistry is shifted from the atomic number of an element to the basic properties of its ions, in particular to their sizes, charges, and electronic configurations. The classical concept of isomorphism (E. Mitscherlich) stresses the "chemical similarity" as a prerequisite for substances to crystallize in the same system. Because of this "similarity" in a chemical sense, isomorphism played an important role in decisions concerning the determination of the valence state of elements. Selenates are isomorphous with sulfates, permanganates with perchlorates, phosphates with arsenates, etc. Hence, the principle of chemical similarity could be used in the determination of the valence states of elements.

With the advent of X rays, chemists could identify insoluble crystals and thus extend their work toward high temperature reactions. High temperature chemistry was first practiced by some mineralogists during the eighteenth and nineteenth centuries but more systematic efforts could be made only when it was possible to identify submicroscopic crystals by their X-ray patterns. The extension of chemistry to high temperatures produced many substances which violated the classical rule of isomorphism.

There is no chemical similarity in the usual sense between the oxide of silicon and the phosphate of aluminum. Nevertheless, from a crystal chemical point of view, the compound $AlPO_4$ shows some striking resemblances to the compound SiO_2 in its various crystalline modifications. M. Strade, in 1934, obtained $AlPO_4$ in a cristobalite-like modification, H. F. Hüttenlocher, in 1935, reported a quartz-like modification, and J. W. Gruner, in 1945, found a tridymite-like modification. This far-reaching similarity in the crystallographic properties of two chemically unrelated substances is one of the characteristic features of the crystal chemistry of high temperature reaction products.

In this particular case, the crystal chemical similarity is the result of the fact that Al^{3+}, P^{5+}, and Si^{4+} ions have the same coordination requirements. This makes it possible to retain the structure of $SiSiO_4$ by replacing one half of the silicon ions by Al^{3+} and the other half by P^{5+} ions. The only change that this substitution causes in the structure is that the size of the elementary cell is doubled.

The quartz structure can also be retained if one half of the Si^{4+} ions is replaced by Al^{3+} ions and the deficiency of positive charges made up by the addition of the small Li^+ ion. Thus, the compound $LiAlSiO_4$ has a quartz-like structure. If the large Na^+ ion is used to compensate for the charge deficiency, the compound $NaAlSiO_4$ is formed, which forms a cristobalite-like and a tridymite-like but not a quartz-like modification.

In spite of the far reaching structural similarity between the different crystalline modifications of $SiSiO_4$ and those of $AlPO_4$ A. Dietzel and H. J. Poegel (44) found no similarity for these substances in the glassy state, because in the fused state the condition for the structural similarity, namely, the alternation of AlO_4 and PO_4 groups, is missing. This difference expresses itself in several ways. Firstly, the melting point of $AlPO_4$ is higher than that of $SiSiO_4$ whereas all other phase transformation temperatures are lower. Secondly, on melting, $AlPO_4$ decomposes. The interaction of PO_4 groups now no longer separated by AlO_4 groups leads to the formation and vaporization of P_2O_5. In their glass-forming properties the two substances show drastic differences. The system Na_2O-$AlPO_4$ is pseudo-binary. Additions up to 17% Na_2O produced crystallization of corundum. In the system Na_2O-$AlPO_4$ H. J. Poegel (45) obtained glasses only in the narrow composition range of 17 to 29% Na_2O.

$AlPO_4$ and $SiSiO_4$ do not form solid solutions for the same reason. The classical concept of isomorphism was based on the ability of two substances to form solid solutions. $AlPO_4$ and SiO_2 are isostructural but not isomorphous in the classical sense.

H. G. Grimm and K. F. Herzfeld found that the formation of most solid solutions is a weakly endothermic process. The formation of a solid solution increases the disorder of the system. The gain of entropy by this disorder contributes to the free energy and is proportional to the absolute temperature. At absolute zero solid solutions should not be stable. Indeed, we find many systems in which "exsolution" takes place if the temperature is lowered. The crystallization of NaCl and KCl from an aqueous solution does not give a solid solution. However, a melt of the two chlorides when cooled rapidly produces a solid solution which is metastable at ordinary temperature. The clear crystals turn turbid with time because even at room temperature they segregate into two phases.

The formation of perthite from anorthoclase is a typical exsolution which occurs in nature. F. Becke, in 1913, calculated that this process caused the volume to decrease by 0.5%. The gain of electrostatic energy exceeds the loss of entropy on cooling.

3. Polymorphism

E. Mitscherlich, a few years after he had discovered isomorphism, found that a single compound may occur in two or more crystal "forms" or, as we prefer to express it today, structural types: polymorphism.

Polymorphism refers to crystal structures only. In many instances the difference between lattice energies, e.g., of the NaCl and the CsCl structure of an alkali halide, is rather small so that a change in temperature or pressure may cause the stabilities of the two structures to reverse. The differences between two polymorphous forms, e.g., their different colors, disappear if polymorphous substances are dissolved in a liquid or if they are vaporized. If two solids, e.g., urea, $CO(NH_2)_2$, and ammonium cyanate, NH_4CNO, have the same molecular weight in solution and the same chemical composition they are called isomers. The differences between isomers persist in solution and in the vapor phase. Chemists also use the word "allotropy" and speak of allotropic modifications if an element, e.g., sulfur or carbon, occurs in different forms. Allotropy is restricted to elements but not to crystals. The gases oxygen and ozone are called allotropic modifications. One can express the difference by giving the electronic configuration of those molecules by their quanticule formula; namely,

$$e^- \; O^{6+} \; (\bar{e}_{10}) \; O^{6+} \; e^-$$

for O_2 and

$$\begin{array}{ccc} & (\bar{e}_2) & \\ & O^{6+} & \\ O^{2-} & & O^{2-} \end{array}$$

for O_3 so that today no real need exists for the term "allotropy."

Cesium chloride (Cs^+ in eightfold coordination) changes its structure into an NaCl structure when the temperature is raised above 460°C. Frequently one finds that a substance at high temperature assumes a structure in which the cations have a lower coordination than at low temperature. Increasing the pressure has the opposite effect. The coordination number of Ag^+ ions in AgI at ordinary temperature is 4, but under hydrostatic pressure it changes into 6: AgI assumes the NaCl structure. The iodide of rubidium (NaCl structure) under pressure assumes CsCl structure, i.e., the coordination number of the Rb^+ ions increases from 6 to 8.

Increasing the temperature increases the internuclear distances and thus decreases the mutual polarization of the ions. Hence, as a rule, the high temperature modification of a substance has the higher symmetry because induced dipole moments in anions and cations disappear with increasing inter-nuclear distances. Even ions such as $(OH)^-$ or $(CN)^-$ which have permanent dipoles or multipoles can lose their polarity at higher temperature by free rotations or they can increase the entropy of the crystal by assuming statistical rather than oriented positions.

4. Goldschmidt's Model Substances

Isostructural substances, e.g., the couple $SiSiO_4$-$AlPO_4$ or the couple $BaSO_4$-$KMnO_4$, have the same structure and the same valence sum. More than fifty years ago F. Zambonini discovered the crystallographic similarity between the fluoborate of rubidium and the sulfate of barium. There was no obvious relation between the salts $RbBF_4$ and $BaSO_4$ until Goldschmidt (4) discovered the basis on which the two compounds could be compared. These crystals have the same structure but they are neither chemically analogous nor do they have the same valence sum.

Applying his fundamental law of crystal chemistry, namely, that the structure of a crystal is determined by the ratio, the sizes, and the polarization properties of its building units, Goldschmidt systematically designed structures which would represent "models" of other crystals. His primary aim was to produce a "weakened" or a "strengthened" model of the structure of a compound by changing its "valence sum." According to his concept, the pair $RbBF_4$ and $BaSO_4$ have the relationship of weak and strong structures, respectively.

A single example may illustrate his ideas. The replacement of

TABLE XII

Model Structures and Their Melting Points

Weak structure	M.P., °C.	Strong structure	M.P., °C
BeF_2	538	SiO_2	1713
LiF	870	MgO	2800
MgF_2	1240	TiO_2	1830
CaF_2	1360	ThO_2	3050
Li_2BeF_4	458	Zn_2SiO_4	1509
$KMgF_3$	1070	$SrTiO_3$	2050
NaCl	800	CaS	2000

TABLE XIII

Comparison of Zinc Orthosilicate and Lithium Beryllium Fluoride

	Zn_2SiO_4	Li_2BeF_4
Lattice parameters	a = 8.04 A.	a = 7.60 A.
	c = 9.34 A.	c = 8.85 A.
	ratio c:a = 1.161	c:a = 1.165
Crystal properties	Rhombohedral	Same
	Habitus: prismatic	Same
	Cleavage parallel 1010	Same
Optical properties	Birefringence, weak positive = 0.02	Very weak, positive = 0.006
	Refractive index, 1.70	1.3
Hardness	5.5	3.8
Melting point	1510°C.	470°C.
Solubility	Insoluble in H_2O	Soluble, may be recrystallized from dilute HF

Th^{4+} ion (1.10 A.) by Ca^{2+} ions (1.06 A.) and of O^{2-} (1.32 A.) ions by F^- ions (1.33 A.) makes CaF_2 (valence sum = 2 + 1 + 1 = 4) the weakened model of ThO_2 (valence sum = 4 + 2 + 2 = 8). ThO_2, on the other hand, can be described as the strengthened model of CaF_2. In order to produce a weakened structure, one replaces the anions O^{2-}, S^{2-}, and Se^{2-} by singly charged ions that have similar sizes and comparable polarizabilities; namely, by F^-, Cl^-, and I^-, respectively. In Table XII we find some of these model structures in which the valence sums of the two series differ by a factor of two. Weakening a certain structure produces a crystal with similar lattice parameters and the same habitus and cleavage but one which has a lower hardness, a lower melting point, and a lower refractivity. The weak model has a greater solubility and a greater chemical reactivity as can be seen from a comparison of the properties of Li_2BeF_4 with Zn_2SiO_4 (Table XIII).

V. M. Goldschmidt's observations that the tendency of fused SiO_2 and of some silicates to form glasses on cooling is also a characteristic feature of the weakened models: BeF_2 and some complex fluoberyllates form complex glasses.

CHAPTER VII

REAL CRYSTALS

Most crystals we deal with in our laboratories do not conform with the pictures in our textbooks. A picture is necessarily static but, in reality, the atoms are in permanent thermal motion even at absolute zero. One can give only the positions of atoms or ions over a time average—no picture can show their spheres of action. Furthermore, a picture at its best gives only a few elementary cells. This is sufficient to indicate the relative positions of the atoms but, unfortunately, it gives the impression that this order extends throughout the crystal. It is important for a solid-state chemist to be aware of the fact that a crystal is not an infinitely extending network with self repeating units, but that it contains flaws. In order to interpret the intensities of the X-ray diffraction patterns of simple crystals, the early workers in this field were forced to assume some kind of permanent disorder, either a warped lattice or a mosaic structure. Such a mosaic or block structure also explains the scattering of light by crystals.

Real crystals have at least two kinds of defects, their thermal motion and their block structure.

Any crystal will develop vacant lattice sites and other kinds of disorder if the temperature of the crystal is raised close to the melting point. For a given crystal at a given temperature, an equilibrium is established between the different types of defects. The equilibrium concentration increases with increasing temperature and it is possible to "freeze in" a higher concentration of defects by cooling a crystal rapidly.

When the temperature of a crystal is raised several changes occur, all of which are important for its chemical reactivity, in particular for the rate of its reaction with gases, liquids, or other crystals. One thinks of the energy of the crystal primarily as determined by the vibrations of its atoms, by kT, the thermal energy. This relation is important but it represents only a part of the basis of solid state reactions.

On heating, a crystal expands and thermal expansion by itself can increase the chemical reactivity. The anions become loosened and more penetrable for protons (hydrolysis) and the cations, being screened to a lesser extent, can attract anions and temporarily increase their coordination. Even at constant temperature, lattice expansion can increase the reactivity. This feature is most important for the understanding of stress corrosion. A metal or a glass under tension becomes more reactive than the same solid unstressed.

Another result of increasing the temperature is that the number of lattice vacancies increases. These defects, too, increase diffusion and chemical reactivity at constant temperature partly because a defect leads to a disproportionation of the binding forces and the internuclear distances. This is important because it is possible to vary the number of vacant lattice sites at constant temperature by introducing foreign atoms.

In 1926, G. Tammann (1), the pioneer in the field of solid state reactions, found that a rapid increase in the reactivity of a crystal took place at a certain fraction (approximately one half) of its absolute melting temperature. Above this so-called "Tammann temperature" the course of the reaction of the crystal is dominated by its lattice defects.

1. Effect of the Entropy upon the Stability of a Defective Crystal

A system is stable only if its free energy F is a minimum. The free energy of a crystal, F, is determined by its internal energy, E, and its entropy S.

$$F = E - TS$$

The entropy which is a measure of the degree of disorder of a system increases with increasing number of defects. This leads to the conclusion that at any given temperature above 0°K. a stable crystal contains a finite concentration of defects. Crystals which have a lower or a higher concentration of defects have a higher free energy and are not in equilibrium.

Lattice defects increase the energy E of a crystal approximately proportional to their concentration n/N (n = number of defects and N = number of atoms in the lattice). Plotting the energy E as a function of the concentration of defects gives approximately a straight line (Fig. 1). The decrease of the configurational

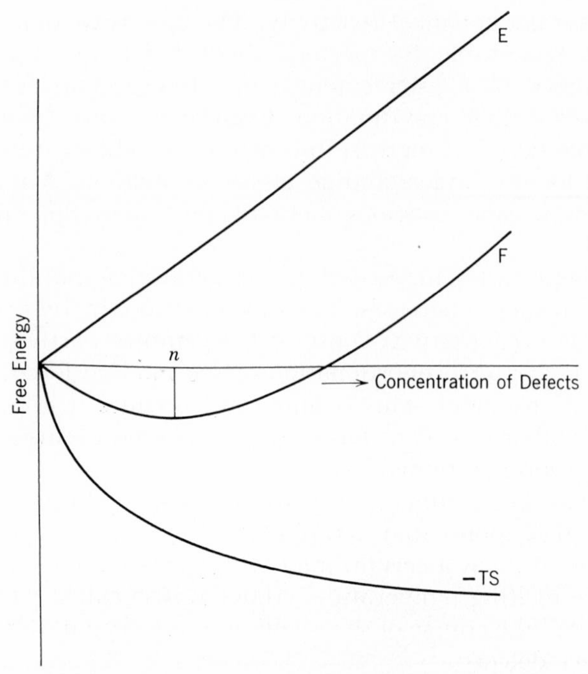

Fig. 1. Effect of defect concentration upon the stability of crystals. n = Number of defects in equilibrium at the temperature, T.

entropy as a function of the concentration of lattice vacancies is given schematically in the same figure by the curve $-TS_{\text{config.}}$. Subtracting the last curve from that for E gives the curve of the free energy F. The curve for the free energy goes through a minimum for a certain concentration of vacancies.

The entropy S which we used in the equation for the free energy consists of two parts, the thermal and the configurational entropy, and we can write:

$$S = S_{\text{thermal}} + S_{\text{configurational}}$$

The thermal entropy, $S_{\text{th.}}$, is determined by the number of different ways, $W_{\text{th.}}$, in which the total vibrational energy of the crystal may be distributed over all possible vibrational modes.

The configurational entropy, $S_{\text{config.}}$, of a crystal is determined by the disorder of the crystal which is a function of the number of defects and vacant lattice sites.

Let us assume that a lattice contains N_A atoms of the type A and N_B atoms of the type B. If all lattice sites are equivalent, meaning that each available lattice site can be occupied by either an atom A or an atom B, the configurational entropy is determined by the number of different ways, $W_{config.}$, in which the total number of cations $(N_A + N_B)$ can be distributed over the existing lattice sites

$$W_{config.} = \frac{(N_A + N_B)!}{N_A! N_B!}$$

The configurational entropy associated with the number of possible ways to distribute the atoms is given by the Boltzmann relation

$$S_{config.} = k \log W_{config.} = k \log \left[\frac{(N_A + N_B)!}{N_A! N_B!} \right]$$

in which k is the Boltzmann constant.

The same relation applies to a crystal which contains defects. For a perfect crystal containing identical atoms, for example, a crystal of metallic gold, there is only one way of distributing the gold atoms over the available lattice positions ($W_{config.} = 1$) and the configurational entropy of such a crystal is zero:

$$S_{config.} = k \cdot \log 1 = 0$$

The entropy of a perfect crystal is due only to its thermal entropy $S_{th.}$. If we produce defects in this crystal by removing at random n atoms from the interior by bringing them to the surface of the crystal, we have produced exactly n vacancies. The n vacant lattice sites increase the disorder of the system because now several ways exist in which the total number of atoms, N, and the n vacant lattice sites can be distributed over the N + n positions; namely,

$$W_{config.} = \frac{(N + n)!}{N!\, n!}$$

The presence of n vacancies in the lattice increases the total entropy of the system by

$$S_{config.} = k \log \left[\frac{(N + n)!}{N!\, n!} \right]$$

In crystals the number of vacancies can be derived from a

comparison between the actual measured density and its theoretical value calculated from the structure.

The density, d, of the crystal is equal to its weight divided by its volume:

$$d = \text{weight}/\text{volume}$$

A crystal containing 1 mole of a substance has the weight M. Its volume is equal to the number of elementary cells multiplied by the volume of each cell. The volume, V, of an elementary cell and the number of atoms which it contains can be determined with great accuracy by X-ray diffraction methods. If each elementary cell contains n atoms, such a crystal must contain $(1/\text{n}) \cdot N$ elementary cells, N being the Avogadro number, 6.0228×10^{23}. Hence, the density of the crystal is given by the formula

$$d = \frac{M}{1/\text{n} \cdot N \cdot V} = \frac{\text{n}M}{N \cdot V}$$

In 1951, N. W. H. Addink found that crystals of KCl obtained from an aqueous solution have the ideal density within experimental error. However, single crystals of KCl grown by the Kyropoulos method which involves crystallization at a temperature near the melting point showed imperfections of the order of 0.02%. This percentage agrees very well with the number of vacancies in KCl crystals near the melting point (1.2×10^{-4}) as derived from conductivity measurements by C. Wagner and P. Hantelmann (46).

Several types of defects may occur in a crystal. They all increase the entropy contribution to the free energy. However, as a rule, a crystal is dominated by only one kind of defect; namely, by the one which has the lowest energy of formation.

2. Types of Defects

Many crystals are not "close packed" arrays of ions but have structures in which a fraction of all lattice sites remains unoccupied. Therefore, in the course of its thermal vibrations an ion may leave its normal lattice site and move into an empty place, an interstitial position. A crystal A_mB_n with x cation vacancies and x interstitial cations per mole can be given the formula

$$A_{m-x}\ (\text{C.V.})_x\ (\text{I:C})_xB_n$$

In our description of defective structure we use the following symbols: Cation vacancy, (C.V.); anion vacancy, (A.V.); interstitial cation, (I:C); electrons, (e^-); and missing electrons, (+).

There is no generally accepted classification of defects. The kinds of deviations from the ideal structures which are chosen as prototypes depend to a great extent upon the field in which a scientist is working. We shall restrict ourselves to a discussion of a few types of lattice defects.

A. Frenkel Defects

The formation of a vacancy by an ion assuming an interstitial position is called a "Frenkel defect" after one of the pioneers in the field of research on defective structures. Because of the existence of vacant sites, this particular ion, can move easily through the rigid lattice at temperatures far below the melting point if an electrical field is applied.

A vacant lattice site expands the volume of the crystal because of additional repulsive forces which come into play. If an Ag^+ ion is taken out of an AgCl crystal the adjacent six Cl^- ions will repel one another much more than when held together by the Ag^+ ion. Lattice expansion as determined by X rays and precision density measurements have, therefore, contributed much to our understanding and classification of lattice defects.

It is now generally accepted that the silver halides, in particular AgCl and AgBr, develop primarily Frenkel defects at elevated temperature. This suggestion was made on the basis of energy considerations by W. Jost and G. Nehlep in 1936.

The high temperature form of silver iodide, the α-AgI (stable above 146°C.), is characterized by a looser packing of its I^- ions than in the low temperature form. Each I^- ion touches only eight others. However, below this temperature, where the β-AgI is stable, the I^- ions are close-packed, each one touching twelve others. The α-AgI shows an unusually high cationic conductivity of the order of 1 ohm^{-1} cm^{-1}. C. Tubandt, in 1920, explained this unusually high unipolar conductivity by an abnormal mobility of the Ag^+ ion, and he called the α-AgI a crystal that consists only of an anionic lattice, whereas its cationic lattice is already in the "molten state." In 1935, L. W. Strock showed that the silver atoms are randomly distributed over all possible lattice sites, meaning that they must assume different coordination numbers; namely, 2, 3, and 4. This concept that a crystal can melt in two steps, the cationic part of the lattice at 146°C. and the anionic structure at 555°C., can be used for describing the reversible structural changes of glasses on heating and cooling below the softening range.

If the stepwise melting is important for the understanding of the properties of solids as simple as AgI, CuI, etc., one may visualize how important this phenomenon becomes for crystals and glasses which contain a high melting rigid framework of SiO_4, or SiO_4 plus AlO_4 groups, and weakly bonded ions such as the alkali ions which are distributed within this rigid network. Ordering of the alkalies may lower the potential energy of the system but if the gain of energy by order is small compared with kT, disorder will prevail. The optical properties of feldspars are used for their identification and some confusion has arisen from the observation that crystals of identical chemical composition can have different optical properties. The same situation exists in optical glasses in which annealed, strain-free glasses can undergo changes in their indices of refraction. Most disturbing is also the drift of volume in thermometer glasses (secular rise and ice-point depression). All these phenomena are due to order-disorder that arises from the fact that structures contain a greater number of possible lattice sites than alkali ions.

B. Schottky Defects

Whereas the Frenkel defect requires unoccupied lattice positions in which an ion can move without materially raising the energy of the crystal, the Schottky defect is less specific and occurs in all lattices if the temperature is raised sufficiently. On heating, an equal number of vacant cation sites and vacant anion sites are formed. The Schottky defect is the dominating structural defect in pure alkali halide crystals close to their melting points.

The formation of defects in crystals at high temperature is the result of their contribution to the entropy which increases and thus lowers their free energy. The effect of defects upon the potential energy of a crystal is more complex; it depends greatly on the additional mutual deformation that is introduced by the asymmetry of vacant lattice sites. The deformation energy is a function of the polarizing power of the cation and, hence, we can understand why the equilibrium concentration of defects in the alkali halides near the melting point is of the order of 10^{18} per $cm.^3$ or 1/100 of 1 $M\%$, but that of the silver halides is a hundred times greater, $10^{20}/cm.^3$, in spite of their lower melting temperatures.

Schottky defects can be introduced into a crystal by bringing into the lattice suitable foreign atoms that have a charge which differs from that of the ion which they replace. KCl, for example, can accommodate in its structure a small concentration of $SrCl_2$ because the Sr^{2+} ion has approximately the same size as the K^+ ion. However, the Sr^{2+} ion has twice the charge of the K^+ ion. This means that one Sr^{2+} ion occupies the lattice site of one K^+ ion but replaces 2 K^+ ions as far as electroneutrality is concerned. Such a crystal has the formula

$$K^+_{1-2x}\, Sr^{2+}_x\, (C.V.)_x\, Cl^-$$

indicating that x Sr^{2+} ions per mole produce x vacant cation sites. C. Wagner and P. Hantelmann (46), who performed this experiment, found that this anomalous solid solution KCl-$SrCl_2$ had a much higher ionic conductivity than pure KCl. Vacant cation sites enhance the mobility of the K^+ ions.

C. Berthollide-Compounds

In 1803, Berthollet in his *Essai de Statique Chimique* advanced the hypothesis that the chemical composition of a compound must not necessarily be uniquely defined but it may depend on the mode of its formation. This view was contrary to Proust's law of constant proportions and, consequently, it raised violent and widespread opposition. Today, more than 150 years later, the nonstoichiometric compounds play an important role in physical sciences. One often refers to this group of homogeneous but nonstoichiometric solids as "Berthollides" in contrast to the classical compounds, the "Daltonides."

Both Schottky defects and Frenkel defects can occur in crystals of exact stoichiometric composition; therefore, they cannot be detected by chemical analysis. Berthollides, at least in principle, can be detected by chemical analysis.

In semiconductors the deviation from stoichiometry is usually very small, scarcely detectable by analysis. There are, however, some Berthollides that show large deviations from stoichiometric composition.

3. Semiconductors

Compounds that contain ions of transition elements can form crystals which have unusual electronic properties.

E. Friederich, in a paper on "Chemical Valency and Electrical

Conductivity" in 1925, called attention to the electrical conductivity of compounds in which the valencies were not completely saturated. Whereas TiO_2 is an insulator with a specific conductivity at 20°C. of less than 10^{-12} reciprocal ohms, the compound TiO is a fairly good metallic conductor (2500 $ohms^{-1}$ $cm.^{-1}$).

The nitride of aluminum, AlN, is a good insulator but that of titanium, TiN, is a conductor. The carbide of aluminum, Al_4C_3, is a good insulator but that of vanadium, VC, is a conductor. The highest oxides of niobium and molybdenum, Nb_2O_5 and MoO_3, are insulators but lower oxides are electrical conductors. However, Friederich's rule that compounds with "unused valence electrons" have metallic conductivity had exceptions in both directions. As_2O_3 with "unused valencies" is an insulator and the compound CuS, which should not have unused valencies, is a metallic conductor.

At the beginning of this century, K. Bädeker and J. Königsberger and associates developed the concept of semiconductors (Halbleiter). The conductivities of semiconductors are much smaller than those of metals. They are characterized by a positive temperature coefficient of conductivity, the absolute value of which can be many times greater than that of metals which have a negative temperature coefficient of conductivity.

Semiconductors can be treated as ionic crystals which contain some "available" or "mobile" electrons as anions. Due to the high mobility of these electrons, fused semiconductors nucleate easily and are not likely to form glasses. It is important, therefore, to realize what causes the formation of a semiconductor.

Oxides such as V_2O_5 and Fe_2O_3 lose oxygen before they melt because of the increase in entropy. Reactions such as

$$V_2O_5 \rightarrow V_2^{5+} (e^-)_{2x}\, O_{5-x}^{2-}\, (\text{A. V.})_x$$

or

$$3Fe_2O_3 \rightarrow 2Fe_3O_4 + 1/2\, O_2$$

are not the result of an intrinsic instability of V^{5+} and Fe^{3+} ions above a certain temperature. These reactions occur because of the gain in entropy through the formation of a defective structure and of mobile particles such as O_2 molecules. These oxides can be retained in their stoichiometric composition by additions which increase the configurational entropy of the system. Small additions of oxides such as P_2O_5, MgO, BaO, etc. make it possible to produce vitreous V_2O_5 that cannot be obtained in the pure state.

The sintering of magnesite bricks is possible at relatively low temperatures through the addition of Fe_2O_3. In the crystal

$$Mg^{2+}_{1-3x}\ Fe^{3+}_{2x}\ (C.V.)_x\ O^{2-}$$

the ferric ion is stable up to much higher temperatures than in pure Fe_2O_3. The addition of TiO_2 to Fe_2O_3 produces a brown stain because the solid solution of Fe_2O_3 in TiO_2 is sufficiently defective so that it will not increase its stability at 1500°C. by changing some Fe^{3+} ions into Fe^{2+} ions. The defective black oxide of cobalt is changed into a red pigment by "alloying" it with MgO. The black oxide of manganese forms a stable purple pigment when "alloyed" with Al_2O_3.

Physicists use the band concept for describing the electronic conductivities of crystals such as nonstoichiometric TiO_2. The band concept pictures the energy distribution of all electrons in a crystal. We desire to interpret the conductivity of nonstoichiometric crystals from a chemical point of view. The white stoichiometric TiO_2, rutile, is an insulator. Its lattice consists of Ti^{4+} ions each of which is surrounded by six O^{2-} ions. Each O^{2-} ion participates in the screening of three cations.

The removal of oxygen from the rutile, e.g., by reduction with hydrogen gas at 900°C., produces a dark crystal which has vacant anion sites. The chemical composition lies between that of TiO_2 and Ti_2O_3 and the rutile structure is retained in spite of the non-stoichiometric composition. In order to be electrically neutral, the crystal must contain either electrons that take the place of the missing anions or titanium ions that have a charge lower than 4. The lower-valent Ti^{3+} ion is stable in aqueous solutions. Its occurrence in Ti_2O_3 (corundum structure) suggests the possibility that the semiconductor contains Ti^{3+} ions. Hence we can write:

$$Ti^{4+}_{1-2x}\ Ti^{3+}_{2x}\ O^{2-}_{2-x}\ (A.V.)_x$$

The removal of some oxygens (x per mole) produces Ti^{3+} ions ($2x$ per mole) that occupy the positions of regular Ti^{4+} ions.

We learned earlier that a sodium chloride crystal on heating develops anion vacancies. In order to retain its electroneutrality the same number of cation vacancies are formed. TiO_2 can form anion vacancies without vacant cation sites because it can retain its electroneutrality by changing some of its cations into a lower valence state. Offhand, we have no justification to write the formula as it has been given because one might also assume that divalent or monovalent titanium is formed rather than trivalent titanium.

We can avoid committing ourselves with respect to the details of the structure by writing into the formula of the semiconductor the number of electrons per mole without referring to their state of quantization:

$$Ti^{4+}\,(e^-)_{2x}\,O^{2-}_{2-x}\,(A.V.)_x$$

Looking at the structure of rutile we find that a missing O^{2-} ion affects three Ti^{4+} ions equally and simultaneously. This raises the problem of how to distribute two electrons among three Ti^{4+} ions. We may go one step further and ask why should we restrict the possibility of quantization of the two electrons to the three immediate neighbors of the vacant anion site? Considering the coulombic attraction between the electrons and the anion vacancy which in reference to the crystal lattice has a positive charge, it is to be expected that the electrons will remain close to the anion vacancy. Space charges would result from the removal of the electrons to more remote parts of the lattice. On the other hand, the gain of entropy by a more random distribution of the electrons and the fact that at higher temperature the value of kT of the lattice is sufficiently large to separate the electrons from the anion vacancy by some distance leads to a modification of our picture. We assume that each vacant anion site is the center of a volume element which contains two electrons. This procedure makes it unnecessary for us to single out two titanium atoms and assume that these two have the quantum state Ti^{3+} whereas the third remains a regular Ti^{4+} ion. The size of the sphere around the anion vacancy depends upon the temperature of the crystal or upon the value of kT which is available in the lattice. The higher the temperature of the crystal the greater will be the probability of finding the electrons in a more remote position with respect to the vacancy which means that the size of the sphere which encompasses the two electrons increases with increasing temperature.

The electron density distribution around the vacancy will remain spherical until an external electrical field is applied to the crystal. In such a field the electron density distribution around the anion vacancy will not remain spherical but will change into an ellipsoid. Each ellipsoid represents a dipole and all dipoles in such a crystal will be lined up in the external electrical field. The dielectric constant of such a crystal can be extremely high, e.g., several thousand times higher than that of the insulator TiO_2.

These concepts are pictured schematically in the three drawings of Figure 2. Figure 2*a* shows a rutile crystal that contains

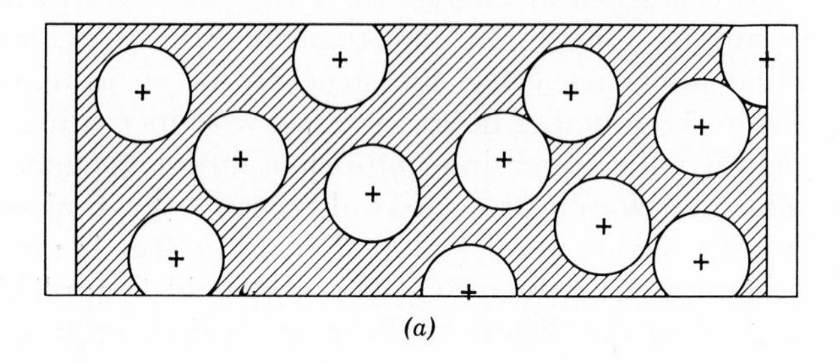

(*a*)

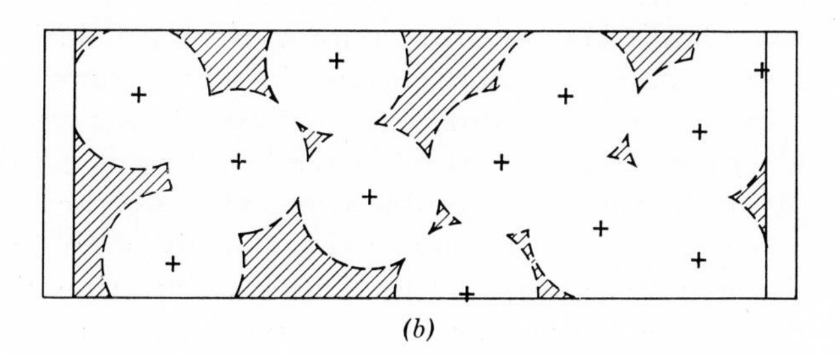

(*b*)

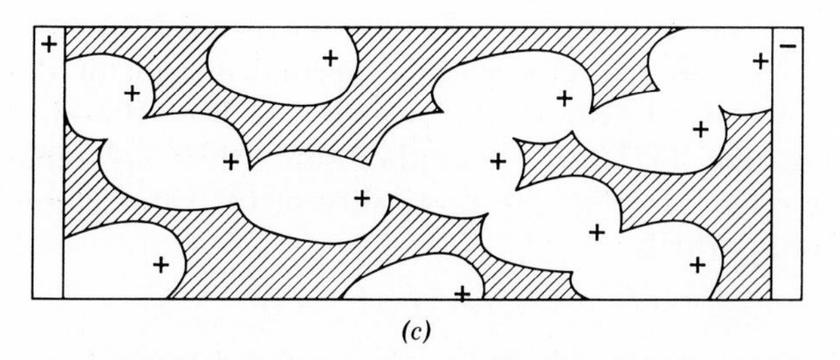

(*c*)

Fig. 2. Atomistic interpretation of semiconducting rutile crystal. *a*, Temperature = t_1, no field applied; *b*, Temperature = $t_2 > t_1$, no field applied; *c*, Temperature = t_1, in electrical field applied.

anion vacancies (+). Each anion vacancy is surrounded by a circle which contains the electrons. Figure 2*b* is the same crystal at a higher temperature. The diameters of the circles have increased. This increase in size of the places in which one may find the electrons causes them to partly overlap. This means that at the higher temperature, electrons can move through the crystal without requiring more activation energy than the thermal vibrations of the lattice supply. One might say that the crystal behaves as if some metallic fibers traversed the structure of an insulator. The number of these conducting fibers increases with increasing temperature as well as with increasing number of lattice vacancies.

A similar path for electrons may also form if the semiconductor is exposed to a strong electrical field. This effect is pictured in Figure 2*c*. Here a strong external electrical field is applied to the semiconductor and the distorted electron clouds overlap occasionally and form paths for electrons. This means that the highly polarizable (high dielectric constant) insulator becomes an electronic conductor when a high voltage is applied. Such a system no longer obeys Ohm's law. If an increasing electric field is applied to such a semiconductor, the current increases more than the voltage or more than one would expect if Ohm's law were valid.

The electronic conductivity of the semiconducting TiO_2 crystal is the result of the undefined positions of some electrons. There is no reason for assuming that two particular titanium ions have trapped the extra electrons. If we prefer to describe the semiconductor as a TiO_2 crystal which contains some Ti^{3+} ions we have to add to this description that the Ti^{3+} ions are not localized in the lattice, i.e., their positions cannot be defined. The electrons are free to move from one Ti^{4+} ion to another one and we may assume that the distance the electron moves away from the anion vacancy increases with increasing thermal energy of the crystal. If one wants an answer to the question of how the electron can move from one Ti^{4+} ion to another since they are separated by anions, one can refer to the possibility of O^{2-} ions changing into O^- ions temporarily:

$$Ti^{4+}\ O^{2-}\ Ti^{3+} \rightarrow Ti^{3+}\ O^{-}\ Ti^{3+} \rightarrow Ti^{3+}\ O^{2-}\ Ti^{4+}$$

This concept, that the migration of an electron from one spot to another consists of a wave of O^- quanticules moving in the opposite direction, makes it possible to account for the ease of formation of good semiconductors from oxides and sulfides and the difficulty of obtaining conducting fluorides.

W. A. Weyl (47) assumes a similar electron transfer to occur in glasses during solarization or when Fe^{2+} and Fe^{3+} ions participate in the glass simultaneously.

Crystals which are electronic conductors because of the participation of electrons in undefined positions in their structure are called N-type semiconductors. They can be formed through partial reduction of insulators through the introduction of interstitial atoms and through the substitution of anions (F^- for O^{2-}) or cations (Ta^{5+} for Ti^{4+}) which call for additional electrons because they would give the crystal an excess positive charge. A more detailed discussion of the roles of impurities on the electrical conductivity and their atomistic interpretation can be found in a publication by W. A. Weyl and N. A. Terhune (48).

CHAPTER VIII

AMORPHOUS SOLIDS

With the advent of X rays the term "amorphous" changed its meaning. Many elements which had been described as amorphous were revealed to be "cryptocrystalline." Their crystallinity was called "hidden" because the crystals were too small to be detected microscopically. The amorphous state is associated with colloids as well as with glasses. The experimental work of P. P. von Weimarn, in 1910, proved the continuity between the amorphous and the crystalline state. Even typically crystalline substances such as $BaSO_4$ or NaCl can be precipitated as colloids when the concentration of the reactants and the types of solvents are chosen properly.

In 1931, P. Scherrer and H. Staub showed that colloidal gold is not amorphous to X rays but that it consists of small individual crystals which in their lattice dimensions were not noticeably different from massive gold.

Originally the word "amorphous," meaning "without shape," referred to visual observations; namely, the lack of cleavage, and the irregular outline. Introducing X rays as a yardstick for measuring order and disorder, we enter the realm of atomic dimensions.

When, in 1916, L. Vegard examined the mineral thorite, $ThSiO_4$, he selected what he thought to be a perfectly good crystal. However, although visual observation classified thorite as crystalline, the X-ray pattern revealed it to be amorphous, in spite of its crystalline outlines. Today we use the term "amorphous" in the sense of "X-ray amorphous," i.e., noncrystalline when examined by X-ray methods.

There are four ways of producing amorphous silica. Cooling fused silica produces a glass. Precipitating silica from a solution of sodium silicate and calcining the precipitate produces a gel. Milling quartz produces an amorphous surface layer (Beilby layer). Exposure of quartz to a heavy neutron flux also causes amorphization. These solids are unstable with respect to quartz but they cannot be characterized by their energy content alone.

The structures of amorphous solids in contrast to those of liquids are not equilibrium structures because solids can have very long relaxation times. Hence, an amorphous solid may remain metastable for geological times (obsidian), and its structure and properties depend on the way it was formed. Amorphous is not synonymous with "absence of structure" and the description of an amorphous solid in contrast to that of a crystal must in one way or the other refer to the way it was prepared and, in any such description, *time* is an essential factor.

In our discussion of the structures of crystals we did not find it necessary to refer to the ways in which the crystals were obtained. The structure of NaCl is essentially the same whether the crystal has been obtained from an aqueous solution, by sublimation, or from its melt. No experimental method is available which can give us the same information for amorphous solids which the X-ray diffraction method gives us when we identify crystals. As the situation is now, we depend to a considerable extent on speculating about the most probable structure of an amorphous material by taking into consideration the method of its preparation.

1. Energy Profile Scheme

Amorphous solids have an energy content that can be considerably higher than that of the stable crystals. The phenomenon of pyrognomy, i.e., the sudden evolution of heat, was observed by Berzelius when he heated certain amorphous minerals before the blow pipe. Substances that had been amorphized by mechanical deformation were found to explode when the strain energy was released suddenly.

In order to better understand the physical chemistry of amorphous solids, the authors (49) developed a pictorial description of the energy distribution in solids that characterizes amorphous solids and distinguishes them from defective crystals.

A crystal at any temperature which is not close to the limit of its stability, at which limit the thermodynamic quantities may fluctuate strongly, has a potential energy that is uniform throughout its lattice. The potential energy of an elementary cell or a sphere of 10 to 100 A. in diameter has the same value throughout its lattice. There are two exceptions, however: (1) The crystal must not be close to its melting temperature or to a temperature at which it undergoes a phase transformation; and (2) the volume element that we examine must not be too close to the surface of the crystal.

The opalescence of quartz crystals near 575°C. indicates that the crystal is in a state close to its "essential instability," as this state has been called by W. C. Gibbs. In this temperature region the potential energy of the system demonstrates remarkable deviations from the average. The density and the refractive index varies from one volume element to the next and this condition causes light scattering. Below and above 575°C., i.e., in the state of thermodynamic stabilities of the low quartz and the high quartz, respectively, the energy distribution is much more uniform.

The second exception, the deviation of the higher potential energy in volume elements close to surfaces and interfaces, does not average out over long times; therefore, it has to be considered not only for the kinetics but also for the equilibrium of chemical reactions. The phase rule does not apply to a system in which the surface energy plays a major role. Taking into consideration the higher potential energy near the surface of a crystal, and plotting the potential energy of a group of 1000 to 10,000 atoms, for example, over a time average as a function of the distance from the surface, one obtains a straight line, A, which has a tail toward higher potential energy at the beginning (Fig. 3). We call this curve the "energy profile" of the crystal. The energy profiles of gases and

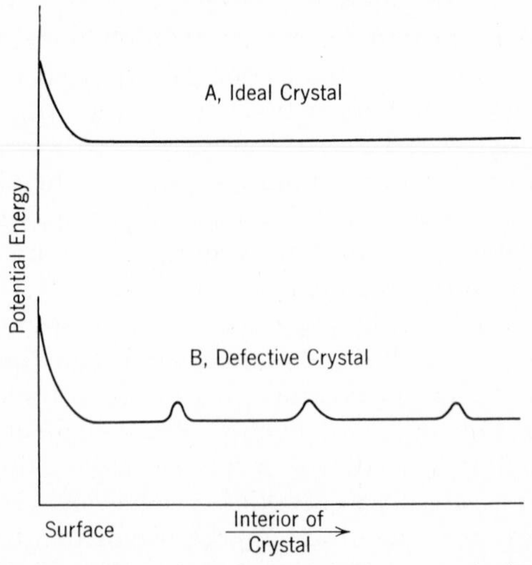

Fig. 3. Energy profiles of ideal and defective crystals. (From (49).)

liquids are straight lines. Only at low temperature can the energy profile of a stable crystal be a straight line. Crystals that are defective have energy profiles which show the peaks of higher energy due to those volume elements which contain the defects (curve B). The incomplete coordination of surface atoms is responsible for the higher potential energy of surface layers. The interior of a crystal can also contain volume elements that have a higher than average potential energy due to defects such as vacancies.

No defect is limited in its effect on the lattice to its first coordination, it will exert a depth action relayed to more distant atoms, mainly through the polarization of the anions. In our energy profiles of a crystal we can bring out differences in the energy levels and the concentration of defects as well as their depth actions.

2. Amorphous Solids from Vapors

The most obvious and direct method of producing an amorphous solid consists of a rapid condensation of one or more vapors on a surface that is so cold that the kinetic energy of the particles does not permit their orientation. In the extreme case, a solid will form that consists of a chaotic pile of vapor molecules frozen onto a wall. It is interesting to note that the first pure oxide which was obtained as a glass, namely, vitreous arsenic trioxide (see Chapter XVII,14,G), condensed from the vapor phase during metallurgical operations.

The first systematic efforts to produce amorphous solids of this type were made by St. von Bogdandy, J. Boehm, and M. Polanyi, in 1926 and 1927, who used a rotating copper drum which was cooled with liquid air and placed in a vacuum. One or two jets of vapor were directed toward the drum and substances such as metals and sulfur were condensed, forming a molecular mixture that exploded when it reached room temperature.

W. Rühl, by a similar condensation process in 1956, obtained films of thallous halides which were amorphous and which gave the X-ray diffraction pattern of a liquid. One describes the chaotic structures of these amorphous solids by an energy profile which is that of a defective crystal, but in which the defects are exaggerated both in height and in number so that no straight line remains (Fig. 4*a*). Annealing such an amorphous solid changes it into a more or less defective crystal (Fig. 4*b*) and the energy which is released leads to the glow phenomenon (pyrognomy).

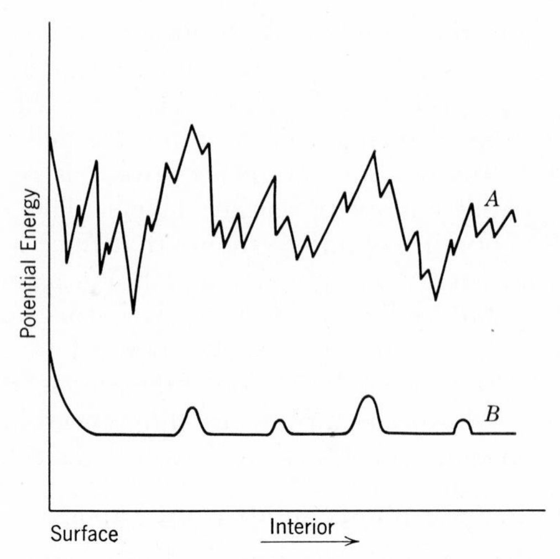

Fig. 4. Energy profile of metamict mineral (*A*) in the original chaotic state and (*B*) after annealing. (From (49).)

Substances which have a very low solubility may be precipitated from a solvent in a similar chaotic condition.

Explosive antimony is such an amorphous solid which forms when antimony chloride is reduced by an electric current of high density. The anodic oxidation of metals, e.g., aluminum, can also lead to an amorphous phase.

3. Amorphous Solids from Crystals

Crystals can be changed directly into amorphous solids without going through the molten state if they are strongly deformed by mechanical forces or exposed to a bombardment with α-particles or neutrons.

A. Metamict Minerals

A. Pabst (5a) gave us the properties of metamict minerals and the colorful history of their discovery.

Wollaston drew Berzelius's attention to the phenomenon of 'glowing" exhibited by gadolinite when the mineral was heated gently. Berzelius, who examined the phenomenon more closely reported it in 1815 as follows: "If a piece of gadolinite is slowly heated before the blowpipe to incipient incandescence it comes to ignition as though it took fire and this ignition will spread over the whole mass the more rapidly, the more uniformly the piece has been heated."

This behavior was found to be characteristic for several minerals. The minerals before heating were isotropic but became birefringent afterwards. The glow process also changed the density of the mineral and to a certain extent, its chemical reactivity. Pabst (50) summarizes the properties of metamict minerals as follows:

1. Optically isotropic.
2. Pyrognomic, i.e., readily becoming incandescent on heating.
3. Lacking in cleavage, fracture conchoidal.
4. Density increases by heating. This is commonly the case but the change is slight.
5. Crystalline structure reconstituted by heating. This conclusion was drawn from the optical changes noted by Des Cloiseaux and later workers.
6. Resistance to attack by acids increases by heating. This curious effect of heating, just the opposite of heating to fusion in many instances, was found in 1841 by H. Rose, also noted by W. Peterson in 1890, and investigated by A. Bauer in 1939.
7. Contains uranium or thorium. The content of uranium or thorium may be low; e.g., 0.41% ThO_2 in gadolinite.
8. Some minerals are known in both the crystalline and metamict states. In these cases little if any chemical difference can be found. There is evidence of hydration attending isotropization but no direct or general correlation has been established.
9. X-ray amorphous. Vegard in 1916 first reported the absence of X-ray diffraction in thorite. This has since been noted for many other metamict minerals.

TABLE XIV

Effect of Neutron Bombardment on the Density and Refractive Index of Quartz (51)

Intensity of irradiation	Density and % decrease		Refractive index and % decrease			
			ϵ_D		ω_D	
0	2.6501	—	1.5534	—	1.5444	—
1.3	2.6483	0.07	1.5530	0.026	1.5441	0.019
49	2.5257	4.7	1.5272	1.7	1.5224	1.4
1100[a]	2.2510	17.7	1.4666	5.6	1.4666	5.1

[a] Carried out at 250 to 300°C.

TABLE XV

Effect of Neutron Bombardment on the Density and Refractive Index of Vitreous Silica (51)

Intensity of irradiation	Density and % increase		Refractive index, n_D, and % increase	
0	2.2050	—	1.4589	—
1.3	2.2094	0.2	1.4597	0.055
59	2.2677	2.8	1.4673	0.58
1100[a]	2.2510	2.1	1.4667	0.54

[a] Carried out at 250 to 300°C.

V. M. Goldschmidt, in 1924, discussed the "isotropization" of minerals and arrived at the conclusion that it must be the result of a number of factors, none of which alone can produce the metamict state. Thus, radiation alone is not sufficient. No strongly ionic crystal is known in the metamict state, nor are all occurrences of thorite isotropic.

The isotropization of crystals by bombardment with particles is distinctly different from glass formation. Vitreous silica also undergoes a change when it is bombarded with neutrons. W. Primak, L. H. Fuchs and P. Day (51) found that exposure to a heavy neutron flux causes the density of quartz to decrease and that of vitreous silica to increase. Tables XIV and XV show the changes of the densities and of the indices of refraction of both quartz and vitreous silica as a function of the neutron flux.

B. Mechanical Amorphization

There is considerable evidence that amorphous films are formed when metals are polished. These thin layers of noncrystalline metals are called Beilby layers after Sir George Beilby who, in 1921, called attention to their formation and who carried out most of the early work in this field. Later workers confirmed the existence of amorphous films on polished metals and showed that a gradual transition exists between the crystalline metal and its amorphous surface.

The application of mechanical forces, in particular of shear forces, to a crystal may lead to the destruction of its long range order. The conversion of mechanical energy into chemical energy is not very efficient, the major part of the mechanical energy is converted into heat.

4. Amorphous Solids from Melts

Some liquids can solidify on cooling without crystallization and form a rigid amorphous solid. If this solid on heating softens and turns into a liquid in a reversible fashion, the solid is called a glass.

Glass became of interest to scientists because of its use in optical instruments. In the middle of the last century it became known that further perfection of the microscope required glasses which had a much wider range of refractive indices and dispersions than those that were then available; namely, the alkali lime and the alkali lead silicates. Harcourt in England and Fraunhofer in Germany developed glasses of new compositions and studied their optical properties. The increasing demand for new optical glasses finally led to the successful teamwork of Abbe and Schott in 1881. Systematic variations of glass compositions, the introduction of many more elements, and the measuring of physical and chemical properties led to the foundation of the modern glass industry and a science of the glassy state. The work did not remain restricted to optical glasses but resulted in superior glasses for chemical apparatus, boiler gauges, and thermometers.

Color is another property which attracted scientists to the study of glass technology. The colors of beads of borax and microcosmic salt were used widely for identifying minerals and during chemical analysis. M. W. Lomonossow in Russia experimented with colored glasses as early as 1760. D. I. Mendeleev who spent his childhood in a glass plant remained interested in glass throughout his life. One of his pupils and close collaborators, W. E. Tistschenko, developed a superior glass for laboratory ware. R. Zsigmondy, a Nobel laureate, was a consultant to some Bohemian glass plants during the last quarter of the past century. His work on the striking of gold ruby is one of the classics in glass research.

At the end of the last century, in 1888, W. Spring in Belgium, and, J. Cobb in England, at the beginning of this century, studied chemical reactions related to those taking place in a glass batch. These were some of the first reactions between ionic solids which were ever studied in a laboratory. Later G. Tammann and J. A. Hedvall studied solid state reactions between oxides, carbonates, sulfates, etc., in a more systematic fashion. Whenever the reaction product was a glass it was considered a mutual solution of the oxides.

The primary difficulty encountered by scientists when they worked with glasses was the proper grouping of the glass within the accepted states of aggregation. At one time the suggestion was even made to call the glassy state the "fourth state of aggregation."

G. W. Morey (6), in his book *Properties of Glass*, pointed out the difficulties involved in arriving at a proper definition of "glass." After a critical discussion of earlier efforts, he suggests the following definition: "A glass is an inorganic substance in a condition which is continuous with, and analogous to, the liquid state of that substance, but which, as the result of a reversible change in viscosity during cooling, has attained so high a degree of viscosity as to be for all practical purposes rigid."

I. I. Kitaigorodski (52), in his book on glass technology, offers a definition that was developed by the committee on terminology of the Russian Academy of Sciences: Glass is a term used for all amorphous solids which are obtained by supercooling a melt, regardless of its chemical composition and the temperature region in which the solidification takes place. Because of the increase in viscosity on cooling, glasses assume the properties of solids. The transition from the liquid into the glassy state has to be reversible.

G. W. Morey (6) suggests reserving the term "glass" for inorganic substances, a restriction which from a physical chemical point of view is arbitrary and which is not shared by all scientists. Morey's and Kitaigorodski's definitions, however, have in common the emphasis on the reversibility of the change liquid-glass on cooling and heating.

Morey is concerned with glasses that are products of high temperature reactions. Kitaigorodski's definition, on the other hand, refers to the glassy state rather than to a product. The features that distinguish glasses from crystalline and from other amorphous solids offer no good reasons for separating inorganic and organic glasses. G. Tammann's (1) fundamental work on the glassy state was performed primarily with glasses which have no technical significance, e.g., selenium and organic substances (salol, brucin, rosin).

Until 1936 no distinction could be made between the structures of vitreous selenium, salol, glycerol, on the one hand, and silicate glasses on the other. It was not realized that these organic glasses consisted of discrete molecules, whereas the silicate glass had an ionic structure that extended in all three dimensions. It was customary to talk about silicate and borosilicate molecules in the same fashion as one talked about phenolphthalein molecules. The fact that organic and inorganic glasses showed the same behavior in the softening range could therefore not surprise the workers in this field.

Gradually, however, the ideas of Goldschmidt (4) on the structural principles of crystals and glasses began to exert their influence. W. H. Zachariasen (3) presented a comparison between the atomic structures of glasses and crystals using and elaborating on Goldschmidt's crystal chemical approach.

The work of Tammann (1) and his school on the behavior of organic glasses remains rather isolated and it is unfortunate that later workers showed little interest in continuing research in this promising field. In the period following Tammann's work, research restricted itself to ionic glasses: mostly oxides, and their fluoride models. B. E. Warren (5) and his school studied some oxide glasses by means of X rays and reached the conclusion that their amorphous patterns could be interpreted on the basis of Zacharaisen's picture. Hence, glasses were called "three-dimensional random and continuous networks" of ions, a description which ruled out the concept of molecules and their association and dissociation products. The fundamental characteristics of the glassy state were established and the work of Tammann on the physical chemistry of the glassy state found a natural termination.

CHAPTER IX

STRUCTURE OF LIQUIDS

About 30 years ago G. Hägg (53) suggested that the glassy state should be explained primarily on the basis of the structure of the liquid from which the glass has formed rather than on the basis of the structure of the crystal which has to be melted first in order to change it into a glass. The major difficulty in elaborating on Hägg's ideas at this time was the lack of knowledge concerning liquid structures.

Physicists have approached the structures of liquids experimentally by measuring their X ray and neutron diffraction, and interpreting the angular distribution of the scattered radiation. Curves with a few peaks are obtained that reveal the presence of some short range order but the absence of any periodicity or long range order. The structure of liquids cannot be described by static pictures such as unit cells. The establishment of a radial distribution function of the atoms in a monoatomic liquid is about as far as one can hope to go at the present time, which means that much of the structure has to be left to speculation.

In exploring the metallic state the physicist can study the short range order of these monoatomic liquids and augment this information by measuring their electronic conductivities. The decrease in the electronic conductivity during melting is an indication of the change in order.

The compressibility of liquids has also been used to obtain a better insight into their structures. The direct experimental approaches to liquid structure are scarce, and hence our factual knowledge of the structures of even the simplest liquids is very scanty. We need a picture of the constitution of liquids that goes beyond the radial distribution function of the atoms as averaged over long periods of time. We need a dynamic picture and the dynamics of a liquid cannot be understood unless we have information concerning the forces that act between atoms or molecules. Averaging the geometry and the forces over large volumes and long periods of time cannot aid our understanding of liquids. The picture necessary for understanding liquids, supercooled liquids and glasses must contain a parameter for bringing into the picture the chemical nature of the liquid. Attempts have been made to treat the liquid state on the basis of statistical mechanical theories (see Chapter V,4,A). These attempts fail to use parameters which are meaningful to the chemist. We cannot expect that a physicist can give us a quantitative explanation of nucleation in liquids but his equations should contain factors which permit us to discriminate between compounds such as V_2O_5 and P_2O_5, substances which can be similar in their geometry, their bond strength, and their melting temperature but which behave fundamentally different with respect to their nucleation rates and their abilities to form glasses.

1. Problems of the Liquid State

Modern physical methods provide considerable information about the sizes, shapes and forces of simple molecules. On the basis of this information we can understand the mechanism by which the cooling of a gas brings about condensation. For atoms, e.g., argon, and for simply-shaped molecules such as methane or benzene, we may even be able to predict the geometrical pattern of the solids formed when these particles are deprived of their thermal energies. We have no difficulty in visualizing the formation of an ordered solid when we consider the geometry of the particles and the existence of attractive forces between them.

However, the fact that the gradual withdrawal of thermal energy from benzene vapor does not necessarily cause its molecules to orient themselves into a crystal lattice, but that such withdrawal can first produce a liquid that is stable from 80 down to 5°C., is not obvious and cannot be predicted. Indeed, if we cool carbon dioxide rather than the vapor of benzene we do not encounter the formation of a liquid under normal pressure. The liquid state is not an obvious state of aggregation and many substances under ordinary pressure exist as gases and crystals but not as liquids.

In order to understand the existence of liquids we must realize that the "mobility" of the particles contributes to the stability of the system because it raises its entropy. This statement is obvious from the thermodynamic expression for the free energy but it can easily lead to fallacious thinking. There is no rigorous relation between temperature, the average forces which are acting between particles, and their mobility. The fact that gallium is a liquid but zinc and cadmium are solids at ordinary temperature presents a temptation to attribute this difference to the forces which are acting between Zn and Cd atoms and assume that they are stronger than those which act between Ga atoms. The boiling points of these metals, however, reveal that the thermal energy necessary for changing metallic gallium into atoms exceeds by far that required for changing metallic zinc or metallic cadmium into atoms. The boiling points are: Zn, 908°C.; Cd, 767°C,; and Ga, 2000°C.

Thus, in addition to the experimental difficulties and limitations which impair our efforts to explore the liquid state, we face two obstacles even when thinking about a plausible picture of the structure of liquids. Firstly, in contrast to gases and crystals, the liquid state is not an obvious state of aggregation, the existence of which could be predicted from the available knowledge of the shape of molecules and the intermolecular forces. Secondly, the liquid state cannot be fully understood on the basis of measureable forces or energy relations. We cannot hope to find a simple relationship between the temperature range in which a substance exists in the liquid state and parameters such as its lattice energy and its heat of vaporization.

Here we meet one of the major problems which confronted scientists when they attempted to derive a picture of the constitution of a liquid.

When a solid, say a piece of metal, is heated it changes abruptly into a liquid that has a very low viscosity. We can easily understand the drastic change in all properties if this metal vaporizes because its conductivity vanishes and the volume changes drastically. During melting no major changes occur with respect to the volume or the electrical conductivity. Let us see what one of the pioneers in this field has to say about the relation between the solid state and the liquid state. In his book on the kinetic theory of liquids, J. Frenkel (54) introduced the chapter "Properties of Liquids and Mechanism of Fusion" as follows:

"Fusion is accompanied, as a rule, by a relatively small increase of volume amounting to 10%. This fact alone serves to show that the arrangement of molecules in a liquid—in the neighborhood of the crystallization point, at least—must be more or less similar to their arrangement in the corresponding solid bodies, in spite of the fundamental difference existing between the amorphous structure of the liquids and the crystalline structure of the solids (in a state of thermodynamic equilibrium).

"We must further note the well-known experimental fact that the latent heat of fusion is much smaller than the latent heat of vaporization. In the case of sodium, zinc, lead, and mercury, for example, the former is equal to 630, 1800, 1170, and 560 cal./mole, while the latter amounts to 23,300, 27,700, 46,000, and 14,200 respectively, exceeding thus the heat of fusion by a factor of 30 to 40.

"This means that the cohesive forces between the molecules decrease only very slightly in the process of fusion, in agreement with the fact that their distance apart is increased by a very small figure of the order of 3 to 4%."

All pictures of the liquid state which have been suggested in the past are the result of extrapolations. Van der Waals thought it appropriate to start out with gases and to speculate on what happens if the atoms or molecules are forced together more closely. His classical approach to the liquid state has been refined and elaborated on by many scientists.

With respect to glass formation we are interested in the viscosity of liquids but the viscosity seems to follow very different laws for liquids and for gases. The viscosity of a gas is not very sensitive to density changes and it increases with increasing temperature. Gases have the opposite temperature coefficient of viscosity than most liquids.

L. Boltzmann started out with solids and he speculated on the effect which increasing thermal vibrations might have upon their structures and their properties thus extrapolating from crystals to the liquid state.

If we want to explain the thermodynamic and kinetic aspects of gases we start out with the description of an "ideal gas." Later we point out the limitation of this concept and add the necessary refinements. We use the same approach in teaching crystal chemistry. Our textbooks give us the geometry of ideal infinitely extending crystals and these pictures provide the basis for our teaching and scientific discussions. Later we point out that these pictures represent idealized structures, that they do not correspond to real crystals because the latter have surfaces and defects which are important for the understanding of some of their properties.

We shall approach the constitution of liquids in the same way as we approach the constitution of gases and crystals. We cannot expect the resulting pictures to be identical with their real structures but they will provide a basis for our discussions. We will be aware of the fact that we must modify these idealized concepts and add refinements whenever they are needed.

2. Concept of Liquid Structures

A. Bernal Model

J. D. Bernal (55) concerned himself with the geometry of simple monoatomic liquids. However, he stated that it would be possible to build a theory for ionic liquids on this basis provided one takes into consideration the opposite signs of the component ions and their radii. The condition for an ionic liquid is that the charges should be evenly distributed so as to balance one another and ionic liquids should obey statistically the same rules which hold for ionic crystals.

One can assume that fused cristobalite corresponds closely to Bernal's model of a liquid. He describes his liquids as homogeneous, coherent, and essentially irregular assemblages of molecules which contain no crystalline regions or holes which are large enough to admit another molecule. The most characteristic feature of Bernal's model is that the irregularity of a liquid is the result of a very small concentration of atoms which show a slight departure from the normal coordination number. Starting out with a regular layer of a close-packed hexagonal aggregate, Bernal was able to show that the distance of one atom from its nearest neighbors can be varied without introducing a widely spread disorder. However, if the coordination of an atom is changed in one place from 6 to 7 or from 6 to 5, the configuration of the whole array becomes irregular and it is practically impossible to return to a regular arrangement within an area which contains less than 100 atoms. The irregular area is characterized by a variation of distances. Bernal (55) described his liquids by the coordination number of the particles and an irregularity function. Bernal's model resembles closely a perfect crystal because it is essentially free of flaws. We refer to such a liquid in its idealized form as "flawless."

The condition which causes this "flawless" arrangement of particles to be liquid is that the thermal energy is of a magnitude sufficient to overcome the energy barriers which oppose their motion. The neighborhood relations of molecules in a liquid are necessarily in continual flux, thus providing a mechanism for self diffusion and on a macroscopic scale for its fluidity.

In applying Bernal's model to ionic liquids we should add that the continual flux does not need to involve place exchanges between anions and cations. One can assume that in such a flawless liquid the anions are mobile within the anionic part and the cations within the cationic part of the structure. Bernal's model describes a liquid which resembles closely the crystal from which it has formed. Slightly above the melting point of the crystal, a melt that corresponds to Bernal's model should be very viscous and it should be easy to supercool it and form a glass.

B. Frenkel Model

We consider Bernal's model of a liquid an idealization of one extreme liquid structure. Another extreme structure of a liquid is described by a model developed by J. Frenkel (54). According to his model the homogeneity of a liquid is only an apparent one. Frenkel assumes that a liquid is permeated by a large number of surfaces of rupture which due to the lack of time cannot develop into a macroscopic size. These fissures are dynamic in nature, they close spontaneously in certain places while new fissures form in neighboring regions. At any given instant, however, the whole volume of the liquid contains a system of cavities in the form of holes and cracks. While Frenkel speaks of "heterophase fluctuations" and "cavitation fluctuations" he points out that for the usual thermodynamic treatment of liquids, in which one deals with average values of different quantities which are integrated over long time intervals, his model will give the same results as one which is based on a general increase in the intermolecular distances and which operates with ordinary density fluctuations. However, if one is interested in the instantaneous and not in the average distribution of the molecules within a liquid, Frenkel considers that the concept of a uniform distribution is substantially incorrect.

In contrast to Bernal's model, the Frenkel model of a liquid bears no similarity to the crystal. Even just above the melting point of a crystal one cannot speak of lattice vacancies or holes in the sense these terms are used in describing defective crystals.

When W. A. Weyl and E. C. Marboe (21) derived the structural changes that must take place in a sodium chloride crystal during its melting because of the disproportionation of all binding forces into weaker and stronger ones and of all interatomic distances into larger and smaller ones, they arrived at a picture which corresponds to the Frenkel model of a liquid. The high fluidity of fused NaCl can be attributed to the ease with which the melt forms fissures. We refer to Frenkel's model as a "fissured liquid."

Crystals which form fissured liquids on melting cannot be overheated. Fissured liquids cannot be supercooled to the extent of forming glasses. The X-ray investigations of J. Zarzycki (56) support our view that molten alkali halides are fissured liquids which correspond closely to Frenkel's model of a liquid. Summarizing his extensive work on the atomic structures of fused fluorides and chlorides, Zarzycki (56) wrote:

"Analysis of the radial distribution curves deduced from the spectra by means of the spherical Fourier transform shows that for the alkali halides the short range order of the crystal is maintained in the molten state whereas the coordination numbers are much lower. This confirms the existence of 'holes' in these molten salts.

"With the aid of supplementary data it is shown that these 'holes' are actually 'fluctuating fissures' between ion clusters consisting on an average of one to two ionic shells surrounding a central ion."

The models of Bernal and of Frenkel represent two extremes and some scientists, e.g., H. Eyring (57), use models which range in their structures between two extremes. Eyring assumes that a liquid must contain a considerable concentration of "holes" which are instrumental in permitting diffusion and viscous flow.

These two extreme models and the transitions between them would form a satisfactory basis for a discussion of the structures of simple alkali silicate glasses.

However, vitreous sulfur and selenium have structures which are complex inasmuch as they contain helical chains and ring-shaped molecules. We assume that vitreous boric acid and some borate and phosphate glasses also have complex structures in spite of the simplicity of their chemical compositions. In order to accommodate these glasses in our structural picture we must include a third model of a liquid structure.

C. Stewart Model

G. W. Stewart (58) on the basis of X-ray studies suggested that molecular liquids may contain swarms of molecules which show some degree of temporary order. As it is necessary to differentiate between ordered crystalline regions and noncrystalline groups of molecules which also show some order he coined the word "cybotaxis" and he called these swarms "cybotactic regions."

The application of X-ray methods to the determination of liquid structure can neither prove nor disprove the concept of temporary ordered regions because the method averages the interatomic distances. There are other experiments, however, which indicate that order may arise in a liquid. The existence of "crystalline liquids" and of the "smectic phases" provide visible evidence for the fact that a crystal must not melt to a clear isotropic liquid but that it can form a mixture of two "phases." One of these "phases" can be oriented so that it shows birefringence. The "smectic phases" will assume a high degree of order and orientation in contact with solids, even with the surface of an amorphous solid such as a microscope slide.

Raising the temperature causes the ordered regions to become smaller and at a certain reproducible temperature the liquid becomes optically clear and shows no more birefringence. However, the viscosity of this liquid changes with the intensity of an applied magnetic field, a phenomenon which reveals that the "clearing up" has not eliminated the ordered regions. Ordered regions still persist in the melt above this temperature but they are not observable by methods based on their response to visible light.

The macroscopic, microscopic, ultramicroscopic, and submicroscopic heterogeneity of melts has been studied primarily with rod-like organic molecules by D. Vorländer (59). Research on the physical properties of the anisotropic liquids was carried out by C. Weygand (60) and his school as well as by W. Kast (61).

G. W. Stewart (58) proposed a model of liquids which reminds us of these "crystalline liquids." He does not limit his model to molecular liquids as can be seen from his remarks:

"The current discussions concerning order and disorder in solid alloys evidently have a definite bearing upon liquids. When two liquids form a homogeneous solution there is a single common liquid structure, but with an unknown degree of order. The phenomenon of solution, whether electrolytic or non-electrolytic, is concerned with forces that produce structures and that have a tendency to produce order corresponding to a superlattice. But in a liquid the effect of temperature, on account of fluidity, would be quantitatively different. Thus the details of the theory will not be the same for the solid alloys and liquids, but probably there will be a strong similarity. The superlattice found for ions has its correspondence in the alloy superlattice."

The Stewart model can best be illustrated by the structure of amorphous sulfur. According to J. A. Prins (37), amorphous sulfur is heterogeneous on an atomic scale because it consists of a mixture of S_8 molecules and helical chains of sulfur atoms. The simultaneous presence of several molecular species in itself would not make sulfur a Stewart liquid but the tendency of chainlike molecules to become oriented, in particular when stretched, justifies the description of amorphous sulfur on the basis of the Stewart model. We refer to Stewart's model as an "orientable liquid." The chain molecules even when they are ordered do not represent crystals of sulfur nor do they nucleate crystallization because no crystalline modification of elemental sulfur is known which consists of chains. Amorphous selenium has a structure similar to amorphous sulfur but unlike sulfur it can form a crystalline modification which consists of ordered chains. Using sulfur rather than selenium as an example, we can better understand why the formation of ordered regions is not necessarily identical with, or even a step in the direction toward, the formation of crystals. A liquid may contain ordered regions which cannot act as nuclei for crystallization

J. J. Trillat and H. Forestier (62), as well as K. H. Meyer and Y. Go (63) examined vitreous sulfur and selenium by X rays and were able to introduce order by stretching. The importance of the phenomenon lies in the fact that it provides a means for distinguishing between glasses which are supercooled "flawless liquids" corresponding to the Bernal model and others which have complex heterogeneous structures corresponding to the Stewart model.

The numerous efforts to find a molecular orientation within fibers have failed as far as silica, silicate and borosilicate glasses are concerned. This failure to induce orientation reveals that these glasses have structures which correspond rather closely to the Bernal model of a liquid even if their chemical compositions are complex.

X-ray patterns revealed that fibers of vitreous B_2O_3 and of $NaPO_3$ did show orientation according to M. Goldstein and T. H. Davies (64) and B. K. Banerjee (65). The alkali phosphate glasses are the only oxide glasses that permit a direct chemical approach to their structures. The molecular species which are present in these phosphate glasses can be determined by chemical analytical methods (chromatography), and we know, therefore, that some phosphate glasses contain chainlike polyphosphates.

The presence of oriented groups in fibers of a boric oxide glass as revealed by X rays has been confirmed recently by their magnetic anisotropy. B. K. Banerjee (65) measured the magnitude of the diamagnetism of glass fibers as a function of the direction. A few of his data shall be listed because they lend strong support to our view that a B_2O_3 glass in spite of its chemical simplicity has a complex structure resembling the Stewart model of an "orientable" liquid. The magnitude of the magnetic anisotropy is given for the following substances:

Boric oxide fibers	0.3111 to 0.4921×10^{-6}
Na borate fibers (10% Na_2O)	0.0307 to 0.0595×10^{-6}
Na borate fibers (31% Na_2O)	0.0091 to 0.0197×10^{-6}
Borosilicate fibers	0
Silica fibers	0

The three types of liquids which we have discussed are not the only types of liquids but they are the ones which interest us most with respect to oxide systems and their tendencies to form glasses.

Liquid argon or liquid mercury are atomic liquids. Benzene is a molecular liquid in which strong forces prevail between the atoms within the molecules (intramolecular forces) and only weak forces between the molecules (intermolecular forces). If we were particularly interested in organic glasses we would have to pay more attention to these molecular liquids and to their changes into orientable liquids. When the molecules become larger through polymerization and the intermolecular forces become stronger because van der Waals forces increase with the molecular weight, the normal liquids change into polymers which can form glasses. Among inorganic systems we also find molecular liquids. The monoclinic form of sulfur and the hexagonal form of phosphorus pentoxide form "normal" liquids on melting. These liquids which contain S_8 and P_4O_{10} molecules respectively are fluid and they do not form glasses on cooling. Just above the melting points liquid sulfur and liquid phosphorus pentoxide consist of the same type of molecules as their vapors. These molecular liquids, however, become "associated" liquids if the temperatures are raised. Their viscosities and their average molecular weights increase. When that happens liquid sulfur and liquid phosphorus pentoxide become orientable liquids which can form glasses. For a better understanding of inorganic glasses we can restrict ourselves to the three types of liquids which we represented in their idealized forms as the flawless Bernal liquid, the fissured Frenkel liquid and the orientable Stewart liquid.

For us it is important to realize that changes of temperature, pressure, and composition are likely to affect the structure of a liquid. These changes are of paramount importance for the understanding of the constitution of glass because any change of a system in the direction toward the Frenkel fissured structure impairs glass formation.

Hydrostatic pressure tends to make the interionic distances more uniform and thus changes a Frenkel fissured liquid in the direction toward a Bernal flawless liquid. We attribute the formation of glasses in the system K_2CO_3-$MgCO_3$ under high pressure to the change of the fissured liquid into one which resembles the Bernal flawless type. Normally, carbonates are not likely to form glasses; neither are nitrates. We would describe a fused alkali nitrate as a liquid which bears some resemblance to the Bernal type but which still has sufficient fissures to permit easy nucleation. Lowering the liquidus temperature by mixing together the nitrates of alkalies and of mangesium or zinc reduces the number of fissures and changes the liquid structure toward that of the Bernal type. These changes, i.e., addition of $MgCO_3$ to K_2CO_3 and $Mg(NO_3)_2$ to KNO_3, introduce cations of a higher charge which are less likely to participate in fissures than the singly charged alkali ions. Very likely the formation of carbonate glasses (W. Skaliks (66)) and of nitrate glasses (A. P. Rostkowsky and A. G. Bergmann (67)) is the result of several factors and should not be attributed to one parameter only. The low liquidus temperatures of these systems are no doubt most important.

When discussing amorphous solids we learned that mechanical forces can transform a crystal into a highly defective amorphous solid. Shear forces acting upon a glass have a very similar effect and we may describe their action as producing a structural change in the direction toward a Frenkel fissured liquid. It is well established that a diamond scratch or the grinding of a glass in a mortar will disproportionate the binding forces and, thus, can induce crystallization.

3. Description of the Real Structure of a Liquid on the Basis of Three Idealized Extreme Models

If an ideal crystal is heated and approaches its melting point it can soften gradually and melt because the thermal energy becomes sufficient to overcome those energy barriers that oppose the motion of its constituents. The substance yields to gravity and assumes the shape of its container. The increase in temperature causes the volume of the crystal to expand, the interatomic distances to increase, and the forces acting between the particles to decrease (Bernal liquid).

The absence of long range order in a liquid, however, does not require that all interatomic distances increase at the same rate on heating. A liquid structure can tolerate fluctuations in density and in the forces acting between the particles. This type of melting leads to the liquid which resembles the Frenkel model and which bears no resemblance to the crystal from which it has formed. All liquids lack the long range order of the crystals from which they form on melting but the liquids of the Frenkel type have short range orders which can be very different; e.g., the average coordination number is likely to be smaller than that which was characteristic for the crystal. The internal fissures which characterize the Frenkel model of a liquid are internal surfaces and an atom in a surface has a lower coordination number than those in the interior.

The melting of a crystal to form a Bernal "flawless" liquid is very different from that which leads to a Frenkel "fissured" liquid. The thermodynamic changes, however, cannot account for this different behavior. Thermodynamics deals with parameters which are averaged over long times, and neither geometry nor time are used in thermodynamic considerations. Thermal data cannot offer a clue to tell us whether we deal with a Bernal-type or a Frenkel-type liquid.

One can understand that many scientists have made attempts to connect the different tendencies of substances to be supercooled and to form glasses with parameters such as: The heat of fusion; the shape of the liquidus curves within binary and ternary systems; and the bond energies and other thermodynamic properties. However, as it turned out there are no such relationships. The decision of whether one deals with a liquid of the Bernal type or with one of the Frenkel type has to be based on kinetic phenomena. We describe the transition cristobalite–liquid as the formation of a Bernal liquid primarily because the resulting phase has a very high viscosity and does not readily crystallize on cooling. A Bernal liquid is "flawless" and the lack of vacancies causes this liquid to have a very low ionic conductivity. On the same basis we assume that fused NaCl is a Frenkel fissured-type liquid, its viscosity just above the melting point is very low, it crystallizes readily when cooled and its ionic conductivity is high.

Obviously, intermediate structures between these two extremes can exist and the degree to which a liquid is fissured depends upon the nature of the substance as well as upon the absolute temperature. As compared with the Bernal liquid, the fissured liquid has the higher entropy because of the higher mobility and the greater disorder of its particles. As the contribution of the entropy to the stability of a system increases with increasing temperature we must assume that any liquid, whether a Bernal type or a Stewart type, will change its structure in the direction toward a Frenkel liquid when the temperature is raised.

Our third model of a liquid, the Stewart-type liquid, contains structural units which can be oriented when the viscous liquid is drawn into a fiber. We call this type of structure "orientable" because of its ability to develop orientation or anisotropy. The geometry, in particular the close resemblance to the crystal, distinguishes the Bernal-type from the Frenkel-type and the Stewart-type liquids. A distinction between the Frenkel-type and the Stewart-type liquid cannot be based on thermal data; it is not sufficient to know the distribution of binding forces.

The melting of NaCl to a Frenkel-type liquid is accompanied by a drastic change in the geometry and by a corresponding drastic change in the distribution of forces. We have strong forces acting within the clusters and weak forces acting across the fissures. Why, then, can we not call the clusters "molecules" or "polymers" and refer to fused NaCl as a Stewart-type liquid? Simply because the lifetime of clusters and fissures in liquid NaCl is too short to permit any orientation. The flow of liquid NaCl does not involve these clusters as flow units. We have to introduce "time" as a parameter in order to classify fused NaCl as a Frenkel-type and fused B_2O_3 as a Stewart-type liquid.

We can understand now why it took scientists so long to arrive at a reasonable concept of the structures of liquids. Even if one simplifies the problem by referring to idealized models, the usual thermodynamic factors do not permit us to distinguish between different possible structures. Even the knowledge of the distribution of forces is not sufficient to distinguish between the Frenkel type and the Stewart type of liquid and these two types are so very different with respect to their rheological properties and their abilities to form a glass. We need an experiment which is time consuming in order to classify B_2O_3 as an orientable liquid. We have to study its ionic conductivity, its viscosity, its rate of nucleation and crystallization or we have to examine its anisotropy after it has undergone flow or stretching.

We can also carry out an experiment with Bernal-type liquids which corresponds to the experiment performed by C. Wagner and P. Hantelmann (46) when they added some $SrCl_2$ to KCl. They found that the substitution of Sr^{2+} ions for an occasional K^+ ion increased the ionic conductivity of KCl because it led to the formation of vacant cation sites. We know that liquid SiO_2, B_2O_3, and BeF_2 have very low ionic conductivities at temperatures not too far above the melting points of the respective crystals. If these liquids had structures resembling the Frenkel type they would be good ionic conductors because of the ionic mobility in the fissured liquids. Let us assume we deal with a substance such as CaF_2 which melts at a temperature at which the thermal energy permits easy nucleation. CaF_2 cannot be obtained as a glass. How can we decide whether liquid CaF_2 is a Frenkel-type liquid or whether its structure resembles that of the crystal. This decision can be made by using the approach which Wagner and Hantelmann (46) used. Experiments of this type have been performed by T. Bååk (68). He added CaO, which in itself has a very low ionic conductivity, to fused CaF_2 at temperatures well above the melting point (1500 to 1545°C.) and he observed that these additions led to a strong increase in the ionic conductivity of the melt. The addition of about 7% CaO to CaF_2 caused the conductivity to rise from 4 ohm^{-1} $cm.^{-1}$ to nearly twice this value. T. Bååk (68) explains the phenomenon as follows: "The reasons for these very interesting features can be explained if we remember that the ionic radii of F^- and O^{2-} are nearly equal ($r_{F^-} = 1.36$ A. and $r_{O^{2-}} = 1.40$ A.). At lower percentages of CaO we can suppose that the oxygen ions can be built into the 'liquid lattice' of the fluorine ions, similar to the situation in the solid state in mixed crystals of KCl-$SrCl_2$ where the cation vacancies produced by the unequal charges of the cations increase the ionic conduction. In our case, the unequal charges of O^{2-} and F^- will also cause anion vacancies and an increase in the conduction."

The formation of a large number of vacancies leads to asymmetries and increases the thermal expansivity of the mixture. Indeed, Bååk found that the addition of about 0.1 mole CaO changed the density at 1545°C. from 2.75 to 2.44. If the mixing would not have caused a profound structural change, the addition of CaO would have lowered the density to only 2.65. The fact that CaO produces such a structural change in CaF_2 can be interpreted as follows: Liquid CaF_2 at 1500°C. has a structure which can be changed by introducing vacancies so that it assumes the formula:

$$Ca^{2+}\ F^-_{1-2x}\ O^{2-}_x\ (A.V.)_x$$

On this basis we could expect liquid BeF_2 to increase its conductivity if BeO or AlF_3 would be dissolved in its melt.

In order to cover all possible liquid structures we present a scheme (Fig. 5) in which the three extreme models are arranged in the corners of an equilateral triangle in the same way as we plot a three-component system. Vitreous silica has a structure that can

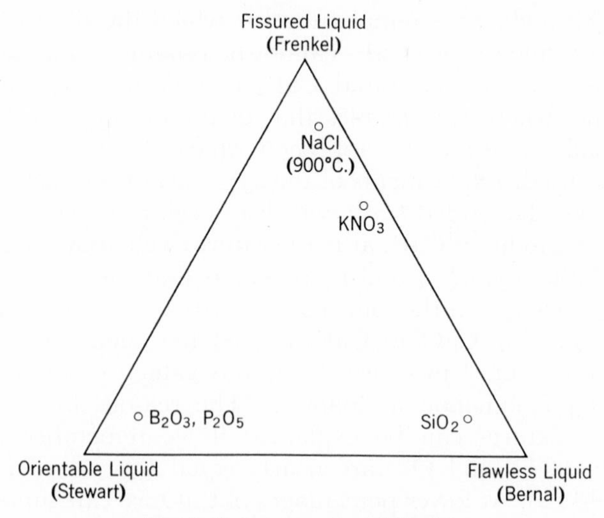

Fig. 5. Structures of real liquids.

be represented by a point close to the corner which we call the "flawless liquid" (Bernal model). Vitreous boric oxide can be represented in this scheme by a point close to the corner which we call the "orientable liquid" (Stewart model). The area of the triangle close to that corner which represents the "fissured liquid" (Frenkel model) is occupied by all those liquids which do not form glasses on cooling. Molten NaF and NaCl are very close to that corner but the nitrates and carbonates of the alkalies should be represented by points which lie farther away from the "fissured" corner and closer to the Bernal-type corner because complex alkali alkaline-earth nitrates and carbonates have been prepared in the glassy state. This suggests that at least the low melting nitrates and carbonates in the molten state resemble the crystal more than molten NaF or NaCl.

Our representation of the structure of liquids and glasses in a ternary diagram reveals a rather startling feature. We find organic high polymers now grouped together with vitreous P_2O_5 and B_2O_3, whereas some borates and phosphates have to be grouped together with the silicates.

We will apply this scheme to the constitution of glasses and learn more about the details of the structural changes which take place in glasses as a function of the temperatures and compositions when we discuss properties of specific inorganic glasses.

We will return also to these ideas when we discuss properties of glasses involving surfaces. The surface in itself is a flaw that causes a disproportionation of all binding forces. For this reason, vitreous silica can be called a Bernal liquid only when we refer to its bulk structure and bulk properties. Its indentation hardness reveals that it can flow at ordinary temperature because of the disproportionation of its binding forces under stress. Brittle solids can undergo plastic deformation when the particles are sufficiently small. Polishing a glass which has the structure of a Bernal liquid reveals that its surface can behave as an "orientable" liquid of the Stewart type. The observations that some glasses devitrify most readily in their surface can be attributed at least partly to the fact that the surface resembles a fissured liquid more than the bulk structure.

For these reasons we must mention here that our classification of glasses according to their structures refers to bulk structures and that it is not applicable to surfaces and interfaces.

4. Structure of Water and Some of Its Manifestations

In our endeavor to understand reality we are somewhat like a man trying to understand the mechanism of a closed watch. He sees the face and the moving hands, even hears its ticking, but he has no way of opening the case. If he is ingenious he may form some picture of a mechanism which could be responsible for all the things he observes, but he may never be quite sure his picture is the only one which could explain his observations. (69)

A. Einstein and L. Infeld, 1938

Water is by far the most common liquid and a major part of our knowledge of the chemical reactions of ions is based on aqueous systems. Water as a substance, in particular liquid water, is abnormal in many respects. Water as a liquid does not fit into our description of liquid structures. Water is not a molecular liquid like benzene, nor is it comparable to associated or polymerized liquids, it definitely has a character of its own.

No matter how we approach water its properties do not fit into those patterns which are established by analogous substances. We may treat it as the lowest member in the series of alcohols and find its boiling point and its viscosity too high. We might treat it as the oxide of hydrogen and compare it with its sulfide, selenide, and telluride and again we find that its boiling point and freezing point are much too high.

The substance water exhibits a number of unique chemical and physical properties. The need for a better understanding of the behavior of water is apparent to both chemists and physicists. The physicists and meteorologists interested in cloud physics are especially concerned with the unique behavior of water.

Why, for example, do water molecules in their vapor state fail to form a liquid in the absence of nuclei unless their concentration exceeds three to four times the equilibrium concentration? What is the nature of the energy barrier which separates the metastable supersaturated vapor from the stable liquid? Is it the same energy barrier which makes it possible to heat water above its boiling point in an open vessel and which gives liquid water a considerable tensile strength? These questions are of vital interest to the understanding of water because the apparent inertness of the water molecules and their failure to condense or even to form dimers stands in striking contrast to the fact that water is one of the most powerful catalysts.

In the absence of water many chemical reactions do not take place. Ammonia combines with hydrochloric acid only reluctantly if no moisture is present. Mixtures of CO and O_2 cannot be exploded by electric sparks unless water is present. Water has a very strong effect upon lowering the viscosity of fused silicates and it is a powerful catalyst in crystallizing glasses which are most difficult to devitrify as dry systems ($Na_2O \cdot Al_2O_3 \cdot 6SiO_2$, $Na_2O \cdot B_2O_3 \cdot 2SiO_2$, or B_2O_3 in their glassy state). The role of water in mineralogy and in the synthesis of minerals is well appreciated.

The physical chemistry of water has two major aspects. One concerns its atomic structure as revealed by X-ray diffraction, neutron diffraction, Raman-spectrum, infrared absorption, and certain electrical measurements. The other aspect concerns the chemistry of aqueous solutions, in particular the abnormally high ionizing power of water. No liquid other than water can dissolve and ionize substances such as aluminum sulfate or thorium nitrate. These two aspects, the atomic structure and the physical-chemical properties of water as a solvent, have been studied rather independently of one another and only in a few instances has the knowledge gained in both fields been integrated.

We want to present a unified treatment of the physical chemistry of water with respect to its solvent properties. Its interaction with glasses will be discussed later and in order to better understand the chemical durability of glasses we have to know more about the unique properties of liquid water.

The properties of water deviate strongly from those which are obtained by extrapolation from analogous compounds. In Table XVIA, water, the oxide of hydrogen, is compared with its sulfide, selenide, and telluride. A glance at these data reveals that water does not fit into the pattern. Its abnormally high boiling and melting points, the high value of its heat of vaporization and of its surface tension seem to indicate that exceptionally strong forces are acting between the molecules of water as compared with those acting in the analogous compounds.

The same impression is gained if one treats water as the first member of the series of alcohols (Table XVIB).

Decreasing the number of carbon atoms in these alcohols causes the density to change only slightly but when taking the last step, i.e., going from methyl alcohol to water, one observes an abrupt increase in the density. Again, the boiling point and melting

TABLE XVIA
Properties of Water and Analogous Compounds

Property	H_2O	H_2S	H_2Se	H_2Te
Boiling point, °C	100.0	−60.7	−41.5	−1.8
Melting point, °C	0.0	−85.6	−60	−51
Heat of varporization, kcal./mole	9.72	4.5	4.7	5.7
Surface tension at boiling point, dynes/cm.	58.9	28.7	28.9	30.0

TABLE XVIB
Properties of Water and Alcohols

Properties	HOH	CH_3OH	C_2H_5OH	C_3H_7OH
Density	1.00	0.79	0.79	0.80
Boiling point, °C.	100	64	78	98
Melting point, °C.	0	−94	−112	−127

point of H_2O are much higher than those derived from the alcohols by extrapolation.

Treating H_2O as the hydride of oxygen and comparing its melting and boiling points with the hydrogen compounds of neighboring elements, namely

H_4C	H_3N	H_2O	HF
	H_3P	H_2S	HCl

leads to the same result. Among these hydrogen compounds, H_2O is the only one which is liquid at ordinary temperature. Water has the highest boiling and melting points in this group confirming that the intermolecular forces among water molecules must be stronger than those of all its analogues. We may conclude also that the anomaly is connected with the specific interaction of the hydrogen atom with the oxygen atom. Whenever hydrogen is bonded to elements other than oxygen, the properties of the compounds change in a more normal way. For example, the boiling points of the chlorides are as follows: n-C_4H_9Cl, 130°C.; n-C_3H_7Cl, 102°C.; C_2H_5Cl, 12°C.; CH_3Cl; −22°C.; HCl, −85°C. The boiling points decrease with decreasing number of the carbon atoms and there is no abrupt change when the methyl group is replaced by hydrogen, i.e., when going from CH_3Cl to HCl. Also, the properties of the carboxylic acids do not reveal any abrupt change when formic acid is reached, as can be seen from the following gradation of the boiling points: C_3H_7COOH, 163°C.; C_2H_5COOH, 141°C.; CH_3COOH, 118°C.; HCOOH, 101°C.

Molecules in close proximity attract one another. The attractive force is small for H_2 or N_2 molecules but it increases with the size, the molecular weight, and the polarizability of the molecule (van der Waals' forces). Carbon dioxide is a gas at ordinary temperature but the heavier and more polarizable carbon disulfide is a liquid. The attractive forces which act between these molecules are not strongly oriented. The molecules of such a liquid, in spite of their close proximity, may rotate without a major energy barrier. As a result of these unoriented attractive forces between molecules many molecular liquids have a structure which comes close to one of closely packed spheres.

There are, however, some very important exceptions to this rule. The forces acting between the molecules of acetic acid

$$\begin{array}{ll} & O^{2-} \\ (CH_3)^- \; C^{4+} & \\ & (OH)^- \end{array}$$

are very different from the van der Waals' forces. The carbon of the carboxyl group is screened by three anions; namely, a methyl group, an O^{2-} ion, and an OH^- ion. The $(OH)^-$ ion is not as good a screener as the O^{2-} ion. The symmetry of the charge distribution around the central carbon would be increased if the polarizability of the two anions O^{2-} and OH^- would be equalized. The screening of the proton within the OH^- ion can be increased also if it is screened by two O^{2-} ions. As a result, the electrostatic energy of acetic acid molecules can be lowered and the screening of the C^{4+} core and of the protons can be improved if two molecules cooperate and form a dimer:

$$\begin{array}{lcccr} & O^{2-} \cdots H^+ & & O^{2-} & \\ (CH_3)^- \; C^{4+} & & & & C^{4+} \; (CH_3)^- \\ & O^{2-} & & H^+ \cdots O^{2-} & \end{array}$$

The dimerization is the result of directional forces between the molecule, the "hydrogen bond," which is effective in addition to the van der Waals' forces. Owing to binding forces, the molecules are no longer free to assume all possible positions with respect to one another with equal probability. The preceding position pictured corresponds to an energy well. The distances between the molecules are determined by their angular charge distributions so that association takes place in preferred angles. Such an association through hydrogen bonds is not likely to favor a close packed structure.

Molecules of the acetic acid type condense to a liquid that has a much higher boiling point than liquids that have the same molecular weight but in which the intermolecular forces are independent of the angular distances between neighboring molecules. Liquids of the latter type are called "normal liquids" and those which show hydrogen bonding are called "associated liquids." The "degree of association" depends upon the nature of the molecule and on the temperature. Acetic acid forms dimers in the vapor phase or when dissolved in an inert solvent such as benzene. Associated liquids due to the stronger intermolecular forces also have higher viscosities than normal liquids of the same molecular weight and some of them form glasses when supercooled sufficiently. Glycerol and many of the organic substances which G. Tammann (1) examined in his studies on glass formation belong in this group. Acetic acid can form only a dimer. However, if a molecule has more than one OH^- ion, e.g., glycerol or glycol, polymerization can go beyond the dimer stage and now glass formation is likely to occur.

When chemists realized that the physical properties of water were abnormal in many respects, it was only logical to classify water as an associated liquid. Tammann (70) was one of the first physical chemists to elaborate on a theory which describes water as consisting of a mixture of different molecular species, monohydrol, dihydrol, etc. In this country W. D. Bancroft was the main exponent of this theory.

J. D. Bernal and R. H. Fowler's (71) investigation of the atomic structure of liquid water on the basis of X-ray diffraction, classified water as a three-dimensional network.

It is important to realize that both pictures, the three-dimensional network and the polymer concept, have one feature in common; namely, the idea that liquid water does not contain an abundance of free single H_2O molecules. The most serious objection to the description of water as an associated liquid in the same sense as used for acetic acid is, no doubt, the reluctance of water to associate in the vapor phase. Even saturated H_2O vapor does not contain dimers, whereas acetic acid vapor consists predominantly of the dimer $(CH_3COOH)_2$.

When comparing water with other associated liquids, we are forced to conclude that the directional forces cannot operate between only two or three water molecules but a cooperation of a very large number of molecules seems to be essential for nucleation. This failure to dimerize in the vapor state sets water apart from the rest of the associated liquids.

If small amounts of a strong electrolyte are added to pure water the conductivity increases from practically zero to relatively high values which depend upon the nature of the salt and its quantity. One can make reasonable assumptions and explain the electrolytic conductivity on the basis of the mobility of hydrated ions. A comparison of their radii with those obtained from crystal structure allows one to go one step further and to calculate the degree of solvation. The theoretical treatment of diluted strong electrolytes is straight forward and offers no principal difficulties. One finds fair agreement between the degree of hydration as calculated from the mobilities and the energies of hydration of the ions.

The energy of hydration of an ion is the result of several factors. Ions with high charge, e.g., Al^{3+} ions, cause a considerable loss of entropy of the water. For the singly charged, noble gas-like alkali ions the hydration energy increases with increasing field strength or with decreasing size.

Hydration energies: Rb^+, 76 kcal./mole
K^+, 82 kcal./mole
Na^+, 102 kcal/mole

On this basis one can understand the greater mobility of Rb^+ or K^+ ions in water as compared with the smaller Na^+ ions. The Na^+ ion has a larger hydration shell which more than compensates for its smaller size.

The hydration energy of the H^+ ion has been calculated to be 260 to 270 kcal., which means it is much greater than that of all other ions. However, the mobility of the H^+ ion is far greater than that of all other ions.

The very low electrical conductivity of pure water increases strongly if substances are added which provide either an excess of protons or a deficiency of protons. This phenomenon is analogous to the electronic conductivities of certain defect structures.

The presence of an excess of protons over the stoichiometric ratio can be interpreted as a defect in the liquid water structure in the same sense as an excess of electrons represents a defect in pure TiO_2. Just as we may describe such a crystal as containing Ti^{3+} or $[Ti^{4+}(e^-)]^{3+}$ ions we may refer to water as containing $(H_3O)^+$ ions. This description is satisfactory as long as we are aware of the fact that these units are not located. The paradoxical feature that both an excess of protons as well as a deficiency of protons changes water from an insulator into a good ionic conductor is readily understood on the basis of its forming a defect structure.

The high dielectric constant of HCN, 120, can be understood on the basis of the dipole molecules being oriented in an electrical field. The high dielectric constant of water, 80, can be attributed to the ease of shifting protons within their respective electron clouds, e.g.;

$$\cdots O^{6+}\ (e_2^-)\ H^+\ (e_2^-)\ O^{6+} \cdots$$

$$\cdots O^{6+}\ (e_2^-\ H^+)\ (e_2^-)\ O^{6+} \cdots$$

$$\cdots O^{6+}\ (e_2^-)\ (H^+\ e_2^-)\ O^{6+} \cdots$$

The ease of shifting the proton within the electron cloud between two neighboring O^{6+} cores can account for the relatively high dielectric constant of water. It has been suggested that the high dielectric constant of water results from the free rotations of some H_2O molecules. This explanation requires two rather artificial assumptions: firstly, that H_2O molecules can rotate in solid ice just as easily as in liquid water and, secondly, that the ease of rotation of H_2O dipoles is increased if pure water is converted into a diluted gel of a hydroxide such as $Al(OH)_3$. Ice and water have nearly the same dielectric constants, 80. According to L. Havestadt and R. Fricke (72) gels which contain only small concentrations of $Be(OH)_2$ or $Al(OH)_3$ (1.0 g. in 1000 g. H_2O) can have dielectric constants which exceed the value of 100.

The ease of shifting protons in an external electrical field can account for ice and water, both having about the same high dielectric constant. The assumption that the proton can be shifted only within a certain electron cloud and cannot jump from one electron cloud to another one accounts for the combination of a high dielectric constant and a very low ionic conductivity of pure water.

In the spirit of the quotation from the work of A. Einstein and L. Infeld (69) which precedes our discussion on the structure of water we shall now present our view of the structure of liquid water as well as a picture which can account for its anomalies. First, let us review some of the pertinent facts.

The experimental approach to the structure of water is particularly difficult because the main tool, the X-ray diffraction method, cannot provide information concerning the location of protons because only ions which have electrons contribute to the scattering of X rays. The second difficulty arises from the fact that water, unlike hydrogen sulfide, in both its crystallized and liquid state does not consist of discrete molecules. If water had the structure of liquid H_2S which consists of more or less closely packed molecules it would have a density of 1.84. The low density of water indicates a very spacious structure.

The work of J. D. Bernal and R. H. Fowler (71) reveals that every oxygen atom in one modification of ice has four nearest neighbors, the O—O distance being 2.76 A. This structure is very different from that of solid H_2S in which every molecule has 12 equidistant nearest neighbors. Ice has a structure similar to silica with the positions of anions and cations reversed.

There is good reason for assuming that the O—H—O bond is not symmetrical. There is only a small difference between the vibrational frequencies involving the stretching of the OH bonds for ice and H_2O vapor, much less than one would expect if the OH distance had changed from 0.96A. in the vapor state to 1.38A. as found for ice.

The dielectric constant of ice above 200°K. is of the same order of magnitude as that of liquid water, a phenomenon on which A. F. Wells (73) comments as follows: "On this view a crystal of ice can assume any one of a large number of configurations, distinguished by different arrangement of the H atoms, either by rotating some of the H_2O molecules or by movements of some of the H atoms from positions about 1 A. from the one O atom to a similar position near the other O atom of the bond."

J. Morgan and B. E. Warren (74) found that in water at 1.5°C. the number of nearest O atoms is 4.4 at an average distance of 2.9 A. At 83°C. the corresponding figures are 4.9 atoms at an average distance of 3.05 A. This means that with increasing temperature the structure of water changes from the spaceous structure of ice toward that of a close packed liquid.

If an electrical field is applied to an aqueous solution of an electrolyte, the ions, e.g., Na^+ ions, have to move bodily through the water, but the H^+ and OH^- ions can move by what Bernal calls a "relay race" that involves only small shifts of protons.

Water neither consists of close packed single molecules analogous to liquid H_2S nor does it contain defined polymers; e.g., dimers as in acetic acid. The Bernal-Fowler concept of a three-dimensional silica-like structure of liquid water seems to be contradicted by its fluidity. The description of water as ice with some rotating molecules has definite limitations and, therefore, we suggest another approach.

In our discussion of the types of screening of positive cores, we singled out the proton as a particle which can be screened in two basically different ways. A proton can penetrate into the electron cloud of an anion. This type of screening is unique for the proton. In addition to this way of screening, a proton can also be screened in the normal way; namely, by coordinating with anions. Because of its small size the proton has the coordination number of two and in rare cases (H_3BO_3) it is screened by three O^{2-} ions.

The electronic formula of the water molecule in the gaseous state is analogous to that of NH_3, CH_4, HF, or H_2S. These molecules can be described as anions that are stabilized and neutralized by the number of protons which equals their negative charge. This leads to the following quanticule formulas:

$$O^{2-}H_2^+, \qquad N^{3-}H_3^+, \qquad C^{4-}H_4^+$$

It might be useful to emphasize the octet configuration of the anions and to write:

$$(O^{6+}H_2^+)(e_8^-), \qquad (N^{5+}H_3^+)(e_8^-), \qquad (C^{4+}H_4^+)(e_8^-)$$

We prefer to use the last formulation in cases in which we want to explain the relative inertness of NH_3 as compared with hydrazin N_2H_6 or of PH_3 as compared with phosphorus hydrides of higher molecular weight which are self inflammable. Among all hydrocarbons the stability range of methane is the largest.

This electronic structure of the single H_2O molecule in the vapor phase is analogous to that of H_2S, H_2Se, and H_2Te. However, it seems that at ordinary temperature the screening of the proton in water by coordinating with two O^{2-} ions leads to a lower energy level and to the three-dimensional structure. Hence, water is ice-like or quasicrystalline and its structure differs appreciably from that of the close packed molecules in condensed H_2S. The formula of the liquid water is analogous to that of a crystal and can be written as follows:

$$H^+(O^{2-}/4)_2 \quad \text{or} \quad O^{2-}(H^+/2)_4$$

meaning that the H^+ ion is screened by two O^{2-} ions, each of which participates in the screening of four protons. Referring to the anion, the second formula expresses the fact that each O^{2-} ion is stabilized by four protons each of which participates in the neutralization and stabilization of two anions.

If one wants to bring out more clearly the tetrahedral structure of the water and wants to emphasize the contrast between the electron configuration in liquid water and the octet shell of the water vapor volucule, one can write:

$$\begin{array}{ccccc} & & (H^+)_{0.5} & & \\ & & (e_2^-) & & \\ (H^+)_{0.5} & (e_2^-) & O^{6+} & (e_2^-) & (H^+)_{0.5} \\ & & (e_2^-) & & \\ & & (H^+)_{0.5} & & \end{array}$$

The repulsive forces between the four electron pairs can account for the tetrahedral angle. The expression $(H^+)_{0.5}$ in the formula indicates that only one half of each of the four protons neutralizes the charge of the central O^{2-} ion, the other half participates in the neutralization of adjacent anions.

It should be made very clear that the electronic structure of water is not a resonance structure between two types. Water in the vapor state is depicted by one, water in the condensed state (liquid or ice) is depicted by the other. The condensation of water involves a structural change and, therefore, this process differs basically from the condensation of H_2S. Two or three water molecules cannot form the nucleus of the bulk structure of water; in contrast to acetic acid, etc., water molecules cannot dimerize at ordinary pressure and temperature.

The structural change which accompanies the condensation

of water vapor is unique and sets water apart from similar molecules and one should not expect its boiling and melting points to fit into a pattern with H_2S, H_2Se, and H_2Te. However, one may expect H_2O molecules to condense in the same manner as H_2S molecules if the proper temperature, i.e., between -80 and $-90°C$. is reached.

Cooling water vapor very rapidly to sufficiently low temperatures may also lead to a solid, the structure of which is probably analogous to that of solid H_2S or solid H_2Se which consists of closely packed molecules. Such a modification of water would have a higher energy than ice and would convert into ice in an exothermic irreversible reaction when allowed to warm up.

The requantization reaction which accompanies the normal condensation of water vapor also accounts for the paradoxical fact that whereas supersaturated water does not condense in the absence of a solid, the unsaturated water vapor in the presence of a solid can build up a film of condensed water many molecules thick not only on a glass surface which is fairly reactive but also on a quartz crystal.

F. E. Bartell and K. E. Bristol (75) found that in a dry atmosphere acetylene tetrabromide had an advancing contact angle of 10 degrees on a quartz plate. In a humid atmosphere this contact angle was greater and in an atmosphere saturated with water vapor it reached its maximum value of 38 degrees. These measurements reveal three important facts. Firstly, the quartz surface just like a glass surface condenses water from an atmosphere that is unsaturated with respect to H_2O. Secondly, the water film which is built up on the quartz surface has a thickness which increases with the H_2O content of the atmosphere. Thirdly, the surface forces of the water film as revealed by the contact angle of acetylene tetrabromide are a function of its thickness.

Summarizing our reasoning, we may state that the transition of H_2O vapor molecules into the condensed state is accompanied by a requantization; i.e., a regrouping of electrons. The H_2O molecules lose their octet configuration and change into more spacious units in which the cores of oxygen are screened by two lone pairs of electrons and by two pairs of electrons which, in addition to screening the O^{6+} core, screen one proton each. The interaction between these units—usually called hydrogen bonding—results in electrostatic forces which are much stronger than the van der Waals' forces which are responsible for the condensation of H_2S, etc. Each proton is screened by two electron pairs. The position of the protons will be within the electron cloud formed by these two pairs. The proton vibrates between two O^{6+} cores and the magnitude of its thermal vibration increases with temperature. It is not necessary to assume that the equilibrium position over a time average is exactly in the middle between two oxygens. It is important to know that the proton is always screened even if it vibrates or is shifted by an asymmetry in its environment. This shift can take place in solid ice in very much the same manner. As a result, the dielectric constants of ice and water are not very different. It is important to realize that each proton is limited in its mobility to the area occupied by the two electron pairs. This limitation accounts for the low electrical conductivity of pure water.

Our concept of the shifting of protons in a three-dimensional structure is a unique feature of water and it can explain the unique ionizing solvent power of water.

We assume that the condensed state is governed by two basic principles, the need for electroneutrality in small volume elements and the need for screening of positive cores. There can be no doubt that liquid ammonia is a better screener than water but the ammonia molecules cannot establish electroneutrality around a highly charged ion. No matter how large a solvation shell surrounds a Th^{4+} ion, this cluster of dipole molecules around the Th^{4+} ion has a positive excess charge of four.

The unique solvent power of water for salts which contain anions and cations of high charge will be better understood after considering the solvent properties of two other liquids. We will use two extreme solvents: one anhydrous HF which can interact with all compounds which improve the screening of its protons, and, as the other extreme, liquid ammonia. The interaction of NH_3 with solids is the result of its high screening power, which makes it possible for liquid NH_3 to compete with the electron clouds of some metals and dissolve the alkali metals. However, neither of these two solvents can ionize aluminum sulfate.

The unique structure of liquid water, which enables it to dissolve and ionize even those compounds which contain ions of high charges, also plays an important part in the structures of solid-water interfaces. When finely powdered quartz is added to pure water, the water becomes acidic and electrically conducting. The acidity of this suspension is out of proportion to the low solubility of silica in water and to the very low dissociation constant of silicic acid. O. Ruff and B. Hirsch (76) found that fine quartz powder can produce a pH as low as 4.8 in pure water. The system quartz-water lowers its free energy by a proton shift that produces a better screening film of water because it has a lower than average proton concentration. Some protons are shifted away from the quartz surface into the bulk of the water where they produce acidity and electrical conductivity. Quartz particles suspended in pure water assume a negative excess charge because they are firmly surrounded by an adhering film of solidified water which has a lower-than-average proton concentration. If a dilute hydrochloric acid solution instead of pure water is used, it is more difficult for the quartz surface to improve its screening by forming a proton deficient water film; hence, the quartz grains remain electrically neutral (isoelectric point). The importance of this interaction between quartz or clay minerals and water for problems in colloid science and in ceramic technology has been discussed by W. A. Weyl (77).

The opposite phenomenon, namely, improvement of the screening of the protons of the water, can be observed when iron oxide is dispersed in water. Some protons of the water will penetrate into O^{2-} ions of this solid and give it a positive excess charge. Adding dilute NaOH to such a system improves the screening of the protons in the water and thus prevents proton penetration into the iron oxide. The excess charges of finely divided solids in aqueous systems are responsible for the stability of hydrophilic colloids. The solidification of the water through proton shifts is important for the rheology of clay-water systems and has been discussed in detail by W. C. Ormsby and W. A. Weyl (78).

Reactions of this kind are the first steps in the corrosion of glasses by water and will be discussed in some detail later (See Chapter XXIII, 2 and 5).

5. Inorganic Compounds as Solvents

The importance of the gases dissolved in a glass is well appreciated by glass technologists. In order to learn more about this solubility, W. A. Weyl (79) studied the solvent power of different glasses for carbon dioxide under pressures up to 1000 atmospheres and found that the solubility of CO_2 in a glass increases with increasing pressure, that a sodium silicate is a better solvent than a lithium silicate, that increasing alkali content increases the solubility, and that increasing temperature decreases the solubility. This, of course, is exactly what one would expect because CO_2 is not dissolved in these glasses in the form of molecules, but as $(CO_3)^{2-}$ ions.

C. R. Kurkjian and L. E. Russell (80) studied the solubility of water in alkali silicate glasses. They found that the solvent power of alkali silicates for water goes through a pronounced minimum if the alkali content is increased gradually. This behavior of glasses as solvents for water is rather unexpected because at ordinary temperature the hygroscopicity of a glass increases steadily with increasing alkali content. The water, too, cannot go into solution as molecules but participates in the glass structure as OH^- ions analogous to CO_2. This raises the question: Why is the solubility of CO_2 in alkali silicate glasses of increasing acidity different from that of H_2O?

Because of the technological importance of the solvent power of glasses for gases such as CO_2, H_2O, or SO_3 we shall examine the physical-chemical basis of solubility in a few inorganic liquids which may be considered to be extremes. It is very difficult to predict the solubility of even the simplest compounds as this property is determined by the difference which exists in the lattice energy and the energy of solvation of the ions. Both parameters can have large values and the difference between the two might be positive or negative. For this reason no adequate concept is available that would permit us to correlate the solubilities of simple inorganic compounds with their composition and the nature of the solvent. One explains the solubility of NaCl in H_2O by stating that the energy of hydration of the Na^+ and Cl^- ions is greater than the lattice energy. Water molecules have a dipole moment and the dielectric constant of water is relatively high. However, nitrobenzene has a relatively high dipole moment but this liquid is a very poor solvent with respect to ionizable salts. Silver iodide is one of the most insoluble compounds with respect to water but it is readily soluble in liquid ammonia. Aluminum sulfate is very soluble in water but completely insoluble in liquid ammonia, in nitrobenzene, or in hydrocyanic acid, and the latter has a dielectric constant of 120; i.e., 50% higher than water.

We prefer to treat solubility as a process which leads to an improved screening of strong cations. For example, the reaction which takes place when solid KCl is dissolved in HF:

$$KCl + HF = KF + HCl$$

can be attributed to the tendency of the poorly screened protons of the HF molecule to enter into the electron cloud of the Cl^- ion which offers better screening conditions.

The boiling points of the hydrogen halides reveal that the screening of a proton in HF is less satisfactory than in gaseous HCl so that HF molecules polymerize even in the vapor phase. It is incidental for the reaction that HCl escapes as a gas. The reaction would be treated as a solution process and HF would be called a solvent for KCl if the HCl did not escape as a gas. The solubility of simple salts can be used for learning something about the screening conditions of cations both in the solute and in the solvent. We found the principle of screening to be a useful basis for a better understanding of solubility phenomena.

Analogous to the formation of a salt from an acid and a base we treat the solubility of a salt in a solvent as an interaction between two substances containing cations of different degrees of screening leading to a more uniform screening of all cations. The cation, the screening of which is improved, can belong either to the solvent or to the solute. The solubility of salts in water is of primary interest to the analytical chemist. However, in view of the unusual structure of this liquid, the abundance of water should not be a factor in making it the reference system in an attempt to gain a better understanding of solubility.

In order to derive a mechanism for the solubility of inorganic crystals in an inorganic liquid, we will start out with anhydrous hydrofluoric acid as the solvent. HF is a compound in which protons have an extremely low degree of screening. No matter what the composition of the solute may be, one can be sure that it must offer additional screening to the protons of HF.

A. Anhydrous Hydrofluoric Acid

The addition of a small number of neutral molecules, such as NH_3, H_2O, etc., to a salt, can lead to a coordination complex as the first step in a solvation process which finally leads to a homogeneous solution. As far as HF molecules are concerned, they can be added only to solid fluorides. The following compounds containing "HF of crystallization" have been described:

LiF·HF		
NaF·HF		
KF·HF	KF·2HF	KF·3HF
RbF·HF	RbF·2HF	RbF·3HF

The ability to add HF molecules only to solid fluorides is a rather unique situation. An analogous situation would exist for water if the formation of hydrates would be limited to hydroxides.

The protons of anhydrous hydrogen fluoride can improve their screening by coordinating with fluoride ions of a more polarizable kind than those of the HF. The F^- ions of KF and RbF are sufficiently polarizable to improve the screening of as many as three protons. In contrast to RbF and KF the fluorides LiF and NaF can coordinate with only one HF since the Li^+ and the Na^+ ions tighten their F^- ions more strongly than a Rb^+ ion. G. Jander calls attention to this characteristic behavior of HF which distinguishes it from other solvating molecules. Water and ammonia molecules can coordinate with a great variety of salts, such as halides, sulfates, nitrates, etc. Hydrogen fluoride in its coordination is limited to fluorides because it would react chemically with all other compounds which have anions of a greater polarizability than the F^- ion.

From the viewpoint of screening this unique feature of HF can be explained in the following manner: With respect to a fluorine ion, the proton behaves like other cations, i.e., it cannot penetrate easily into the electron cloud of the F^- ion; it prefers to coordinate with two F^- ions. The F^- ion attached to a K^+ ion is a better screener than one which is tightened by a proton. In contact with more polarizable anions, say Cl^- or CN^- ions, the proton of the HF molecule would improve its screening not by coordinating with these anions but by penetration into their electron clouds. This produces an electrically neutral, gaseous molecule of HCl or HCN, respectively. For this reason HF addition complexes with halides other than fluorides cannot be stable.

The transition from a stoichiometric "addition compound" of HF molecules with a salt to the function of HF as a "solvent" is only one step further in the same direction. HF is a powerful solvent because many anions and neutral molecules can provide better screening conditions for its protons. Anhydrous hydrofluoric acid can dissolve most of the hydrocarbons which have double bonds because a double bond represents a place of high electron density which is a good screener. Coordination complexes of metal ions with ethylene are well known.

A substance is soluble in HF if it can improve the screening of the protons of the solvent. All fluorides of singly charged cations are soluble in HF because they provide F^- ions that have a greater polarizability than those of the solvent. Accordingly, the solubility of the alkali fluorides in anhydrous HF increases with increasing size of the alkali ions; i.e., from LiF (1 *M*) to KF (6 *M*).

Fluorides of the alkaline earth metals are much less soluble than those of the alkalies, partly because of the lower screening power of F^- ions which are tightened by cations that have a higher field strength as a result of their twofold charge. Nevertheless, the same rule (a steady increase in solubility) applies to the series which ranges from the sparingly soluble MgF_2 to the BaF_2, which has a fair solubility.

The fluorides of cations of the non-noble gas-type with a charge of 2 or more and of cations of the noble gas-type with a charge of 3 are insoluble. No solubility has been observed for the fluorides of Pb^{2+}, Cu^{2+}, Zn^{2+}, Hg^{2+}, Al^{3+}, Ce^{3+}, Cr^{3+}, Fe^{3+}. The solubility of fluorides in HF decreases with increasing field strength and increasing polarizing power of the cation.

Of particular interest is the low solubility of the hydrogen halides, HCl, HBr, and HI in HF. The solubility increases slightly from HCl to HI according to the increasing polarizability of the anion. The tightening effect of a proton within the electron cloud of an anion is so strong that even the highly polarizable I^- ion cannot easily accommodate an additional proton and form the $(H_2I)^+$ ion.

The nitrates, acetates, and sulfates of the alkalies are soluble in anhydrous HF because their anions can improve the screening of the protons of the solvent.

B. Liquid Ammonia

It should be possible to arrange solvents in a series starting with HF, which has no screening power but a maximum demand for additional screening of its protons, and ending with anhydrous ammonia, whose H^+ ions are well screened in the electron clouds of the N^{3-} ions. The screening power of liquid ammonia is so high that this solvent can compete successfully with free electrons of metals so that some metals will go into solution. The demand of the silver ion to be surrounded by electrons or by highly polarizable anions can be satisfied in liquid ammonia. Therefore, the silver halides which belong to the least soluble compounds in aqueous chemistry are soluble in liquid ammonia. The solvent properties of liquid ammonia are limited not by its screening power but by the principle of electroneutrality. In spite of its excellent screening power, ammonia dissolves and dissociates easily only those molecules which produce singly charged anions.

The reaction:

$$2Na + 2HOH = 2NaOH + H_2$$

has its analogue in liquid ammonia:

$$2Na + 2NH_3 = 2NaNH_2 + H_2$$

However, this reaction takes place only at elevated temperature. As a result, metallic sodium can be dissolved in ammonia. The solubility of metals in liquid ammonia increases with the atomic number of the element or the size of the atoms. It is low for Mg and greater for Ca, Sr, and Ba. The metals Rb and Cs are very soluble whereas Na is the least soluble among the alkalies. The solubility of Li is out of line. It is higher than that of Na and K because a Li^+ ion has properties intermediate between those of Na^+ and H^+ ions (Table XVII). The data in Table XVII show that the solubilities of the alkali metals in liquid ammonia are practically independent of the temperature.

The apparent molecular weight (average molecular weight

TABLE XVII

Compositions of Saturated Solutions of Alkali Metals in Liquid Ammonia (moles NH_3/g.-atom metal)

Metal	Temperature, °C.		
	−63.5	−33.7	0
Li	3.8	3.7	3.6
Na	5.2	5.5	5.8
K	5.0	5.0	4.6

of all particles) of Na dissolved in liquid ammonia is less than 23, which indicates that the atoms must be partly dissociated according to the following:

$$Na = Na^+ + e^-$$

The blue solutions of Li, Na, K, Cs, and Mg in liquid ammonia have identical absorption spectra. Concentrated solutions are deep blue in thin films and have a copper red appearance in reflected light.

The electrolysis of a diluted solution of K in liquid ammonia leads to an increase in the color at the cathode. In the immediate neighborhood of the anode the solution forms a thin colorless layer. Prolonged electrolysis transfers the color (electrons) completely from the anode to the cathode compartment. The current diminishes due to the depletion of ions in the anode compartment. Electrons enter the solution from the cathode where they combine with the K^+ ions of the solution. This behavior of a solution of potassium in liquid ammonia during electrolysis suggests the following mechanism of solubility.

When metallic potassium is dissolved in liquid ammonia K^+ ions form which can be screened by a group of oriented NH_3 dipoles. We assume that the valence electron of the potassium atom is quasifree because it is added to the electron clouds of the group of ammonia molecules which surround the K^+ ion. The presence of an additional electron causes the ammonia molecule to expand considerably, because formally it can be described as a hypothetical N^{4-} ion containing three protons in its electron cloud $(N^{4-}H_3^+)^-$. The addition of an electron to any atom or ion increases the size of the electron cloud because the mutual repulsive forces among the electrons increases. The assumption that these solutions contain $(N^{4-}H_3^+)^-$ anions explains the increase in volume when alkalies are dissolved in liquid ammonia. It can also account for the participation of K^+ ions and "solvated" electrons in the transport of the electricity and the observation that the carrying capacity of the positive and negative carriers is of the same order of magnitude, at least in dilute solutions of metals in ammonia.

With increasing concentration of the metal in the liquid ammonia, the conductivity of the solution reaches the same order of magnitude as that of metallic iron or mercury. This phenomenon reveals that the mechanism of the electron transport must be described in different terms. The conductivity of concentrated solutions of alkali metals in ammonia is no longer due to material transport alone but resembles that of semiconductors.

In our description of semiconducting TiO_2 we treated a certain volume of the crystal comprising many atoms as a unit which contains an available, quasifree electron instead of assigning this electron to any particular cation and calling it a Ti^{3+} ion. In the same fashion we describe the "solvated electron" in liquid ammonia, not as an electron participating in the electron cloud of one particular NH_3 molecule, but as an electron which participates in those NH_3 molecules which are grouped around the K^+ ion. In semiconductors we assume that the size of this volume element increases with increasing temperature. Treating solutions of metals in liquid ammonia as semiconductors agrees with the fact that concentrated solutions, in which the volume elements harboring the available electrons overlap, have electronic conductivities which are characteristic for a metal. Overlapping of the volume elements makes it possible for an electron to move through the solution without requiring more activation energy than the thermal motion can supply.

Some metals are stable also in glasses. However, the mechanism of this solubility is very different. A gold ruby glass has no electronic conductivity comparable to that of solutions of metals in ammonia.

C. Liquid Water

We may wonder why solvents such as NH_3 or HCN, which resemble water in their electrical properties, cannot ionize a salt such as $Al_2(SO_4)_3$ or $Th(NO_3)_4$. However, we should wonder instead how liquid water can separate highly charged cations such as Al^{3+} or Th^{4+} ions from their anions. Water is the only liquid which can accomplish these dissociations. Water and some of its organic derivatives, the alcohols, have solvent properties which are less limited to certain classes of compounds than are other solvents, including liquid ammonia.

We have seen earlier that our concept of acids, which represents systems in which the cations are less screened than those of bases, is applicable to aqueous solutions.

If water is chosen as an arbitrary neutral point, a basic system is obtained when some of the protons of the water are replaced by cations with a weaker electrical field. One can describe an aqueous solution of NaOH as water in which some protons are replaced by an equal number of Na^+ ions. Such a solution is a base because of the lower field strength of the Na^+ ion as compared with that of the H^+ ion.

With respect to the solubility of oxides in water this brings out an important relation. Oxides of high "basicity" are soluble in water because their presence improves the screening of the protons of the solvent. Oxides of high "acidity" are soluble in water because they can improve the screening of their cations by hydrations and by expanding their coordination. Oxides such as Al_2O_3 and SiO_2 which are intermediate and belong to neither of the two extreme groups have a very low solubility in water.

As the electrical field of the cation increases, the acidity of the compound also increases. The replacement of six protons in water by one S^{6+} core represents an aqueous solution of sulfuric acid.

Replacing in H_2SO_4 the S^{6+} core by the weaker field of the larger Te^{6+} core, one finds that the corresponding acid H_2TeO_4 does not exist, but that only its salts are stable. The Te^{6+} core is too large to be screened by four O^{2-} ions, two of which are tightened by protons

$$\begin{array}{ccc} & O^{2-} & \\ (OH) & Te^{6+} & (OH) \\ & O^{2-} & \end{array}$$

Replacing the two protons by Na^+ ions loosens the electron clouds of the O^{2-} ions sufficiently to stabilize the $(TeO_4)^{2-}$ ion.

Free telluric acid is either orthotelluric acid H_6TeO_6 or a polymer $(H_2TeO_4)_n$ called allotelluric acid or polymetatelluric acid. In both molecules the coordination of the Te^{6+} core is expanded to 6.

$$\begin{array}{ccccc} & OH^- & & OH^- & \\ OH^- & & Te^{6+} & & OH^- \\ & OH^- & & OH^- & \end{array}$$

Orthotelluric acid

We treat the solubility of salts in liquid ammonia and in anhydrous HF as the reaction of an acid with a base. The tendency of cations, either those of the solvent or of the solute, to improve their screening offers a reasonable explanation for the different solvent powers of anhydrous HF and anhydrous NH_3. With respect to its screening power and the demand of its protons for screening, one would expect water to have solvent properties ranging between those of the two extremes: HF and NH_3. Obviously, this is not the case. Water can dissolve and ionize a large number of salts which are insoluble both in NH_3 and in HF.

The solubility of salts in water involves both the screening requirements of the cations of the solute and the screening power of the anions of the solute for the proton of the water. A salt is soluble in water if the gain in energy by these two processes overcomes the lattice energy of the salt. Alkali compounds are the most soluble salts in a great variety of solvents because the solvation of the Li^+, Na^+, K^+ ions, etc., by molecules such as SO_2, H_2S, HCN, NH_3, is sufficient to screen the singly charged alkali ions. The limited solvent power of nonaqueous solvents with respect to $Al_2(SO_4)_3$ or $Th(NO_3)_4$ can be attributed to the difficulty of neutralizing highly charged ions within a small volume. Apparently, this difficulty does not exist for water as a solvent. Salts producing Al^{3+} ions or Th^{4+} ions can be soluble in water but are insoluble in the better-screening liquid ammonia. The dipoles of the ammonia molecules can screen the Al^{3+} and Th^{4+} ions but they cannot neutralize their high excess charges within a small volume.

The anion to cation ratio in $Th^{4+}(NO_3)_4^-$ is only 4 whereas the coordination of the Th^{4+} ions in crystals is usually 8. If the $(NO_3)^-$ ions were better screeners, such as Br^- or I^- ions, one might attribute the solubility of $Th(NO_3)_4$ in water to the formation of solvated but undissociated molecules. This mechanism governs the solubilities of $SnCl_4$, $SnBr_4$, and SnI_4 in anhydrous HCN. The solutions of the tin halides in HCN are nonconductors of electricity. The solutions of the thorium salts in water are conductors of electricity indicating the presence of hydrated ions.

The problem of neutralizing the excess charge of an ion within a small volume arises as soon as the anion has an excess charge of two or more. No sulfate or carbonate, not even $(NH_4)_2SO_4$ and NH_4HCO_3, is soluble in liquid ammonia. However, anions with a charge of 2 and more can be accommodated easily within the structure of water.

With respect to the structures of aqueous solutions, H. S.

Frank and M. W. Evans (81) introduced an important pictorial concept: the "iceberg," meaning a submicroscopic volume of water around the solute (molecule, atom, or ion) which is quasi-solid. The name "iceberg" was not supposed to imply that the structure of this rigid water resembles that of ice, because ice has a spacious structure and dissolved ions may reduce the volume of water.

The analysis of this phenomenon by Frank and Evans (81) leads to the concept that the introduction of a large atom into the structure of liquid water produces the following two antagonistic effects:

1. The normal solvent action: Disorder in the structure of the solvent, gain of entropy.

2. The "iceberg" effect: Change of the structure of water toward clusters which have greater order or "crystallinity," loss of entropy. At low temperatures at which the thermal motion does not seriously interfere with the establishment of ordered islands around the dissolved particle, this effect overshadows the first one so that the solubility of many gases in water goes through a minimum if the temperature increases.

The presence of ions in water lowers the entropy because their forcefields superimpose a new ordering principle on the structure of water. Our atomistic picture agrees with the one which has been derived on the basis of thermodynamics. We assume that around an ion of high charge the protons have been repelled into positions where they have lost their mobility. The water in this region has changed into an "iceberg." Hence, the hydration entropy of all ions is negative.

The influence which the charge of an ion has upon the hydration entropy can be seen from the series (in entropy units per mole):

Na^{+}, −20; Mg^{2+}, −70; Al^{3+}, −120

The size of the ion has the opposite effect as its charge. This is illustrated by the steady decrease of the entropy charges in the series of anions:

F^{-}, −25; Cl^{-}, −11; Br^{-}, −8; I^{-}, −4

or the series of cations:

Mg^{2+}, −70; Ca^{2+}, −62; Sr^{2+}, −50; Ba^{2+}, −42

In an aqueous solution the environment of an ion is symmetrical over a time average so that the electronic configuration and the polarization properties have no major influence upon the entropy of hydration. The values of Pb^{2+} and Ba^{2+} or of Mg^{2+} and Cu^{2+} are practically the same.

The atomistic interpretation of the interaction with water of ions that have high charges can explain the unique solvent power of water. Water can accommodate ions of high charge within its structure because the shift of the protons in directions away from the cations produces a volume element of water which has a proton deficiency and, therefore, an excess negative charge. The negatively charged shell of water partly neutralizes the charge of the cation within a relatively short distance, thus avoiding major space charges. This neutralization of an excess charge is a feature that no other solvent has to offer. From the viewpoint of screening, liquid ammonia should be superior to water. From the viewpoint of the dielectric properties, liquid HCN should be the better solvent. However, the only salts which ionize completely and which can produce electrical conductivity in anhydrous HCN are the alkali salts. The salts of the alkaline earths are practically insoluble in HCN and compounds of trivalent or tetravalent metals ($SbCl_3$, $AsCl_3$, $SnCl_4$, SnI_4) go into solution as solvated molecules without being ionized.

The unique structure of water governs its solvent power for highly charged cations. In addition to this thermodynamic property, the structure of water also governs the kinetics of solution processes; water is also unique with respect to the way by which solution equilibria can be reached.

Many crystalline compounds contain "water of crystallization" in the form of individual molecules. The structure of the aqueous solution of a thorium salt contains Th^{4+} ions surrounded by water with a lower-than-average proton density, but not by individual H_2O molecules. Thorium sulfate can form hydrated solids with two, four, six, eight and nine molecules of water. In these crystals some water molecules are present as individual dipoles which participate in the screening of the Th^{4+} ions. This structural difference and the rigidity of the water which surrounds the Th^{4+} ion in an aqueous solution account for the slow reaction rates of thorium salts. According to H. W. B. Roozeboom (82), anhydrous $Th(SO_4)_2$ dissolves in water up to 25% at 0°C. This solution, however, is metastable with respect to the crystal

$Th(SO_4)_2 \cdot 9H_2O$, which is soluble only to the extent of 1%. Long times (hours, or even days) are required for establishing the equilibrium in an aqueous solution of a thorium salt. According to I. Koppel (83), cerous sulfate behaves similarly to thorium sulfate.

The long period of time required for establishing phase equilibria in aqueous solutions of $Th(SO_4)_2$ and $Ce_2(SO_4)_3$ indicates that these reactions involve considerable energy barriers and that the transition:

$$Th^{4+} \text{ hydrated} + 2(SO_4)^{2-} \text{ hydrated} \rightarrow Th^{4+}\ (SO_4)_2^{2-} \cdot 9H_2O$$

cannot be merely a regrouping of ions. According to our approach, the formation of crystalline hydrates from the metastable aqueous solution involves the requantization process:

$$2H^+ + O^{2-} \rightarrow (O^{6+}H^+H^+)(e^-)_8$$

i.e., an energy barrier similar to that which opposes the condensation of water molecules from the vapor phase or the formation of H_2O molecules in the interior of liquid water under high negative pressures.

The regrouping of electrons with respect to the positive cores and the formation of H_2O molecules is a time-consuming process, as can be seen from the hydrogen-deuterium exchange. The H^+-D^+ exchange in the system H_2O-C_2H_5OH, takes place practically instantaneously, whereas it is slow in the system H_2S-C_2H_5SH, because the H_2S molecule contains the H^+ and D^+ ions within the electron clouds of S^{2-} ions.

D. Water Vapor

All properties of the liquid and of the vapor phase approach the same value as the temperature of the system approaches the critical temperature. The atomic structures of both phases become identical at the critical temperature so that the two phases can no longer coexist as separate entities above the critical temperature. Keeping in mind that not only density and refractive index but also the atomic structure become the same, one should not be surprised to find that the solvent properties of water with respect to salts change continuously and that water vapor has a distinct solvent power for compounds such as NaCl. The solvent power of water vapor is utilized in some hydrothermal reactions.

The concept that water vapor can be a solvent for salts created considerable difficulties in the minds of physical chemists and of engineers. The solubility of inorganic compounds, salts, and even silica in high pressure steam can give rise to serious disturbances in the maintenance of high pressure steam turbines. As the steam pressure is released solids are precipitated. They change the critical shape of the turbine blades and make the engine less efficient. Because of the importance of this phenomenon much of the work on this subject was carried out in connection with engineering problems. Calculations of A. Kleinhaus (84) revealed that in high pressure boilers operating at temperatures around 300°C. the partial pressure of NaCl is still far too low to be responsible for its presence in the steam or the condensate.

On the basis of the screening concept we describe the condensation of NaCl vapor as the result of the screening demand of the Na^+ ions or the electrostatic interaction between $Na^+ Cl^-$ molecules. For this case, screening and lattice energy become practically identical. However, the formation of a crystal lattice represents only one particular case of screening. Elemental iodine has a higher vapor pressure in an atmosphere of compressed CO_2 than in a vacuum. For water one could always assume that a hydrate forms which increases the concentration of water in carbon dioxide over that in vacuo. It would be artificial, however, to use this explanation for carbon disulfide. Nevertheless, it has been established that the partial pressure of iodine, water, and carbon disulfide are higher in carbon dioxide than in its absence.

The solvent power of steam is a special case of the general rule that the tendency of a substance to volatilize increases in an atmosphere of molecules which can improve screening. A. Eucken (85) pointed out that in these examples the interaction between the molecules exceeds the van der Waals' interaction and that it bears no immediate relation to the latter. This type of interaction of constituents of the glass with the water vapor of the melting furnace can play an important role in changing the composition of the surface glass. Very little exact information on this subject is available.

O. Fuchs (86) made a thorough study of the solvent properties of high pressure steam. He was very critical in the analysis of his own and of earlier experiments with respect to the possibility of a mechanical transfer of the salts either in the form of droplets of water solution or of tiny crystals. The lack of a theoretical basis on which a true solution of a solid in steam could be explained made investigators very suspicious of whether such a transfer of a salt would be possible. The experimental results, however, leave no doubt that some solids are truly soluble in steam.

R. Willstätter, H. Kraut, and K. Lobinger (87) developed a method of preparing an aqueous solution of monomeric silicic acid and found that orthosilicic acid, $Si(OH)_4$, was volatile when its aqueous solution was subjected to a vacuum distillation. Geologists were well aware of this possibility but in order to prove the reaction of quartz with water much more rigorous conditions were required. Thus, C. J. van Nieuwenburg and H. B. Blumendahl (88) had to go close to 400°C. and 300 atm. in order to prove the solubility of silica in steam.

M. von Stackelberg, F. Quatram, and J. Dressel (89) investigated the volatility of boric acid in the presence of water vapor when they studied the phase relationship B_2O_3-H_2O. They recognized the cause of the drastic differences in the vapor pressures of B_2O_3, HBO_2, and H_3BO_3. Only the latter compound, the orthoboric acid, was "coordinatively saturated" (a condition which we call "screened") and thus had a considerable vapor pressure.

In contrast to the solubility of NaCl, KCl, and NaOH in steam, Fuchs found that the sulfate and phosphate of the alkalies were insoluble. Only alkali ions, i.e., no sulfate and phosphate ions, could be discovered in the condensate. This result is of interest with respect to our earlier remark on liquid water as a solvent. We attributed the unique solvent power of liquid water as compared with liquid ammonia to the possibility of a "proton shift" which enables water but no other liquid to compensate excess charges of ions. The proton shift of liquid water is a characteristic feature resulting from its three-dimensional structure. Obviously, it cannot occur in steam, which consists of single molecules. With increasing temperature the three-dimensional structure of water breaks down gradually and water vapor consists of single molecules. In its vapor state water is quite normal as a solvent. Its dipole molecule can screen ions of low charge, e.g., Na^+ ions and neutral molecules like $B(OH)_3$ and $Si(OH)_4$, but they cannot compensate for the excess charges of SO_4^{2-} and PO_4^{3-} ions.

CHAPTER X

MELTING OF CRYSTALS

Most solids expand on melting as their constituents form a less ordered array. Hence, melting is accompanied by an increase in the entropy due to the increase of the volume and the decrease of order. The conventional theoretical approach to melting is based on thermodynamics and is restricted to those solids that consist of atoms (rare gases, metals) or to molecules that can be treated as having a spherical symmetry. The physical model used for picturing the entropy and energy changes during the transition from solid to liquid involves the "hole formation" by shifting particles from their regular lattice sites into interstitial positions. The energy requirement for moving a particle into an interstitial position is considered to be one of the main factors in determining the melting point. For details concerning the thermodynamic approach to melting of monoatomic solids, the work, in 1938, of J. E. Lennard-Jones and A. F. Devonshire (90) should be consulted.

We do not know much about the structure of fused salts. Their melting involves a structural change which cannot be described accurately. For this reason the melting process is much more difficult to understand than volatilization.

The volatilization of an ionic crystal with a low anion to cation ratio involves what is often called the breakage of existing bonds and the formation of new bonds. The boiling point of AgCl (1837°K.) is higher than that of NaCl (1738°K.) in accordance with the stronger binding forces which exist between Ag^+ and Cl^- ions as compared with those acting between Na^+ and Cl^- ions. The higher lattice energy of the AgCl (214 kcal.) as compared with that of NaCl (180 kcal.) can, therefore, account for the different vapor pressures. However, the melting process does not involve a breakage of bonds. A change occurs in the mobility of the ions which involves a temporary lowering of the degree of screening of the cations. The stronger Ag^+—Cl^- bond does not increase the melting temperature of AgCl above that of NaCl as one might expect from the fact that the boiling point of AgCl is higher than that of NaCl: AgCl melts at 728°K.; NaCl at 1073°K.

1. Fundamental Aspects of the Melting of Ionic Compounds

The melting point of an ionic compound such as NaCl is defined as the temperature at which two phases of the same composition are in equilibrium because their free energies are the same. One, a crystalline phase, has the lower potential energy and the symmetry of the environment provides better screening of the cations. The other phase, a liquid, has the higher entropy but it cannot provide the same degree of screening for its cations. Many molten salts can be easily supercooled but for most substances the transition solid-liquid takes place spontaneously.

The fact that analogous compounds may have widely different melting points has challenged many scientists to speculate on the relationship between their melting points and their constitution. Most attempts to elucidate these relationships emphasize a single parameter to account for the differences. N. V. Sidgwick (91) selected the fluorides of the second row elements in order to demonstrate the role of the bond character on the melting points of compounds:

NaF	MgF_2	AlF_3	SiF_4	PF_5	SF_6
980°C.	1396°C.	1040°C.	Gases at room temperature		

He attributes the gaseous nature of SiF_4, PF_5, and SF_6 to their high covalency. The high melting fluorides are considered to be salts of ionic character. L. Pauling (92) prefers to restrict the ionic type of bond to NaF and MgF_2. According to his view covalency starts with AlF_3 rather than with SiF_4 and he assumes that little difference exists between the character of the Al—F and the Si—F bond. He points to the geometry of these compounds and considers their polymerization in three dimensions to be a more plausible reason for the abrupt change in properties. When V. M. Goldschmidt (4) developed his "model structures" he gave an impressive demonstration of the importance of the "valence sum" as a factor which determines the melting temperature of ionic crystals having identical structures. Thus, CaF_2 (melting point, 1633°K.), the weakened model of ThO_2, has a much lower melting point than ThO_2 (3323°K.). This relationship between the melting points of solids which have the same crystal structures but ions of different valency such as CaF_2 and ThO_2 or NaCl and CaO made it a real temptation to correlate the melting temperature with the "strength of the bonds" which have to be "broken." The misconception that melting or the ability of a system to flow is connected with the strength of bonds is so deeply rooted that recently A. Bondi (93) tried to correlate the viscosity of fused salts with the van der Waals attractive forces acting in their lattices. Pointing toward the low viscosity of fused LiCl, NaBr, etc., he wrote: "One might conclude that the motion of ions in flow takes place within a uniform electrostatic field and is restricted only by van der Waals' forces."

The different approaches to melting and the failure to arrive at a consistent picture seem to indicate that no single parameter can account for the melting temperatures of even the simplest compounds. For simple salts (such as the halides of the alkalies), it is possible to explain the diffusion of ions, the formation of defects and, finally, the melting on the basis of coulombic forces, in particular the repulsive forces which come into play when one cation has to pass another one. The screening of cations improves with increasing anion to cation ratio as well as with increasing size and polarizability of the anions. The better the cations are screened the less is the mutual repulsion and the more readily can the compound gain entropy through melting.

The melting points of the halides of the alkaline earths fit well into this picture. For all alkaline earth halides the melting points drop from the fluorides to the iodides.

In order to derive a picture of the melting process of an ionic crystal the authors (21) start out with an ideal crystal and follow its changes on heating. The crystal becomes defective because a defective crystal has a higher entropy than the ideal crystal. Each defect exerts a certain depth action the extent of which depends upon the nature of the crystal, in particular its polarizability.

Let us now consider the effect which a defect has on the binding forces among the ions. A missing Cl^- ion in a crystal of NaCl represents a spot in which the surrounding six Na^+ ions exert repulsive forces upon each other because the negative ion which had bound together those cations is now missing. These repulsive forces lead to a widening of the first coordination sphere around the anion vacancy. Being pushed closer to the second coordination sphere the Na^+ ions introduce an asymmetry which increases the binding forces between the sodium ions of the first and the chlorine ions of the second coordination sphere (Fig. 6).

One can describe the binding forces of an ideal NaCl crystal as the coulombic forces resulting from the charge and the distances

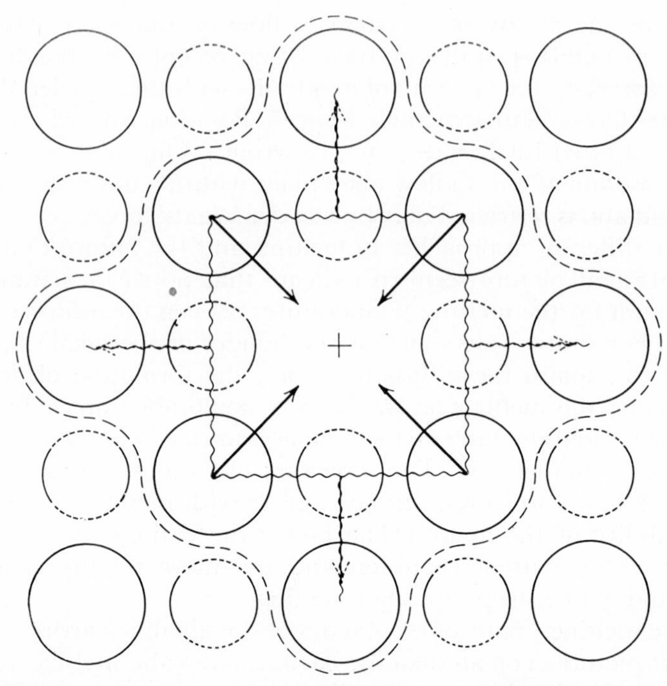

Fig. 6. Disproportionation of forces and distances around anion vacancy.

of the ions. These forces are subject only to those fluctuations which result from thermal vibrations. This picture no longer applies to the defective crystal. Even if we average over the time, the binding forces between some Na^+ and Cl^- ions have become stronger, whereas others have become weaker, than the average. Each defect is the center of a disturbance in which the binding forces between ions show deviations from the average (See Chapter IV). This disproportionation of binding forces around the vacancy produces a cluster in which the ions are bound more strongly because of the diminished internuclear distance; this is followed by a shell in which the bonds are weaker. When the melting temperature is reached, the ionic clusters around the defect increase the entropy of the system by free rotation.

2. Factors Determining the Melting Points of Simple Compounds

Cations, as a rule, are less polarizable than anions. This also means that the repulsive forces between two cations are greater than between two anions at the same distance apart. Fluidity of molten salts and formation of anion and cation vacancies involves several energy barriers, but we may assume that in the first approximation the cation-cation repulsive forces dominate the melting process.

This concept, that the magnitude of the repulsive forces between cations influences the melting temperatures of analogous compounds, provides a useful qualitative basis on which to interpret their melting temperatures. In the following paragraphs the chief factors which determine the repulsive forces between cations and, with it, the melting points, will be discussed. As it is not always possible to change only one parameter, the relations between melting temperature and composition are sometimes obscured by antagonistic effects.

A. Charge

The most obvious factor determining the repulsive forces between two cations is the magnitude of their charges. The role of the "valency" of the elements in similar structures has been used by V. M. Goldschmidt in the development of his "model structures." It has been pointed out earlier (Table XII) that the "weakened" models have much lower melting points than their "stronger" counterparts. The fluorides as the weakened models of oxides have lower melting points because the lower charges of their cations lower the cation-cation repulsion. In the same fashion, nitrides containing the N^{3-} ion with a threefold charge are "strengthened models" of oxides and fluorides. Their melting points are higher than those of the oxides.

B. Anion to Cation Ratio

Let us consider the melting temperatures of the fluorides of the second row elements beginning with sodium. The higher melting temperature of MgF_2 as compared with that of NaF agrees with our concept that more energy is required to move a Mg^{2+} ion past another Mg^{2+} ion and keep it there for any length of time than to move a Na^+ ion past another Na^+ ion. However, as we proceed in this row the melting points go down and the next fluoride, AlF_3, has a lower melting point than MgF_2 in spite of its containing the more highly charged Al^{3+} ion. This lowering of the melting point is due to the improved screening of the cation as the result of the increased anion to cation ratio. The last fluorides in this row, SiF_4, PF_5, and SF_6, are gases because their central cores are sufficiently screened by the number of F^- ions that is needed for neutralizing the charges of the cores. Their melting and their volatilization does not involve cation-cation repulsion. We may state, therefore, that the occurrence of a maximum in the melting points of this series of fluorides is the result of two antagonistic effects. As the charge of the cation increases, the cation-cation repulsive forces increase, but the number of anions per cation also increases. This means that the probability decreases that the cations have to become neighbors, even temporarily, in the liquid.

Because of the strong influence of the anion to cation ratio, the melting point of a compound is a function of the charge of the anion as well as that of the cation as can be seen when comparing the melting points of the fluorides with those of the corresponding oxides.

Going from the oxides to nitrides and carbides one finds a further increase in the melting points. The highest melting compounds are carbides, silicides, borides, and nitrides because the high excess charges of the C^{4-}, Si^{4-}, B^{3-}, and N^{3-} ions lead to an anion to cation ratio which is very unfavorable with respect to the screening of the cations:

	SiF_4	SiO_2	SiC
Melting point, °C:	−77	1710	2600

C. Size of the Cation

A drastic influence of the size occurs in the oxides of the general formula XO_2 as can be seen from Table XVIII. In this series of oxides the charge of the cation and the anion to cation ratio are constant. With increasing size of the cation, however, it becomes impossible for two O^{2-} ions to provide proper screening and the

TABLE XVIII

Melting Points of Oxides of the Formula XO_2

	Melting point, °C.				
	C^{4+}	Si^{4+}	Ti^{4+}	Zr^{4+}	Th^{4+}
Oxide	Gas	1710	1830	2677	3050
Ionic radius (A.)	<0.2	0.39	0.64	0.87	1.10

melting temperature increases to a very high value. Only the very small core of carbon can exert such a deforming influence upon its O^{2-} ions that it is screened by two strongly deformed O^{2-} ions.

D. Polarizability of the Ions

A comparison of compounds which contain cations of similar size, identical charge, and different electronic configuration reveals that increasing polarizability decreases the melting point. The classical example is provided by Fajans' discussion of the properties of the sodium and silver halides. In Table XIX, compounds containing cations of the noble gas-type (Mg^{2+}, Rb^{+} and Sr^{2+}) are

TABLE XIX
Melting Points of Compounds

Compound	Melting point, °C.	
A. Magnesium and Zinc Compounds		
	Magnesium	Zinc
XO	2800	1975
XF_2	1396	872
XCl_2	708	262
$X_3P_2O_8$	1184	900
X_2SiO_4	1900	1509
B. Rubidium and Thallium Compounds		
	Rubidium	Thallium
XF	760	327
XCl	715	430
XNO_3	305	206
C. Strontium and Lead Compounds		
	Strontium	Lead
XO	2430	888
XF_2	1190	855
XCl_2	873	501
X_2SiO_4	>1700	743
$XSiO_3$	1580	766
$X_2B_2O_5$	1130	497
$X_3As_2O_8$	1635	1042

TABLE XX
Effect of the Polarizability of the Anion on the Melting Points

Compound	Melting point, °C.			
	O^{2-}	S^{2-}	Se^{2-}	Te^{2-}
Ga^{3+}	1740	1255	1020	790
B^{3+}	450	310	—	—
Al^{3+}	2050	1100	—	—

compared with others which have either an 18 shell (Zn^{2+}) or an incomplete outer electron shell (Tl^{+} and Pb^{2+}). In all cases those compounds containing the noble gas-type cations have the higher melting points.

The polarizability of the anion also plays an important role. Because of the greater polarizability of the S^{2-} ion as compared with the O^{2-} ion, the melting points of sulfide are generally lower than those of oxides. The data given in Table XX illustrate the reduction of the melting temperature which occurs if the O^{2-} ions are replaced by S^{2-}, Se^{2-}, and Te^{2-} ions. One can explain the lower melting points of the compounds that contain highly polarizable cations on the basis of the lesser repulsive forces between cations on passing one another in the liquid state. However, one may also emphasize that a lesser cation–cation repulsion is conducive to a higher concentration of defects, which in turn would lower the melting point.

3. Anomalous Behavior of Compounds of Hydrogen, Lithium, Beryllium, and Boron

From the viewpoint of the screening of cations the proton has to be treated separately. We follow the ideas of K. Fajans and N. Bauer (13) and treat the hydrogen halides as halogen ions which contain protons within their electron clouds.

The proton can be screened in two ways. Like other cations, it can be surrounded by anions and for this purpose it requires two anions (hydrogen bonding, liquid water, and ice) or it can penetrate into the electron cloud of an anion (hydrogen halides and water molecules in the vapor state). The electronic structure of the Li^{+}, Be^{2+}, and B^{3+} ions (helium configuration) gives these ions properties which are intermediate between those of the ions with neon configuration (Na^{+}, Mg^{2+}, and Al^{3+}) and the proton. We assume that the polarization of these ions, namely, the repulsion of their 2 K-electrons, expose their nuclei to such an extent that they can penetrate partly into the diffuse electron clouds of polarizable anions. The greater the polarizability of the anions, the greater is the deviation of the properties of Li^+, Be^{2+}, and B^{3+} compounds from those expected by a comparison with Na^+, Mg^{2+}, and Al^{3+} compounds.

If one plots the melting points of the alkali fluorides against the size of the cation (Fig. 7), one obtains an almost straight line relation for the melting points of CsF (684°C.), RbF (760°C.), KF (880°C.), and NaF (980°C.). Extrapolating this line to the radius of the Li^+ ion one would expect LiF to melt at about 1100°C. Actually, LiF melts at 870°C.; i.e., 10 degrees lower than KF. There is no straight line relationship between the melting points of those alkali halides which contain the more polarizable Cl^-, Br^-, and I^- ions, but one can still see that the lithium compounds are completely out of line: their melting points are too low.

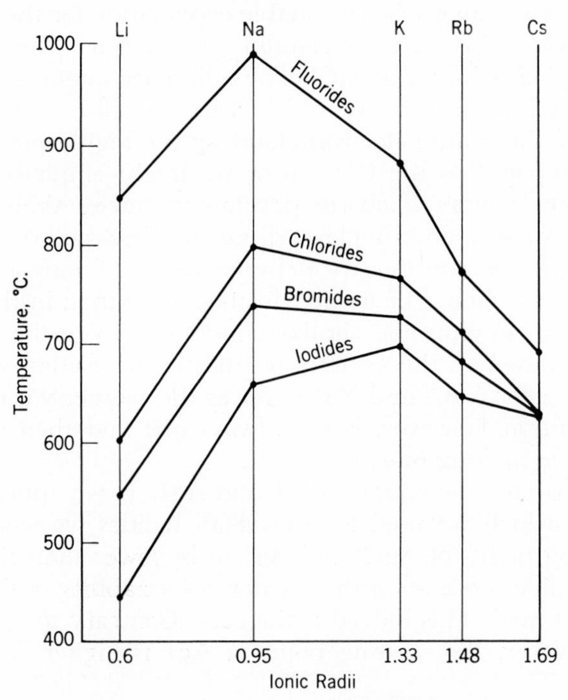

Fig. 7. Melting points of alkali halides.

One finds the same situation for Be^{2+} compounds. No matter whether one starts out with the melting points of the chlorides of the alkaline earths (melting points increase with size) or those of the oxides (melting points decrease with size), the melting points of BeO and $BeCl_2$ are lower than those expected from an extrapolation. Also, the melting points of B_2O_3 and B_2S_3 are very much lower than those of the corresponding aluminum compounds. The same applies to the melting points of the boron halides as compared with aluminum halides.

The drastic difference in the screening demands of Li^+ and B^{3+} as compared with Na^+ and Al^{3+} explains the different properties of those glasses containing these ions. Lithia imparts some unique and desirable properties to glass, and one may safely state that the introduction of B_2O_3 revolutionized the development of technical glasses.

4. Structural Changes during Melting

As long as we limit ourselves to a comparison of related simple compounds we can give a reasonable explanation for their different melting points. We can understand for example, why NaI has a lower melting point than NaCl. The difference might be attributed to the smaller Na^+-Na^+ repulsion which would exist in a melt containing the diffuse electron clouds of the highly polarizable I^- ion as compared to the Cl^- ion or we might emphasize that an NaI lattice is more likely to develop vacancies than the more compact (smaller internuclear distances) less polarizable NaCl lattice. The electron density between two Na^+ ions at the same distance apart should be greater in the iodide than in the chloride melt. This reasoning and similar considerations of the melting of crystals is based on the assumption that the transition solid-liquid is analogous for NaCl and NaI as far as the geometry is concerned. This condition, however, is not always met and then our simple approach to melting must fail.

Let us take the couple AgCl and AgI. If we apply the same reasoning which we used for the alkali halides we would expect the melting points of AgCl and AgI to be lower than those of the sodium halides because of the greater polarizability of the Ag^+ ion with its 18-shell. This indeed is the case. Contrary to our expectations, however, the melting point of AgI is higher than that of AgCl:

Melting point:	NaCl—800°C.	AgCl—455°C.
	NaI —651°C.	AgI —552°C.

This discrepancy can be understood only if one realizes that the melting of AgCl and AgI are not analogous processes as far as the geometry is concerned. Both crystals on heating gain entropy by increasing the number of their defects but AgI at 146°C. undergoes a phase transformation which increases its entropy by placing the cations into random positions. The Ag^+ ions in the high temperature modifications AgI are mobile. C. Tubandt, in 1920, as well as L. W. Strock, in 1935, who examined the phase change by electrical and X-ray methods speak of "molten silver" within a solid framework of iodine atoms. In this case the solid phase has found a way to increase its entropy without melting. Hence, the melting of the high form of AgI cannot be accompanied by the same gain in entropy as the melting of AgCl. Silver iodide is not unique, lithium sulfate undergoes a similar change. The cationic lattice, so to speak, melts before the anionic structure becomes a liquid.

At the melting point a crystal and a liquid of the same composition are in equilibrium, i.e., melting does not change the free energy of the system

$$\Delta F_M = E - T_M S = O$$

$$T_M = E/S$$

The greater the entropy change (S) during melting, the lower must be the melting temperature T_M of the substance. The parameters which we consider important for the melting process, e.g., anion to cation ratio, field strength and polarizability of the cation, etc., refer to energy changes (E) during melting. Hence a regularity in melting temperatures of analogous compounds can be expected only if the structural changes are analogous because they determine the entropy.

AgI has a higher melting point than the other halides of silver because the gain in entropy, S, is smaller for the high temperature form of AgI than for the other halides of silver.

The gain in entropy during melting depends upon the difference which exists between the structures of the solids and those of the liquids. We must expect therefore to encounter a discrepancy similar to that between AgI and AgCl when two analogous compounds have similar crystal structures but different liquid structures. In order to fully understand melting we have to know more about the structure oι the liquids which form.

CHAPTER XI

NUCLEATION AND CRYSTALLIZATION

Our approach to the structures of liquids and to the process of melting required dynamic concepts; namely, the formation of fissures that fluctuate and of ionic clusters or aggregates with very different lifetimes. We heard about crystals that melt in steps, first the cationic part and, at a higher temperature, the anionic part of their lattices. Other crystals which melt to form a Bernal liquid may require considerable time for becoming amorphous, even 50°C. above their melting points (albite, $Na_2O \cdot Al_2O_3 \cdot 6SiO_2$). Glass formation also depends upon a kinetic process; namely, a negligible rate of nucleation. We will have to review, therefore, those factors that influence the nucleation rate of a system and determine whether a liquid can be solidified as a glass. Nucleation is an essential part of the constitution of glass and should be treated on a par with phase diagrams. Most textbooks on glass comment on the static aspects and discuss the phase diagrams such as the Na_2O-SiO_2 system and the ternary system Na_2O-CaO-SiO_2. These diagrams give us some important information; namely, the nature of the phases that separate out of the glass when it devitrifies. It is also important to learn something about the rate at which these phases separate out: Why does silica form a "stone" and sodium fluoride form an opal glass? In books on the structure and the technology of glass, these rate phenomena are not treated as thoroughly as equilibria because they require a very different approach and we do not have a basis as rigorous as thermodynamics for understanding rate phenomena in condensed systems. Where does the difference lie between rate phenomena and equilibria?

1. Equilibria versus Rate Processes

When we discussed our concepts of the acidity and basicity relations of oxides (see Chapter V) we derived an energetic reason for reactions between oxides such as SiO_2 and CaO. The improvement of the screening of the Si^{4+} core or the equalization of the states of polarization of all O^{2-} ions leads to the formation of compounds. We learned why a mixture of 1 mole CaO with 2 moles silica is not in equilibrium and how it can lower its free energy by reacting and sharing O^{2-} ions between Ca^{2+} and Si^{4+} ions. Consulting the phase diagram of the system CaO-SiO_2 we find that a mixture of 1 mole CaO with 2 moles SiO_2 is in equilibrium only when the CaO is combined with SiO_2 in the form of wollastonite, $CaSiO_3$, the most siliceous compound of calcium. Half of the SiO_2 remains unreacted. When we study the reaction by heating the mixture to approximately 1000°C. we find that in spite of the excess of silica the orthosilicate of calcium Ca_2SiO_4 is formed first and not the metasilicate, which is the stable phase. This is rather perplexing. As the reaction proceeds we find that the compound $3CaO \cdot 2SiO_2$ is formed next and that it requires considerable time to change the system into the stable wollastonite-silica mixture.

This sequence of reactions was first observed by W. Jander and E. Hoffmann (94) and it can not be deduced from the phase diagram. Here is an example of a rate phenomenon that involves nucleation of a metastable phase which guides the reaction into a channel that does not lead to the phase with the lowest free energy.

The rates and even the paths of many reactions in which new phases are formed are governed by the formation of nuclei. A nucleus is a fragment of the new phase which is sufficiently large to survive the energy fluctuations so that it is able to grow. The nucleus which forms in a system is not necessarily the most stable phase but it must be a phase which is more stable thermodynamically than the matrix from which it forms.

The phenomenon of nucleation of unstable or metastable phases plays a very important part in chemistry. It makes it possible for us to prepare substances that have no stability region but form only because of their higher rates of nucleation. This phenomenon has an interesting history. Wilhelm Ostwald (95) expressed it as his "Stufenregel" or law of stages.

The CaO-SiO_2 mixture lowered its free energy by reacting but the reaction did not immediately produce nuclei of the stable wollastonite. The equilibrium was approached in several steps (Stufen) so that different stages of the reaction could be frozen in by taking the mixture out of the furnace and letting it cool.

Ca_2SiO_4 has a higher polarizability than $CaSiO_3$. Once a nucleus of Ca_2SiO_4 has formed it will guide the reaction in this direction and cause the nucleus to grow. The most polarizable compound is grown first until by chance a new nucleus forms. The compound next in line, $3CaO \cdot 2SiO_2$ has a better chance of forming nuclei than the least polarizable, most acidic, $CaO \cdot SiO_2$.

The fascinating aspect of this phenomenon is, that in order to guide a reaction toward a certain metastable product one does not even need a nucleus or a seed of that phase: a crystal which resembles it geometrically may be sufficient. In this case we speak about a "nucleation catalyst." Here we meet one of the fundamental differences between experimentation in the field of equilibria (phase diagrams) and rate processes. Rate processes are subject to catalysis.

By choosing the proper nucleation catalyst a chemical reaction can be guided to proceed in a direction which it would not take without the catalyst. For example, I. N. Stranski and D. Totomanow (96) demonstrated that in the stability range of the hydrate $NaBr \cdot 2H_2O$ (below 50.7°C.), anhydrous NaBr can be obtained from its aqueous solution if PbS crystals are used as nucleation catalysts.

In order to understand the speed of a reaction we need a hypothesis concerning its mechanism. An explanation of the mechanism of a reaction, e.g., the formation of the crystal which is stable at a certain temperature-composition point in our system, requires a model of the interaction of those atoms or ions which we choose as constituents of the system. Such a model should be limited to a relatively small number of atoms. In order to understand reaction rates we have to go from the macroscopic description of events as they are pictured in the phase diagram into atomic dimensions, a step which by necessity changes our approach considerably. We cannot expect that the few reacting particles of our model that we observe will interact exactly in the ratio of the mixture which is presented by the point in the phase diagram. Our model has to allow for fluctuations in the composition. Furthermore, it is meaningless to speak about the exact temperature of the few atoms which we observe in our model. The temperature which we chose, 10°C. below the liquidus temperature, has to be replaced by the fluctuating energy of the small group of atoms which we consider in our model. In contrast to the thermodynamic descriptions in which the energy is integrated over long times we have to describe our model in a way which reveals the energy fluctuations with time. Both fluctuations, i.e., of composition and of temperature, are pertinent for the understanding of the kinetics of reactions. The former accounts for the formation of metastable phases and the latter for the existence of metastable temperature regions in which no changes can occur unless seed crystals are added.

According to thermodynamic equilibria the lowering of the temperature to a point which lies 10 degrees below the liquidus temperature should produce crystals. The first step toward crystallization, however, is the formation of a nucleus through the interaction of a small number of particles. As such as group does not have a constant temperature but an energy which fluctuates, we must expect that at 10 degrees below the liquidus temperature nuclei form but that they are also destroyed at this temperature.

For nucleation processes the point in the phase diagram has lost its significance and it has to be replaced by an area which includes the probable variations of both the chemical composition and the energy. The events which take place on cooling depend on the statistical fluctuations of the temperature and the composition of small volume elements. The exact number of atoms or ions which represent a nucleus, i.e., a fragment of a new, more stable phase which can survive the energy fluctuations so that it can grow into a crystal, depends upon the nature of the substances as well as on the external conditions. This approach to rate phenomena leads us into fields that cannot be treated as rigorously as we can treat the equilibria presented in our phase diagrams.

A system such as a supersaturated aqueous solution or a molten silicate below the liquidus temperature that can lower its free energy by precipitating a new phase will frequently do so only after a considerable time has elapsed. The system requires either an "induction period" or "seeding." Experimental studies concerning the rates of reactions confronted the scientist with a new phenomenon; namely, poor reproduceability of an experiment and the need for a large number of experiments in order to draw valid conclusions.

The role of mysterious contaminations, seeds, and catalysts, becomes more and more important. Scientists who studied the rates of nucleation studied events that were subject to chance. A gambler throws a die and hopes for the best, but throwing a die once or twice gives no certainty. Only if this operation is repeated frequently can the results be predicted and can they be treated mathematically.

The chances of throwing a six are 1 in 6, but that does not mean that we can be sure of throwing a six if we throw a die six times. We might get a six two or three times; we might not get one at all. However, if we throw a die 6000 times we find the number of sixes coming rather close to 1000.

Equilibria can be understood on the basis of energy relations but rate processes require in addition some knowledge concerning the path of the reaction. In our last example where the absence or the presence of PbS determines whether the supersaturated solution precipitates $NaBr \cdot 2H_2O$ or NaBr, the catalytic action of PbS can be easily understood. We started out with a homogeneous solution supersaturated with respect to NaBr (I). This system has a high free energy. Stable under this condition would be a heterogeneous system consisting of a saturated solution plus a solid phase which has the composition of $NaBr \cdot 2H_2O$ (III). As far as the free energy is concerned, between these two systems there is one which has an intermediate free energy; namely, a saturated solution with NaBr as the solid phase (II). We may write

(I.) Supersaturated solution of NaBr in water (highest free energy)
(II.) Saturated solution + NaBr (intermediate free energy)
(III.) Saturated solution + $NaBr \cdot 2H_2O$ (lowest free energy)

The energy barrier which keeps the supersaturated solution (I) in a metastable state is the formation of a nucleus of either NaBr or $NaBr \cdot 2H_2O$. PbS has the same lattice dimensions as NaBr, hence it catalyzes the formation of NaBr by epitaxy, i.e., oriented overgrowth. If we had added to the metastable solution a crystal of $NaBr \cdot 2H_2O$ or of an isostructural substance as a seed, the reaction would have proceeded directly from (I) to (III).

The addition of PbS crystals to the high energy system (I) has two effects: it decreases its lifetime and it determines the reaction product. Within seconds we have changed system (I) into system (II). Unmolested it may have remained in its metastable high energy state for many hours and finally would have changed into (III). As far as the rates of these reactions are concerned, the absolute energy differences between the systems (I), (II), and (III) lost their importance and we have to focus our interest upon the nature of the nucleus.

Returning to our first example, the formation of Ca_2SiO_4 in the system CaO-SiO_2, we ask now the question: Why does a nucleus of Ca_2SiO_4 have a greater chance of forming than one of the stable $CaSiO_3$? Before we can answer this question we want to get better acquainted with simpler phenomena which involve nucleation.

2. Theoretical Approaches to Nucleation

Wilhelm Ostwald was the first scientist who was able to bring some order into those phenomena which are connected with spontaneous crystallization or nucleation. He examined the stability of supersaturated solutions, and studied the effects which "seeds" and "catalysts" have upon the rate of nucleation. His work remains one of the fundaments upon which our present knowledge is based. Nucleation and the effects which catalysts have in accelerating crystallization and gas evolution fascinated some of the great scientists during the eighteenth and nineteenth centuries. The supercooling of water in an evacuated vessel and its crystallization when air is admitted was studied by G. Fahrenheit as early as 1724. Through his experiments with glacial acetic acid, J. T. Lowitz established in 1785 the effectiveness of seeding with crystals of the same substance and the ineffectiveness of crystals of unrelated substances. Lecocq de Boisbaudran contributed much experimental material and his observations formed the basis of Ostwald's distinction between "metastable" and "labile" supersaturated solutions. Many solutions which are only weakly supersaturated were found not to crystallize unless seeds were added. In 1866, Lecocq de Boisbaudran laid the basis for a concept which W. Ostwald developed further and which he called the "law of stages" (Ostwald's Stufenregel). De Boisbaudran experimented with salts which could form several hydrates and found that crystallization rarely produced that hydrate which was stable under his experimental conditions. He found that, as a rule, an instable hydrate was formed first.

At the time when scientists experimented on the formation of crystals from supersaturated solutions there was a strong interest in experiments and theories on gas evolution from supersaturated solutions. The controversial opinions and the colorful history of the phenomena which accompany the gas nucleation has been covered by E. C. Marboe (97) in her Marie Curie lecture.

This historical treatment of a major technological problem, gas evolution from supersaturated solutions or superheated liquids, makes very interesting reading, and one may wonder how it was possible for leading scientists to be so narrow in their views and to ignore the possibility that a certain phenomenon may have more than one cause. There is no justification, however, for a condescending smile because in our own times we find the same attitude. One has only to mention the words "cloud seeding" and one finds that the leaders in the field of atmospheric physics are divided in their theories.

Our present difficulties with the constitution of oxide glasses is primarily the result of efforts to provide one and only one picture for their structures. As we will see, even among a group of oxides the formation of a glass can be the result of two very different conditions. The formation of vitreous silica SiO_2 and the formation of vitreous P_2O_5 or B_2O_3 may look as if they were closely related processes but the reluctance of these melts to nucleate have very different causes. The nucleation of gases and of crystals from supersaturated solutions looks simple but the experimental treatment of nucleation processes is tedious because the evaluation of experimental data requires a statistical treatment of a large number of single experiments. Hundreds of experiments had to be made in order to establish the existing relations. Only by the statistical treatment of a great many observations can the nature of the process be elucidated.

De Coppet in his study in 1872 on spontaneous crystallization introduced the "average lifetime" of a solution as a function of the degree of supersaturation. Even the statistical treatment of a large number of experiments did not solve all problems immediately. The effects on nucleation of mechanical vibrations and of scratching the wall of the container have not yet found their final explanations. P. Othmer, in 1915, encountered a new difficulty when he found that the number of nuclei formed under certain conditions is not proportional to the volume of the supersaturated or supercooled liquid but that it is strongly influenced by the surface area of the sample.

We look upon a surface or an interface as an asymmetry that disproportions all binding forces and changes any structure in the direction of a fissured liquid or a molecular liquid. Silica is a "flawless" Bernal liquid only in its bulk; not in its surface.

This concept will be used extensively in Volume II because it explains the surface flow of rigid glasses during polishing, the anisotropy of a glass surface when rubbed in one direction, the fast material transport in grain boundaries, and the higher ionic conductivity of polycrystalline aggregates as compared with single crystals.

We also apply this concept to a liquid such as water or molten glass. The more rigorous attack on glass of cycled humidity as compared with constant humidity, the more intense corrosion of a glass upon a refractory at the "metal line," and the phenomenon of "upper drilling" are all the result of the disproportionation of binding forces. From our viewpoint it is not surprising, therefore, that the surface area plays an important role in all nucleation phenomena. When Tammann encountered difficulties in inducing crystallization in a piece of glass, he powdered some of it and sprinkled the powder upon the surface of the glass. Because of the large surface area of the powder, nucleation was enhanced and crystallization spread to the bulk glass.

W. Ostwald's experimental approach led to the distinction between a metastable supersaturated solution and a labile solution. Only the latter showed spontaneous crystallization within experimental times. Ostwald also attempted to elucidate the nature of the seeds. How much must a crystal weigh in order to act as a seed?

The fundamental, thermodynamic approach to nucleation was chosen in 1876 and 1878 by J. W. Gibbs. In the second part of his writings on heterogeneous equilibria, Gibbs examined the stability of a nucleus as a function of its size and he proved that a phase may have a stable existence beyond its normal stability limits because the formation of a new phase requires energy. He reached the conclusion that there should be a simple relation between the radius of a particle which is stable in another phase, the thermodynamic potentials of the two phases, and the interfacial energy. Only if the radius of the new phase exceeds a certain value does this phase grow. Gibbs' general theoretical approach to nucleation is still the basis of the present scientific work in the field of nucleation. The modern work on nucleation by M. Volmer and his school is based partly on the Gibbs equation. A more atomistic approach to nucleation has been chosen by I. N. Stranski and his school. His work combines the kinetics of nucleation with equilibrium consideration.

The theories of nucleation or irreversible condensation are centered around the experimental fact that for a supersaturated vapor a definite critical supersaturation exists.

In order to precipitate water from the vapor phase the supersaturation has to reach a value of 4 to 6. The supersaturation is expressed as the concentration of water divided by the concentration or vapor pressure in equilibrium: $P/P_{Equ.}$.

M. Volmer and H. Flood (98) point out that even for such a simple system as water or as a supersaturated vapor of a simple alcohol it is very difficult to perform meaningful experiments.

The accurate determination of $P/P_{Equ.}$ is difficult because of the various effects which catalyze nucleation and change the homogeneous nucleation into heterogeneous nucleation, in particular, the walls of the container or the presence of dust particles and of polar molecules and ions. One cubic centimeter of air contains approximately 1000 ion pairs due to ionizing radiation.

In addition to the experimental difficulties, theoretical approaches suffer from the shortcoming that too many assumptions have to be made for which no proof can be given. In 1952, in a symposium on nucleation, H. Reiss (99) commented on the nucleation theory using the following arguments.

The first fragments of the new phase formed are regarded as well defined, spherical droplets that have the same thermodynamic properties as macroscopic drops. Droplets which are smaller than the critical size, i.e., those which have less than the critical number of molecules, are unstable and do not grow. Drops which are larger than the critical size grow due to energy fluctuations which are violations of the laws of thermodynamics.

In order to derive a theory, the assumption has to be made that an equilibrium exists between embryos of different sizes (still smaller than the critical size) which is characteristic for each pressure and temperature. It is assumed that by some constraint upon the system no embryos change into nuclei by reaching a size larger than the critical size. Hence a dynamic equilibrium is established in which the number of embryos of a given size is fixed. The supersaturated vapor is considered as a homogeneous solution of single molecules and embryos of all sizes in equilibrium. Each kind of particle is treated as a molecular species characterized by its own chemical potential.

Analogous to similar rate theories, the crucial step in the

nucleation rate theories is the computation of equilibria. In order to derive a rate function one has to assume that effective collisons between embryos are rare and that the growth of all embryos can proceed only by the addition of single molecules. On this basis one can calculate the rate of growth of an embryo of the size X to the size 1 + X for different values of X.

The main difficulty attending this model is the fact that for a group of about 50 molecules no geometrical dividing line can be drawn between liquid and gas phase. A slight change of the boundary line easily doubles or triples its volume.

A second difficulty arises from the lack of knowledge concerning the density of the embryo. The assumption that a small liquid particle, containing of the order of 50 molecules, has the same density as the bulk cannot possibly be correct. Furthermore, the use of surface tension, a macroscopic property of liquids, should not be extended to a group of a few molecules.

At the present time glass technologists are exceedingly interested in nucleation processes. S. D. Stookey's (100) success in providing a new material with superior properties has opened up new fields of research on nucleation and crystallization of glasses. Of course, a sound theoretical treatment of nucleation would be very desirable. For this reason it is important that one realizes the shortcomings of the conventional theoretical treatment of nucleation from the vapor phase. Nucleation of droplets from a vapor phase should not be used as a basis for developing a theory of nucleation of solids. As far as the physical chemistry of solids is concerned, the authors share R. Smoluchowski's (101) opinion that there is no satisfactory theory of nucleation.

3. Nucleation of Gas Bubbles from Supersaturated Liquids

The problem of gas evolution has occupied the minds of leading scientists for several centuries and it has remained a problem of interest to many technologists. The conditions that catalyze the evolution of gases from a supersaturated solution have been known for a long time but only recently were the authors (102) able to give a consistent explanation. Before we go into the details, we shall review some pertinent experimental observations which E. C. Marboe (97) reported in her Marie Curie lecture.

As far back as 1784 Achard observed the effect of a piece of bread or paper on the release of carbon dioxide from beer or champagne. In 1817 Gay-Lussac observed the added ease with which water boiled in glass containers if iron filings were thrown into the vessel.

The problem of the evolution of gases became of prime importance with the introduction of the steam engine, in which superheating of boilers often led to explosions. As early as 1825 the engine-keepers of Scotland made a practice of throwing a bushel of radicles of barley into the boilers to help raise steam. This waste product from the cleaning of malt was found to be effective for a period of several days.

In the eighteenth and nineteenth centuries, outstanding scientists in France studied the problem of superheating because it was connected with an important French industry, the distillation of brandy. The production of the finest quality brandy required that the distillation be carried out at low temperature. Superheating caused undesirable high-boiling fusel oils to be carried over. Two methods were found to prevent overheating. One method was the nucleation of steam bubbles by means of materials that contained plenty of gas inclusions, such as paper or bread or a coiled brass tube. The other method was the addition of soap, which in contact with the copper retorts formed a hydrophobic layer of copper palmitate.

In 1834 Gagniard-Latour examined the influence of sound on the release of gases from supersaturated liquids. This method has its modern counterpart in the use of ultrasonic waves for degassing a molten metal or a glass.

In 1866 the European scientists were divided into two camps and engaged in an energetic scientific feud over the true cause of gas evolution from supersaturated liquids. Leading the group on one side was Gernez, who saw in microscopic gas bubbles the only cause of nucleation. On the other side was Tomlinson, who denied Gernez' thesis and explained all experimental results on the basis of hydrophobicity or lack thereof. In the light of present-day research, we know that both premises are correct.

An important contribution to the solution of the problem was made by Henrici when he found that stearic acid released gas supersaturation when in the solid state, but not in the molten state. It has been confirmed by present-day research that rigidity is an important condition that aids a hydrophobic substance in catalyzing gas release. Unfortunately, Henrici attributed his findings to "surface roughness," the presence of sharp points or edges, and even today this interpretation has not been eradicated completely.

This brief review of the thoughts which scientists had on gas evolution shows that the important factors aiding nucleation were known at the beginning of this century, namely: (1) the role of entrapped air, gas bubbles, or any gas-liquid interface, and (2) the role of greasy materials or, generally speaking, hydrophobic substances in their solid or rigid state.

The first condition needs no further comment. Any liquid-gas interface is the seat of a molecular exchange requiring little activation energy. In order to test the mechanical strength of a liquid one can seal it in a glass container, let it expand thermally until it completely fills the container, and cool the system. On cooling, the liquid contracts more than the glass container but in the absence of a gas bubble the system can develop considerable mechanical stresses before the liquid fractures.

The second condition, the need for a hydrophobic substance to be in a rigid state in order to be most effective, is less obvious. For example, a drop of a liquid fatty acid in contact with water can orient its molecules so that the hydrophilic groups are turned toward the water. Such an orientation is less likely to occur in the solid or crystal phase because some crystal faces must retain hydrophobic properties and the absence of strong forces between these faces and the water allows gases to escape readily. In addition to this phenomenon one has to remember that no hydrophobic substance is "water-repellent" in the exact meaning of the word, because the van der Waals attractive forces are still active between any two phases. Hence, even those hydrophobic liquids that do not contain hydrophilic groups or molecules (e.g., paraffin oil) are bound to the adjacent water by weak forces. A liquid droplet, due to the van der Waals' forces, will tend to follow the thermal motion of the adjacent water film and is less likely to produce a hole that can act as a nucleus than a hydrophobic solid with its more independent thermal vibrations. The difference between the forces emanating from a liquid surface and those of the same substance in the solid state can be demonstrated experimentally. Using beams of vapor molecules, M. Volmer and I. Estermann (103) found that the adhesive forces between the oncoming molecules and liquid mercury are greater than those between the same molecules and solid mercury. In its liquid state, mercury had the higher accommodation coefficient.

The authors could confirm the earlier observation that the hydrophobic liquid paraffin oil is not as effective as solid paraffin as a nucleating catalyst for a supersaturated solution of CO_2 in H_2O. However, by smearing a film of liquid paraffin onto a glass wall, they are able to convert the liquid into an effective nucleation catalyst.

A molten glass below the liquidus temperature is metastable. Such a glass is not only supersaturated with respect to the primary phase, e.g., devitrite $Na_2O \cdot 3CaO \cdot 6SiO_2$, but also with respect to gases, e.g., CO_2 and O_2. Hence, a better understanding of the nucleation of gases from liquid water can help the glass technologist to better understand his problems connected with the fining of glasses. Experiments, which reveal a surprising parallelism between the behavior of molten glasses and of supersaturated aqueous solutions of carbon dioxide, have been performed by glass technologists.

Opening a bottle of carbonated water carefully and avoiding major vibrations reveals that the supersaturated liquid remains metastable for long times. In spite of the water containing more CO_2 than that amount which is soluble at atmospheric pressure, gas bubbles do not form spontaneously; it takes a long time for the system to reach its equilibrium by the slow diffusion of CO_2 into the liquid-air interface. The metastable aqueous solution of carbonated water can be looked upon as a model of molten glass. In an early stage of the melting, glass technologists are interested in increasing the rate of gas evolution from the melt. There are several methods that permit us to accelerate the release of gases from a molten glass or from water supersaturated with carbon dioxide. Increasing the temperature is the most obvious method to increase the rate of a reaction. E. Zschimmer, E. Zimpelmann, and L. Riedel (104) devised a heating schedule for glass melting which applied high temperatures for short durations to the glass melt at a certain stage in order to release supersaturation.

Pouring carbonated water into a container and stirring it, is an efficient way of accelerating the CO_2 gas evolution and establishing equilibrium. This process had its counterpart in the old custom of glass melters who used "blocking" of glass by immersing into the pot a piece of damp wood. The evolution of steam from the rapidly decomposing wood created a lively agitation which helped to speed up the removal of gases and the fining of the glass.

Sound waves and ultrasonic waves, i.e., mechanical vibrations with a frequency of that of sound or higher, have been used in several industries for releasing supersaturated gases from aqueous liquids, fused metals, and glass melts. The first experiments on the degassing of glasses in a laboratory scale were carried out by F. Krüger (105). Apparently the difficulty of transferring sufficient mechanical energy from an electrostriction generator into a molten glass melt is too great and the efficiency is too low to make this process practical.

According to an electrodynamic principle, mechanical forces are produced when a material conducting an electric current is exposed to a magnetic field. If either the current flowing through the conductor or the magnetic field to which the conducting material is exposed pulsate, mechanical forces can be generated which also pulsate. This phenomenon has been developed into a method that originally was used for degassing molten aluminum alloys. Later this method was adapted to glass melting and used in the Jena Glass Works for degassing certain optical glasses that were difficult to fine by ordinary methods. For a description of this treatment and for pictures which illustrate its effect upon a glass as a function of time the publication of C. Eden (106) should be consulted.

The diffusion of CO_2 from a supersaturated aqueous solution into a gas bubble does not require an activation energy. A bubble of CO_2 can act as a nucleus for the supersaturated aqueous solution as long as the pressure of the dissolved gas exceeds 1 atm. If the equilibrium pressure of the solution is 1 atm. or less, gases other than CO_2 have to be bubbled through the supersaturated water to remove the carbon dioxide. Today glass technologists show renewed interest in the process of bubbling gas through the molten glass to increase the efficiency of the tank. This process has many facets, but in one respect it resembles the old custom of throwing lumps of arsenic into the melting pots. As the heavy arsenic sank to the bottom of the pot it boiled and produced a stream of bubbles. The mixing effect and the removal of residual gases through the bubbles of arsenic vapor must have been beneficial for the melting of glasses because "blocking" with arsenic has been a common practice among glass melters.

4. Nucleation and Crystallization of Supercooled Liquids

The rate of nucleation and crystallization of glasses, in other words, the rate of devitrification, is one of the three major factors that determine the usefulness of a certain composition range. The other two factors are meltability and chemical resistivity. Methods of measuring the rate of devitrification are described in several textbooks and they are practiced in all glass plants. Therefore, there is no need to go into details. G. W. Morey (6) devotes a whole section of his book *Properties of Glass* to devitrification, and W. Eitel (107) deals with this subject in his book *The Physical Chemistry of Silicates*. When glass technology introduced modern, highly mechanized, molding processes, methods had to be found which would ascertain the "safe" working range of a glass. Using G. W. Morey and N. L. Bowen's ternary diagram Na_2O—CaO—SiO_2 as a basis, E. Zschimmer and A. Dietzel (108) made the first systematic study of the rates of devitrification of technical soda lime glasses as a function of their composition.

The early theoretical work on the nucleation rate and the rate of crystal growth in supercooled melts was done primarily in G. Tammann's (1) laboratory and most of the pertinent information was obtained by experimenting with organic substances such as betol, salicin, and others.

G. Tammann (1) and P. Othmer (109) proved the statistical nature of the nucleation phenomena. For parallel experiments under identical conditions the number of nuclei formed in a glass fluctuates around a certain value in the same way as other statistical events fluctuate.

At the melting point of a substance or the liquidus temperature of a system a nucleus can form in the melt only temporarily because the temperature of small volume elements fluctuates. Hence, a nucleus formed at or just below the melting point is likely to be consumed by a temporary rise of the temperature. Nucleation, therefore, requires a finite degree of supercooling. The nuclei are invisible and they might remain invisible for a considerable length of time at the temperature of their formation. In order to measure the number of nuclei, G. Tammann (1) kept a given volume of the supercooled liquid in a temperature bath for a certain length of time. After this time the invisible nuclei had to be "developed" by heating the glass to a temperature several degrees below the melting point. This process of developing the nuclei makes it possible to count them. Each nucleus grows to a visible crystal but no new nuclei can form if the development temperature is chosen properly. Piperine, for example, melts at 129°C. In order to make sure that no crystals remain in the liquid it has to be heated a few degrees above its melting point. A measured volume of the melt is brought into a thin walled glass tube which is kept in a constant temperature bath for 10 minutes. Within this time nucleation takes place only in the temperature region from 0°C. to 80°C. and its rate has a sharp maximum at 40°C. The nuclei formed under these conditions are invisible but they can be developed by heating the sample to 100°C. for four minutes. At 100°C. the growth rate of the crystal is sufficient to permit each nucleus to grow into a visible crystal. The nucleation rate, i.e., the number of nuclei formed per unit volume in unit time, has been studied by G. Tammann (1).

In contrast to the nucleation which in many glasses requires a considerable degree of supercooling (50°C. for piperine) the rate of growth of an existing crystal becomes noticeable at temperatures very close to the melting point of the substance. The rate of crystal growth also goes through a maximum with decreasing temperature. Near its high temperature limit it is slowed down by the heat evolution that accompanies the crystallization (latent heat of fusion) and in its low temperature limit by the decreasing rate of diffusion and orientation of the molecules. The temperature of the maximum of the rate of crystal growth is closer to the melting point than that of the nucleation rate. Figure 8 shows schematically this relation. The value of the rate of crystal growth is usually given as the linear velocity of growth in centimeters per second. It is determined by keeping the supercooled liquid in a constant temperature bath and seeding its surface. In many cases the crystals line up in parallel fashion and grow from the surface into the liquid so that their length can be easily measured.

Rate processes such as nucleation and crystal growth are easily influenced by the experimental conditions, in particular, by impurities. Tammann (1) showed how some additions to betol suppress nucleation, whereas others are strong positive catalysts. It is this catalytic action of water and impurities in the atmosphere, e.g., NaCl, which makes it very difficult to perform valid experiments.

One of the controversial subjects in nucleation-crystallization

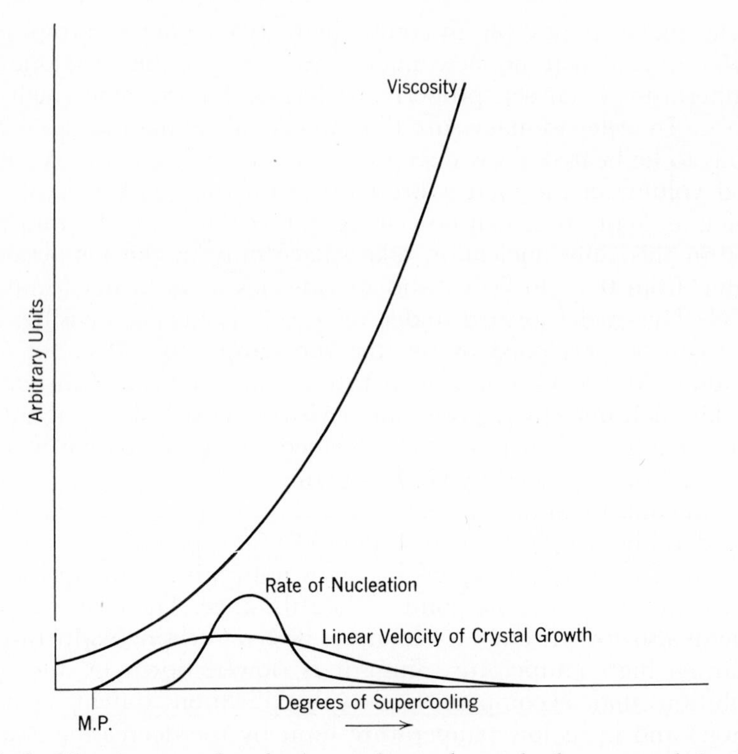

Fig 8 . Viscosity, rate of nucleation, and crystal growth of a supercooled melt.

processes concerns the role which the surface of a glass plays. G. Tammann described the crystallization of a soda lime silicate glass at 700°C. as starting at the surface. Kept for 10 hours at this temperature only the surface of the glass showed visible crystals which grew in an oriented fashion from the surface toward the interior. After heating the glass for 30 hours crystals could also be found in the interior but even then he found crystallization to be initiated by gas bubbles which were present in the glass.

Powdering a piece of the glass and placing this glass dust on the glass surface was found by G. Tammann to increase the nucleation rate at the surface. D. E. Harrison and F. A. Hummel (110) took advantage of this method and enforced the crystallization of a zinc borate glass that resisted all efforts to crystallize by heat treatment alone.

G. W. Morey (6), on the other hand, does not share these

views. He examined the devitrification of many glasses paying special attention to the location where crystallization started and reached the following conclusions: In no case, he reports, has there been observed crystals growing from the surface or from bubbles. He makes two important statements; namely: (1) the surface may have a different composition than the bulk of the glass because those constituents that can lower the surface energy of the system will tend to accumulate in the surface film, and (2) the effect which a composition change of the surface has on the liquidus temperature or the rate of its crystallization cannot be discussed in a general way but must depend upon the composition of the particular glass.

Any surface, even one of pure silica, will attract a water film several molecules thick even from an atmosphere with a relatively low humidity. It has been found that vitreous arsenic can crystallize at ordinary temperature due to a mechanism which involves a temporary hydration. Water even in trace amounts is one of the most powerful positive catalysts in nucleation and crystallization processes as one can see from the use which is made of water in hydrothermal reactions.

As far as the effectiveness of powdered glass is concerned, it need not necessarily catalyze crystallization because of its relatively large surface. We attribute much of its reactivity to mechanical stresses. We describe such a strained glass powder as "activated by the partial unscreening of cations." This crystallization-promoting effect of mechanical stresses is not limited to the transition glass-crystal but is a well known phenomenon in transitions between crystals, e.g., the change of protoenstatite into the stable clinoenstatite.

5. Atomistic Approach to Nucleation

We can easily understand why and how bubbling a gas through carbonated water can release its supersaturation. We can also understand why a hydrophobic solid has a similar effect. Also, the catalytic effect of PbS on the precipitation of a metastable phase, NaBr, offers no difficulty if we regard this process as an oriented overgrowth and are aware of the structural similarity between PbS and NaBr.

However, we still have to answer the question: Why is the probability of forming Ca_2SiO_4 in a mixture of CaO and SiO_2

greater than that of forming $CaSiO_3$ even when the mixture contains an excess of silica? In order to answer this question we have to consider the surface energy of the nucleus as the energy barrier that opposes nucleation. The surface energy of a solid is the result of the incomplete coordination of its surface ions. This energy is partly compensated for by the deformation of the electron clouds, a process which has certain depth action and whose efficiency increases with increasing polarizability of the system. For crystals which contain cations of the noble gas-type such as Ca^{2+} and Si^{4+} ions, the polarizability is vested in the anions and can be described by the molar refractivity of the O^{2-} ions (see Chapter V). Hence, the more polarizable orthosilicate has a better chance to form a low energy surface than the less polarizable metasilicate. With the exception of BeO all oxides of the alkaline earths form compounds with silica which have O^{2-} ions of greater polarizability than those of silica. As we showed earlier, the polarizability of a crystal or the refractivity of the O^{2-} ions increases with increasing basicity of the compound. Hence, orthosilicates have a better chance to form nuclei because their surface energies are lower than those of other silicates which exist in this temperature region (1000°C.).

This phenomenon, namely, that the rate of nucleation is proportional to the polarizability of a crystal, has its counterpart in aqueous systems. The degree to which a solution can be supersaturated is inversely proportional to the polarizability of the compound. Compounds such as CaF_2 require a high degree of supersaturation before nuclei can form whereas the bromide or iodide of mercury cannot form metastable supersaturated solution for any length of time.

The importance of the surface energy or the interfacial energy for the stability of a system can be judged from the following experiment. If a suspension of $BaSO_4$ in water is brought into a solution of $Pb(ClO_4)_2$ one finds that Ba^{2+} ions of the crystalline phase go into solution and that the surface of the $BaSO_4$ crystals is transformed into $PbSO_4$ in spite of the fact that $BaSO_4$ is less soluble in water than $PbSO_4$. A part of the free energy of the system is vested in the surface energy of the crystals and the replacement of Ba^{2+} ions by the more polarizable Pb^{2+} ions lowers the surface energy of the crystals and with it the free energy of the system. Feigl (111) took advantage of this phenomenon for increasing the sensitivity of the analytical test for Ba^{2+} ions. By adding a complex lead salt he made available Pb^{2+} ions and the latter enhanced the nucleation of $BaSO_4$. Nuclei of $BaSO_4$ form at a lower degree of supersaturation in the presence of Pb^{2+} ions because Pb^{2+} ions can lower the surface energy of the nuclei. The influence of large and polarizable cations on the rate of nucleation can be observed in glazes and enamels which are opacified by oxides such as SnO_2, TiO_2, ZrO_2, CeO_2, or colored by compounds such as CdS, $PbCrO_4$, etc., which have high polarizabilities. Crystals of this type, like those of the noble metals Au and Cu, form a large number of nuclei whereas the precipitation of silica or devitrite is characterized by a small number of nuclei and the formation of relatively large "stones."

Nucleation, like all rate processes, is susceptible to catalysis. When we discussed the effect of PbS on the nucleation of NaBr from a solution we got acquainted with one particular kind of catalysis: epitaxy.

Substances that affect the rates of reaction without participating in the reaction product are called catalysts. In the particular case in which a substance increases the rate of crystallization one often refers to it as a "mineralizing agent" or a "mineralizer." The French mineralogists in the nineteenth century made wide use of fluxes which they called "agents mineralisateures" because they enhanced those chemical reactions which lead to synthetic minerals or which increase the rate of crystal growth.

Water is by far the most important mineralizer in nature as well as in the laboratory. Eitel's book (107) *The Physical Chemistry of Silicates* contains numerous references to mineralizers, their roles in changing the viscosity and crystallization rates of magmas, as well as their technical applications in the refractory industries. For details as well as for the historical background of the synthesis of minerals this work should be consulted.

What is the mechanism by which small amounts of water can affect the viscosity of a melt and the crystallization rate of a glass?

The most important single factor that affects the viscosity of a glass is the ratio of anions to cations. The use of fluorspar (german, *Flusspat* fluxing spar) in the middle ages was based on its ability to lower the viscosity of metallurgical slags. The replacement of CaO by CaF_2 results in the substitution of two F^- ions for one O^{2-} ion. This increase of the anion to cation ratio facilitates reactions whose energy barriers consist of a "partial temporary unscreening of cations" (see Chapter V, 4, B). Incorporating fluorides into glasses, glazes, and enamels is widely practiced for lowering the viscosity.

Water is perhaps the most powerful nucleation catalyst for silicates. Water functions in a manner similar to that of fluorides. The addition of water to a silicate system can best be described as the addition of O^{2-} ions which increase its anion to cation ratio and of protons which can move from one O^{2-} ion into the electron cloud of others. By temporarily lowering the anionic charge the proton weakens the binding forces between silicon and oxygen ions:

$$Si^{4+}O^{2-}Si^{4+} \xrightarrow{H^+} Si^{4+}(OH)^{-}Si^{4+}$$

The catalytic effect of water on the rate of mineralization or crystallization is used in hydrothermal synthesis.

CHAPTER XII

COMPATIBILITY IN GLASS-FORMING SYSTEMS

There is one prerequisite for glass formation: in order to obtain a glass one must have a homogeneous liquid. Before we investigate the conditions that are responsible for the failure of some liquids to nucleate and to crystallize when their temperatures are lowered below the liquidus temperature we have to examine the conditions which oxides have to meet in order to be compatible so that they can form a homogeneous liquid.

It will be necessary for us to find an answer to questions such as: Why can one not produce a homogeneous liquid phase containing 15% CaO and 85% SiO_2? Why do these two oxides become compatible upon the addition of alkali oxides?

Compatibility and incompatibility are of considerable importance to the glass technologist. Compatibility of the constituents is essential for a system in order to obtain a homogeneous glass. Incompatibility is equally important for the glass technologist. He takes advantage of the incompatibility of his glasses with certain oxides for producing resistant refractories to be used in the glass tank. Compatibility is a solubility phenomenon and has to be treated as such. As a rule, compatibility increases with increasing temperature. Like solubility, it has its static and its dynamic aspects and both are equally important.

1. Equilibrium Aspects of Compatibility

None of the refractories used in the glass industry are incompatible with the molten glass in a static sense because no refractory is in equilibrium with a soda lime silicate at 1400°C. The usefulness of refractories is based upon their dynamic incompatibility with the glass. In other words, solution rate of a refractory is sufficiently slow as compared with the reaction rates of the batch ingredients so that it can be used as the reaction vessel.

Compatibility and incompatibility in the liquid state are phenomena which are related to solution phenomena. All gases are mutually soluble. The ideal gas laws assume that the particles do not interact, i.e., that the cohesive forces between the molecules are zero. Some gases come closer to this assumption than others. On the same basis one can derive a law for ideal solutions. Here the assumption has to be made that the cohesive forces between molecules are the same throughout the liquid. A mixture of two liquids A and B behaves as an ideal solution if the cohesive forces between A and A, B and B, and A and B are equal. The law of the behavior of ideal solutions was first derived in 1886 by F. M. Raoult on the basis of experimental vapor pressure data. According to Raoult's law the partial vapor pressure of A over the solution is proportional to its mole fraction. The same applies to the vapor pressure of B.

As Raoult's law is based on the complete equality of the cohesive forces one finds rarely that a solution obeys this law over a wide range of concentrations. The deviations from Raoult's law are expressed not only in the vapor pressures of A and B but also in volume effects and in heat effects. Complete equality of the cohesive forces would lead to strict additivity of the volumes and to the absence of heat effects on mixing.

If a solid is dissolved in a liquid the boiling point of the liquid is raised and its freezing point is lowered. This interaction is presented in the phase diagrams. The solution of Na_2O in SiO_2 lowers the melting point of cristobalite. The liquidus curve can be described as a "freezing point depression curve" or as a "solubility curve" of cristobalite in liquids of different SiO_2–Na_2O ratios.

It is very important to be aware of the fact that compatibility in its different forms is a solubility phenomenon because as far as solubility is concerned every one is aware of the paramount importance of the temperature. Nobody would think of presenting data on the solubilities of salts in water without referring to the temperature. In aqueous solutions one deals with a rather limited temperature range but in glass-forming systems one deals with a very wide range of temperature. Nevertheless, in the last few years several papers have appeared in the ceramic literature in which rules are presented which govern mutual solubilities and gaps in the miscibility of liquids which do not refer to the temperatures.

Most of the work on the interaction of substances in the liquid state is based on organic systems which consist of more or less defined molecules. Systems have been found which deviate from

Raoult's law in both directions. In some systems the vapor pressure of the components is higher and in others it is lower than expected from Raoult's law. If the cohesive forces between A and B are smaller than those acting between the like molecules, A and A as well as B and B, their vapor pressures are higher or their tendencies to escape from the mixture are greater than one would expect from Raoult's law. This positive deviation is usually associated with a volume increase on mixing and with a lowering of the temperature through the absorption of heat. We can describe the positive deviation from Raoult's law as a tendency of the two types of molecules to remain by themselves or as the beginning of an incompatibility.

The opposite phenomenon, a negative deviation, means that the unlike molecules interact more strongly than the like ones, hence their tendency to escape into the vapor phase is smaller than expected from Raoult's law. This "affinity" between unlike molecules may lead to the formation of compounds. The positive deviation may lead to partial immiscibility so that the two kinds of molecules may no longer form a continuous series of solutions. In most cases in which two liquids show partial miscibility, one finds that the miscibility gap decreases when the temperature is raised. The system phenol-water is the classical example cited in most textbooks. At ordinary temperature water can dissolve close to 10% phenol and phenol can dissolve about 20% water. Mixtures which contain from 20 to 90% water form two liquids at ordinary temperature. The miscibility gap closes on heating so that the system forms only one liquid phase above 70°C. Among glasses we find that alkali borosilicates behave very similarly. At tempera tures well above 1000°C. the oxides in the system Na_2O-B_2O_3-SiO_2 are compatible but at about 1000°C. and below the system unmixes into two phases.

One can understand the closure of a miscibility gap at high temperature on the basis of the entropy gain on mixing and the increasing importance of the entropy contribution to the free energy of the system when the temperature is raised. The entropy contribution to the free energy, however, is not the only important factor because cases are known in which a single phase, liquid or crystalline, forms two immiscible liquids on heating. The system triethyl amine-water forms a homogeneous phase at low temperature but it unmixes into two liquids above room temperature.

This phenomenon has its analogue in the crystalline borosilicates. Danburite, $CaO \cdot B_2O_3 \cdot 2SiO_2$, is a well defined crystalline compound which is stable up to about 1000°C., at which temperature it changes into two immiscible liquids.

Compatibility among oxides, in the sense that we use the word, requires the possibility of changing the composition of the system continuously over a certain range. Alumina and phosphorus pentoxide are not compatible in spite of the existence of the compound $AlPO_4$. The formation of $AlPO_4$ is based on a very stringent condition, each PO_4 tetrahedron has to share each of its oxygens with one Al^{3+} ion and each AlO_4 tetrahedron has to share each of its four O^{2-} ions with one P^{5+} ion. Each O^{2-} ion has to be bound to one Al^{3+} and one P^{5+} ion. This structural condition can be met only if the Al to P ratio is precisely 1 to 1 and if the structure is sufficiently rigid to retain its geometry. Retention of this geometry is not possible in the liquid state. In order to form a liquid, both the anions and the actions have to be free to exchange their positions. In cristobalite it is possible for the Si^{4+} ions to exchange positions above the melting point (1713°C.) but at this temperature the exchange of Al^{3+} and P^{5+} ions is not possible. Cristobalite melts when the thermal energy, kT, is sufficient to overcome the energy barrier that opposes the exchange of Si^{4+} ions in the cationic network of silica. Such an exchange does not cause the structure to change drastically. We describe the melting of cristobalite as the melting of a "perfect" crystal and we call the resulting liquid a "flawless" liquid of the Bernal type.

The energy barrier which opposes a corresponding exchange between Al^{3+} and P^{5+} ions in the cationic network of $AlPO_4$ is considerably higher. This exchange of cations produces a drastic structural change and would lead to space charges. In the course of exchanging cations two PO_4 groups would become neighbors so that this volume element would assume an excess positive charge over neighboring volume elements. As a result of the increased energy barrier, $AlPO_4$ remains a solid up to temperatures above 2000°C., at which temperature it decomposes forming corundum and P_4O_{10} molecules.

Compound formation between two molecules such as Al_2O_3 and P_2O_5 does not mean that the two molecules are compatible and will form a liquid which is homogeneous. Hydrocarbons are not compatible with water, whether they are gases (methane), liquids (hexane), or solids (paraffin). The fact that methane can form a hydrate does not make it compatible with water because this hydrate has to have a certain stoichiometric composition. A constant $CH_4:H_2O$ ratio can be maintained easily in a crystal but the condition of constancy of the composition in molecular dimensions interferes with the very nature of a liquid.

The oxides MgO and SiO_2 have a very limited compatibility even at 1600°C. A narrow composition region exists around 60% SiO_2 and 40% MgO which is liquid at this temperature. However, increasing the SiO_2 content by 10% leads to the precipitation of cristobalite. Why do the two oxides MgO and SiO_2 have such a narrow composition range at which they can form a homogeneous liquid at a temperature as high as 1600°C.?

In order to answer this and similar questions concerning the phase relations in siliceous systems we have to realize that in order to be a liquid the system has to assume a dynamic structure in which the cations exchange positions. Earlier (see Chapter V,4,B) we described the energy barrier of the reshuffling of ions, e.g., the formation of spinel from MgO and Al_2O_3, as the partial temporary unscreening of cations.

The screening of all cations in such a liquid is governed by two factors: (1) the anion to cation ratio, and (2) the polarizability of the anions. Increasing the silica concentration of our system decreases the polarizability of the O^{2-} ions because they are now exposed to cations of higher charges. Increasing the MgO concentration decreases the anion to cation ratio. Hence, for a variation of the MgO–SiO_2 ratio an optimum of screening of all cations is achieved for mixtures close to 60% SiO_2, the eutectic mixture. Such a system has the ability to flow at 1600°C. because its Mg^{2+} ions and Si^{4+} ions can remain sufficiently screened. The thermal energy available at this temperature (1600°C.) is sufficient to partially unscreen the cations temporarily so that they can exchange positions and increase the entropy of the system.

Increasing the MgO concentration precipitates forsterite Mg_2SiO_4. This process increases the anion to cation ratio in the liquid phase and permits a part of the system to remain fluid at 1600°C. All cations in forsterite have improved their screening by assuming a highly symmetrical crystal structure.

Increasing the SiO_2 concentration precipitates cristobalite from the melt. This process decreases the anion to cation ratio in the liquid but the effect of this change is more than compensated for by the increased polarizability of the O^{2-} ions.

This example shows how the activation energy of cationic exchange processes depends upon the polarizability of the anions and the anion to cation ratio.

Now we shall examine another mixture within the same system MgO-SiO_2, namely, one which contains 80% SiO_2 and 20% MgO. This mixture forms a eutectic melt and cristobalite above 1550°C. As the temperature is raised the amount of liquid increases slightly because some of the cristobalite can go into solution. Up to nearly 1700°C., however, we find that still approximately one half of the mixture remains cristobalite and only one half is liquid. At 1750°C., however, we have two liquid phases, one nearly pure silica and the other containing practically all of the MgO. The fact that the whole system is liquid at 1750°C. must mean that at this temperature the thermal energy is sufficient to overcome the energy barrier that opposes cationic exchanges and the system gains entropy by increasing its mobility. Why is this possible only through the formation of two different liquid phases? Or maybe we should ask a more specific question. The liquid phase which is nearly pure SiO_2 has the advantage of a high anion to cation ratio and the liquid phase which contains the MgO contains more polarizable O^{2-} ions. Therefore, can the system not exist as a homogeneous phase in which the anion to cation ratio and the polarizabilities of the anions have some intermediate values?

The solubility of cristobalite in the eutectic melt does not increase much when the temperature is raised. This is the result of a strictly geometrical condition. The Mg^{2+} ion requires sixfold coordination and the Si^{4+} ion requires fourfold coordination. The formation of a liquid lattice requires mobility of the O^{2-} ions within the anionic lattice and the mobility of the Mg^{2+} ions within an octahedral framework of O^{2-} ions. This condition can be met only for a rather narrow concentration range in the system MgO-SiO_2. Beyond this eutectic range either the octahedra or the tetrahedra are too "diluted," i.e., these polyhedra are too far apart, for the cations to exchange and the low polarizability of the O^{2-} ions in this system is not favorable for a fast change in the polyhedra as they exist in the liquid. When the temperature exceeds the melting point of cristobalite the latter must melt.

One cannot expect liquid silica to be much more soluble in

the MgO-SiO_2 melt than the cristalline form. The solubility of a low melting organic compound such as paraffin in water does not strongly increase when the paraffin melts. The fact that the liquidus temperature (1695°C.) is practically the same as the melting point of cristobalite means that the liquid SiO_2 cannot accommodate in its structure an appreciable quantity of MgO.

In order to understand the phase relationships in the system MgO-SiO_2 we have to consider the structures of the liquids. Liquid structures are based on dynamic processes, not necessarily on the possibility of establishing a complete disorder. In order to be liquid, a mixture of MgO and SiO_2 has to meet the following conditions:

1. The O^{2-} ions have to be able to exchange positions.
2. The Mg^{2+} ions have to be mobile within an octahedral framework of O^{2-} ions. The high melting point of MgO reveals that the Mg^{2+} ions require a symmetrical environment of six O^{2-} ions up to 2800°C.
3. The Si^{4+} ions have to be mobile within a tetrahedral framework of O^{2-} ions.

At 1600°C. these conditions are met only within a narrow concentration range of the system MgO-SiO_2.

Any compensation within the system MgO-SiO_2 is characterized by the anion to cation ratio $O^{2-}/(Si^{4+} + Mg^{2+})_x$ and by the polarizability of the O^{2-} ions which again is a function of this ratio (see Chapter V,1,c). These parameters and the coordination requirements of all cations have to be considered for understanding phase relationships. Therefore, let us discuss the effects that the coordination requirement and the polarizabilities of the anions have upon the phase relations in the systems alkaline earth oxides-silica.

Replacing the Mg^{2+} ion by the Be^{2+} ion, which has the same coordination number as silicon, brings about a drastic change in the phase relationships. The addition of BeO to SiO_2 can lower the liquidus temperature to 1670°C. and no miscibility gap exists. The temperature range is too high for beryllium orthosilicate Be_2SiO_4 to appear in equilibrium with a liquid phase. This compound, the only one known in this system, decomposes at approximately 1560°C.

Be^{2+} ions have the same coordination number as Si^{4+} ions. The Be^{2+} ion can be screened by four O^{2-} ions of low polarizability.

TABLE XXI

Molar Refractivities of O^{2-} Ions in Orthosilicates

Orthosilicate	Molar refractivity (cm^3)
Mg_2SiO_4	3.83
Ca_2SiO_4	4.53
Sr_2SiO_4	4.67
Ba_2SiO_2	4.97

The molar refractivity of the O^{2-} ion in Be_2SiO_4 has an even lower value (3.35 cm^3) than that of SiO_2 (3.52 cm^3).

The alkaline earth oxides, CaO, SrO, and BaO, have the same crystal structure as MgO, but they introduce O^{2-} ions of higher polarizability. The molar refractivities of the O^{2-} ions in the orthosilicates are given in Table XXI.

None of the alkaline earth oxides can enter the structure of silica to an appreciable extent as can be seen from the fact that they barely lower the liquidus temperature. All of these ions require sixfold coordination.

The fact that their O^{2-} ions are more polarizable than that of MgO, however, affects the lowest temperature at which a liquid phase can exist in these binary systems.

Lowest eutectic temperature: $MgO\text{-}SiO_2 \sim 1540°C$.
$CaO\text{-}SiO_2 \sim 1440°C$.
$SrO\text{-}SiO_2 \sim 1360°C$.

Due to its more polarizable O^{2-} ions the liquid phase is a better solvent for SiO_2. Such a melt may contain up to

60 mole % SiO_2 in the system $MgO\text{-}SiO_2$
70 mole % SiO_2 in the system $CaO\text{-}SiO_2$
80 mole % SiO_2 in the system $SrO\text{-}SiO_2$

One can easily visualize a static model of a structure which contains MgO_6 octahedra and SiO_4 tetrahedra in a ratio 2:1 or 1:1 but in order to be a liquid not only geometrical but also dynamic conditions have to be met. It is for this combination of geometrical and dynamic conditions that one cannot prepare a homogeneous liquid which contains 10% MgO or CaO and 90% SiO_2. The screening demands of Mg^{2+} and Ca^{2+} ions are such that they require a symmetrical environment of six O^{2-} ions. Each O^{2-} ion in MgO and CaO crystals participates in the screening of six cations. In contrast to silica in which the O^{2-} ions have twofold coordination with respect to the cations, those in MgO and CaO have sixfold coordination. This difference accounts for the fact that the two oxides are not compatible in the high silica region. They form immiscible liquids but the immiscibility decreases from MgO to BaO, i.e., with increasing polarizability of both the O^{2-} ions and the cations. The more polarizable Pb^{2+} ions are more compatible with silica than the Sr^{2+} ions which have approximately the same size.

As the compatibility is a solution phenomenon the temperature is of paramount importance. We saw that silica at its melting point cannot accommodate much MgO in its liquid structure because of the stringent coordination requirement. Nevertheless, the addition of SiO_2 to MgO does not lead to the formation of two liquids. How is it possible that MgO at its melting point can accommodate SiO_2 in its liquid structure? The explanation lies in the high temperature which makes it possible for the two oxides to be mutually soluble. MgO melts at 2800°C. and in this temperature range the kinetic energy is available for making both Mg^{2+} and Si^{4+} ions mobile, whereas the coordination conditions do not permit mobility at 1700°C.

Unfortunately, the use of high temperature for enforcing compatibility is of little use to the glass technologist. If the temperature is high the kinetic energy available for enforcing compatibility is also available for nucleation and hence these high melting systems are not suitable for forming stable glasses.

The fact that the compatibility is a function of the temperature is important for a number of phenomena such as the striking of fluoride opal glasses and of selenium ruby glasses, etc. Even in glasses that contain only oxides, similar phenomena have been discovered by applying the electron microscope to systems such as borates, borosilicates, and complex beryllium fluoride glasses. We will refer to these incompatibility phenomena later when we discuss the constitution of some representative glasses.

The oxides MgO and CaO can be made compatible with silica by the addition of alkalies. The addition of alkali to a system provides polarizable O^{2-} ions. The screening demands of the singly charged alkali ions are not as severe as those of more highly charged cations.

The presence of alkali in a silicate glass, however, is not

sufficient to make it compatible with Cr_2O_3. This can be accomplished, however by introducing into a glass relatively high concentrations of PbO. Lead borosilicate glasses have been used for dissolving Cr_2O_3 at high temperatures. They precipitate this oxide on cooling in the form of large, thin, hexagonal plates (chromium aventurine glass).

We will learn more about the role which the alkali plays in increasing the compatibility between XO_6 units and SiO_4 tetrahedra when we discuss the use of color indicators for determining the constitution of glasses. The absorption spectrum of the Nd^{3+} ion responds to the compatibility of the constituents of a glass and can be used for estimating the stability of glasses or their tendencies to crystallize.

Our discussion of compatibility and incompatibility was centered around the alkaline earth oxides because they have the same coordination requirement from room temperature to their melting points. Their coordination number is not likely to change in the presence of silica. However, in the presence of more polarizable O^{2-} ions the coordination number may decrease from 6 to 4.

More than 30 years ago N. J. Kreidl (112) in a paper on the role of the basic oxides upon the properties of glass suggested that MgO should be treated as an acid when it participates in an alkali lime silicate glass. In modern parlance this idea would be expressed by saying that Mg^{2+} ions can form MgO_4 tetrahedra or that Mg^{2+} ions are network-formers rather than network-modifiers. For the Co^{2+} and Ni^{2+} ions which have approximately the same sizes as the Mg^{2+} ion, W. A. Weyl and E. Thümen (113) could prove their participation in glass structures in both octahedral and tetrahedral coordination. The change from octahedral to tetrahedral coordination is favored by increasing polarizability of the O^{2-} ions and by increasing temperature. Whether Mg^{2+} ions at ordinary temperature participate in a technical glass in the form of octahedra or tetrahedra is not pertinent for our problem but we should think of the possibility of Mg^{2+} ions entering fourfold coordination in the presence of alkali, a feature which can contribute to the compatibility of MgO with SiO_2 in the presence of alkalies.

Aluminum oxide but not chromium oxide is compatible with silica. The difference in the ionic sizes is not sufficient to prevent Al_2O_3 and Cr_2O_3 from forming solid solutions. However, the phase diagrams Al_2O_3-SiO_2 and Cr_2O_3-SiO_2 are very different because Al^{3+} ions may enter fourfold coordination but Cr^{3+} ions cannot. In such a case, in which a cation can participate in the structure of a liquid in both fourfold and sixfold coordination, the nature of the alkali becomes a prominent factor. One can easily substitute K_2O for Na_2O in soda lime silicate glasses. The differences in such qualtities as workability are not drastic. However, this does not apply to alumino-silicates, as can be seen from the melting points of albite and orthoclase.

(albite) $Na_2O \cdot Al_2O_3 \cdot 6SiO_2$, 1118°C.
(orthoclase) $K_2O \cdot Al_2O_3 \cdot 6SiO_2$, 1533°C.

This couple and the melting points of spodumene and leucite reveal that in alumina-silica systems the addition of alkali has just the opposite effect from that expected from the effects of these alkalies in combination with silica only.

(spodumene) $Li_2O \cdot Al_2O_3 \cdot 4SiO_2$, 1423°C.
(leucite) $K_2O \cdot Al_2O_3 \cdot 4SiO_2$, 1680°C.

The fact that K_2O has the strongest effect upon lowering the liquidus temperature of silica and Li_2O the weakest was explained on the basis of the polarizability of the O^{2-} ions which they introduce. In the alumino-silicates the effect is reversed because of the structural change of the Al^{3+} ion which can form either AlO_4 groups or AlO_6 groups.

A. Dietzel (114) used the refractive index of binary glasses in the system Al_2O_3-SiO_2 to draw conclusions on the coordination number of the Al^{3+} ion. The increment of the refractive index of Al_2O_3 in these glasses was found to be 1.63 which is lower than that of Al_2O_3 in sixfold coordination (1.74 for corundum) but higher than that of AlO_4 groups in feldspar (1.50). Hence, he assumes that both AlO_6 and AlO_4 polyhedra are present.

J. F. Schairer and N. L. Bowen (115) determined the isofracts of glasses in the system Na_2O-SiO_2-Al_2O_3 and found that the addition of Na_2O to silica increased the refractive index but that its addition to a mixture of SiO_2 and Al_2O_3 lowered the index of refraction. The addition of Na_2O to SiO_2 introduces more polarizable O^{2-} ions which raises the index of refraction. Addition of Al_2O_3 to SiO_2 also raises the index of refraction. However the addition of both Al_2O_3 and Na_2O to silica increases the value of n much less than one would expect from additivity. This can be interpreted as follows: the presence of the polarizable O^{2-} ions introduced by Na_2O enables the Al^{3+} ions to form its own tetrahedra; i.e., to assume the role of a network-forming ion.

2. Kinetic Aspects of Compatibility

The compatibility of an oxide with silica can be seen from the phase diagram. The phase diagram tells us the temperature at which a certain mixture forms a stable homogeneous liquid phase.

We have seen that many oxides in a quantity of approximately 10% or more are incompatible with silica; the incompatibility expresses itself either in the insolubility of the added oxide (Cr_2O_3) or in the formation of two liquids (CaO). Compounds other than oxides, e.g., fluorides, chlorides, and sulfides, can be incompatible with silica because of the formation of volatile substances; e.g., SiF_4, $SiCl_4$, and SiS_2.

A. Suppression of the Volatility of Compounds

Glass technologists are well aware of the fact that a considerable fraction of the fluorine that is introduced into the batch in the form of fluorspar escapes during melting. Depending on the melting conditions and the glass compositions, the fluorine loss can reach one-third to one-half of the fluorine which is introduced. Fluorine escapes primarily in the form of NaF which has a noticeable vapor pressure at the melting temperature of glasses (boiling point of NaF: 1700°C.). One should be surprised that a considerable portion of the fluorine can be retained in a glass because not only does it escape in the form of NaF, but there is even the possibility of the formation of SiF_4, a gas even at ordinary temperature.

If the exchange of anions which characterizes the liquid state would be a random process which could be treated on the basis of statistics, one must arrive at the conclusion that it is not possible to retain fluorine in a silicate glass. The relatively high mobility of F^- and O^{2-} ions in the striking range of an opal glass suggests that during melting, the probability of SiF_4 molecules forming and escaping from the melt would be very high. Such a system could increase its entropy by forming mobile SiF_4 molecules. This raises the questions: (1) How is it possible to make an NaF opal glass? Why does not all of the fluorine escape from the melt as gaseous SiF_4? (2) What causes the difference between the behavior of fluorides in a soda lime silicate glass and the behavior of chlorides which cannot be retained to the same extent?

Even if the phase relations in the system Na_2O-NaF-CaO-SiO_2 were known, they would not supply an answer to these questions. Very likely the differences between the phase relations in the system containing the fluoride as compared with that containing the chloride are small. No alkali halide would be retained in the homogeneous system at 1450°C. under ordinary pressure. The difference in the behaviors of the fluoride and the chloride in a glass melt is the result of rate phenomena and not of equilibria.

The replacement of an O^{2-} ion in an SiO_4 tetrahedron by an F^- ion lowers the degree of screening of the central cation. As a result this particular silicon will improve its screening by interacting more strongly with the electron clouds of the three remaining O^{2-} ions. The Si-O bond becomes stronger and the probability of replacing a second O^{2-} ion in an $SiFO_3$ tetrahedron by a F^- ion is lowered. With increasing number of F^- ions the probability of further substitutions of O^{2-} ions by F^- ions must drop off sharply because the formation of SiF_4 molecules from a glass melt is a rare event. It is possible to retain a major concentration of fluoride ions in a soda lime silicate glass because the place changes between O^{2-} and F^- ions are not random and statistical but are governed by the tendency toward keeping the number of F^- ions in the coordination sphere of each silicon as low as possible. The same situation applies to the interaction of boron with fluorine and oxygen. BF_3, like SiF_4, is a gas.

The screening requirements of the silicon explains why and how a SiO_4 group in a melt opposes the substitution of F^- ions for O^{2-} ions. A similar process is responsible for the retention of "water" in silicate glasses which are melted at high temperature for long times. The OH^- ions are also poorer screeners than the O^{2-} ions. Cations such as Ti^{4+} or Ta^{5+} which have a higher coordination number than Si^{4+} ions will be more inclined to form polyhedra in which one or more O^{2-} ions are replaced by F^- ions. Therefore, these cations help to make fluorides and silicates more compatible. This feature is used in some optical glasses for retaining a major concentration of fluorine without opacification.

Boron, too, acts in a similar way. The B^{3+} core is well screened by three anions as can be seen from the fact that BF_3 is a gas. The B^{3+} core can easily expand its coordination to 4 as can be seen from the existence of the fluoroborates; e.g., KBF_4. Hence, the presence of B_2O_3 in a silicate glass increases the compatibility of the glass with fluorides in a way which makes borosilicate glasses unsuitable for opacification with NaF.

Chloride and sulfide ions are better screeners than F^- ions so that $SiCl_4$ and SiS_2 are formed more readily in a glass melt than SiF_4. Experience teaches us that it is not possible to retain a major concentration of chloride and sulfide ions in a soda lime silicate glass because of the formation of volatile compounds. Compatibility of such a glass with sulfides can be achieved by introducing into the glass a cation such as Zn^{2+} or Cd^{2+} which due to its stronger polarizing power (18 shell) surrounds itself preferentially with the more polarizable S^{2-} ions. The retention for sulfur and selenium by a silicate glass is approximately proportional to its zinc oxide content. In this case it is the greater mutual deformation between a non-noble glass type cation and the more polarizable S^{2-} and Se^{2-} ions which modifies the place changes between anions in the glass melt and keeps the number of S^{2-} ions surrounding a Si^{4+} ion to a minimum.

The Cl^-, Br^-, and I^- ions escape readily from a silicate or a borosilicate glass because of the volatility of the halides of silicon and boron. Like the S^{2-} ions, the I^- ions can be retained by cations of the transition elements. W. C. Taylor (116) produced green borosilicate glasses which contain $(Co^{2+} I_4^-)^{2-}$ groups.

When A. Hilsenrod and B. Gehauf (117) needed a glass with a high concentration of I^- ions they found that zinc iodide was the most suitable ingredient for introducing and retaining I^- ions in a sodium metaphosphate glass.

B. Corrosion of Refractory Materials

What constitutes a good refractory material for a glass tank? We realize that this question has many facets and that many different requirements have to be met in order to produce a refractory material which is satisfactory for the construction of glass tanks or for melting pots. The material should of course have a high melting temperature and not soften under working conditions. It should have a fair degree of homogeneity and its attack by glass should not lead to "stones." These aspects are well understood. The refractory has to meet several physical requirements in order to be acceptable. What are the crystal chemical requirements? Let us assume that we can have a refractory brick consisting of a single crystal, i.e., homogeneous with no porosity, and we are in the fortunate position to be able to ignore costs. This next question is: What substance would be most suitable for this refractory; i.e., one which has the lowest rate of going into solution?

Certainly, high melting temperature alone is not a sufficient prerequisite for our refractory because neither the high melting MgO nor CaO would be satisfactory as refractories. Also, we know that Al_2O_3 in the form of β-alumina and the aluminum silicates, mullite and sillimanite, are satisfactory refractories and during the last 15 years zirconium oxide has gained importance rapidly. However, none of these compounds are in equilibrium with a soda lime glass. This means that the equilibrium diagram cannot give us the final answer and that we deal with a rate phenomenon. We saw that neither NaF nor NaCl are in equilibrium with a glass at its melting temperature, nevertheless NaF can be retained in a soda lime glass more easily than NaCl. Neither MgO, Al_2O_3, nor ZrO_2 is in equilibria with a glass but the rate of attack is fast for MgO and slow for Al_2O_3 and ZrO_2.

N. V. Solomin, N. M. Galdina and V. V. Lapin (118) published their studies concerning the microstructure of a refractory "Bacor" which consisted essentially of Al_2O_3 (67%), ZrO_2 (15%), and SiO_2 (15%). This electrocast refractory block contained crystals of corundum (Al_2O_3) and baddeleyite (ZrO_2) embedded in a vitreous matrix. In contact with the hot glass the vitreous matrix reacts faster; corundum is attacked more slowly and is dissolved but partly precipitated as nepheline. The baddeleyite offered the greatest resistance to attack.

Chromium oxide represents another example of high resistance of an oxide toward corrosion by glass. In cases in which chromium ore or other chromium compounds contaminate a glass batch the danger of the formation of "black stones" arises. H. Jebsen-Marwedel devotes a chapter of his book to this particular defect because once these stones have formed they are not likely to dissolve again. Under the microscope these black stones may show the hexagonal outline of Cr_2O_3 crystals but rarely does one find them embedded in a cord of green glass; they do not show the "tail" that is so characteristic for other stones which occur in glass and which go into solution gradually. What is the difference between Al_2O_3 which goes into solution and Cr_2O_3 which does not? Neither of the two oxides is in equilibrium with the glass but Al_2O_3 has a mechanism by which it can diffuse, and Cr_2O_3 has not. The fact that Al^{3+} ions can enter fourfold coordination in a soda lime glass is responsible for the difference in their solution behavior. Cr^{3+} ions require sixfold coordination and their incompatibility is responsible for their resistance to corrosion. Cr_2O_3 cannot easily establish the concentration gradient which is essential for diffusion. The same applies to ZrO_2. Both oxides ZrO_2 and Cr_2O_3 can be dissolved in silicate glasses—Cr_2O_3 is widely used for producing green glasses—but their apparent incompatibilities are dynamic in nature. The high coordination requirement of Zr^{4+} and Cr^{3+} ions is the result of their sizes and charges and both are responsible for their reluctance to diffuse and to dissolve in the glass.

The high charge of Zr^{4+} and Cr^{3+} ions is most important. The high melting MgO owes its high melting temperature not so much to the high screening demand of the Mg^{2+} ion but to the unfavorable O^{2-} to Mg^{2+} ratio. Mg^{2+} ions in a soda lime glass diffuse fast as compared with Cr^{3+} and Zr^{4+} ions because they can easily establish a concentration gradient. If it were not for economic reasons ThO_2 should make a very good refractory.

CHAPTER XIII

CONDITIONS OF GLASS FORMATION

1. Critical Review of Earlier Approaches to Glass Formation

A. The Shape of Molecules

At the beginning of this century progress in glass technology was based on further development of silicate glasses and, to a lesser extent, borates and phosphates. The scientific approach to the vitreous state, especially the work of G. Tammann (1), was centered around low melting glasses such as elemental selenium, rosin, and many other organic substances. At this time all matter was thought to consist of molecules, hence there was no problem in accounting for the viscosity of some macromolecular liquids or for glass formation in general. It was possible to determine the molecular weight of substances that could be vaporized or dissolved in a liquid. As far as the silicates were concerned there was no method of obtaining information about the nature, sizes, and shapes of the molecules.

During the seventeenth century great discoveries were made in the field of mechanics by Newton, Kepler, and others. When chemistry developed into a science, mechanical concepts influenced the thinking of chemists and it was only natural for them to look for mechanical explanations for the forces that are active in the molecules and even for some specific properties of substances. The biting taste of acids and their ability to corrode metals, for example, were attributed to the pointed shapes of their molecules.

Exact knowledge of the shape of molecules has become available only recently; hence, in the past scientists had to speculate on the shapes of molecules and these speculations were based on the properties of substances. It was again natural to look for mechanical concepts that could account for the failure of a liquid to crystallize. Hence, glass formation was associated with the odd shapes of molecules.

The ability of a substance to polymerize and to form chains was one of the most widely accepted prerequisites of glass formation. Firstly, some organic high polymers that consist of long carbon chains have viscosities and transformation temperatures analogous to inorganic glasses. Secondly, the existence of chain structures could be proven for some inorganic glasses, in particular elemental sulfur and selenium, and a group of phosphate glasses. Chain structures are quite common in crystalline silicates and there is no reason to exclude the possibility of silica chains participating in silicate glasses. The original concept of R. B. Sosman (120) that vitreous silica contained silicon chains analogous to the carbon chains in organic polymers could not be maintained. Vitreous silica may contain some chains but it is essentially a three dimensional polymer not very different from cristobalite except that it lacks its periodicity and long range order.

Elemental sulfur owes its ability to form a glass to the shape of its molecules. Molten sulfur just above the melting point consists of ring-shaped molecules of the formula S_8. This liquid does not form a glass on chilling. At higher temperature the molecular structure of liquid sulfur undergoes a change which leads to the formation of high polymer chains. Only when this molecular state is reached can the liquid be chilled to a glass.

Some chainlike organic molecules, e.g., stearic acid, crystallize readily if their melts are cooled; therefore, one cannot assume that anisodimensional molecules are not likely to crystallize but can form glasses.

G. Hägg (53) emphasized that glass formation must be caused by some characteristic features of the constituents of the melt. Without singling out chains in particular, he speaks of large groups that have irregular shapes. These groups of associated molecules were thought to have a certain stability because the atoms within the groups were held together by forces stronger than those acting between the groups. For many years the occurrence of macromolecules of irregular shapes and weight and the presence of association and dissociation products of simple and complex compounds (silicates, borosilicates, etc.) was used to explain the properties of glasses as affected by their compositions and their previous history. The complexity of these melts was cited also as a reason for glass formation itself.

The concept that chains become entangled in a liquid, thus preventing crystallization, is a strictly mechanical picture which is gradually being replaced by one involving forces. The irregularity of a group must not necessarily be vested in its shape but can well be the result of its force field. When A. Dietzel and E. Deeg (36) experimented with glass formation using mechanical models representing silicon and oxygen ions, they substituted magnetic forces for the electrical forces. The formation of SiO_4 groups could be demonstrated with a set of magnets floating on water in a basin. The individual "ions" were round and the ratio of their sizes corresponded to that of the sizes of Si^{4+} and O^{2-} ions. Such a model system, when given the necessary mobility, "crystallized" but did not form a glass. In order to induce glass-forming properties into the mechanical model, it was not necessary to change the shape of the "ions," it was sufficient to introduce an asymmetry into their force fields by moving the individual magnets out of their central positions.

Today when scientists talk about chain structure in glass they think much more in terms of the distributions of binding forces than of the shape of molecules, i.e., aggregates of atoms which have a high degree of permanency in the melt. Thus, J. B. Murgatroyd (121) in his work on the delayed elasticity of glass fibers assumed the formation of chains; however, he speaks of the orientation of weak and strong bonds during the drawing process. As the bonds are electrical in nature the original mechanical concept is being replaced by one which is electrical and which considers forces rather than shapes.

When we look at the pictures which Tammann (127) used for explaining the effects of pressure on the properties of glasses by the "bending" of molecules during compacting and their "straightening out" on heating, we should interpret their shapes in terms of forces and electrical symmetries. The concept of "bent molecules" has disappeared in the current literature and has been replaced by that of "bent bonds" or "changed bond angle."

As the situation presents itself today we know of inorganic glasses that consist of real molecular chains in the classical sense (sulfur, selenium) and others that contain chainlike arrangements of polyhedra in very much the same fashion as they occur in crystals (phosphate glasses).

The formation of strongly anisodimensional particles presents a fascinating problem in itself but nobody has yet been able to answer the questions: Why does the reduction of solid Ag_2S or CuBr vapor by hydrogen gas produce metallic silver and copper in the form of "hairs"? Why does the condensation of silica around places where silica glass is blown or drawn lead to a condensation of SiO_2 which has the form of spider webs? There are many examples of chain formation in systems which are not described as consisting of molecules.

B. Nature of the Chemical Bond

Three kinds of forces are known to us: electrical, magnetic, and gravitational forces. In glasses we can ignore the gravitational and the magnetic forces and regard the binding forces as electrical in nature. The electrical interactions which are responsible for the formation of the condensed state have been grouped into several types, and one speaks of van der Waals', metallic, ionic, and covalent bonds. As far as these bond types are concerned the metallic bond is the only one which cannot lead to glass formation. Some molten metals, especially those of the iron and platinum group, can be supercooled to a considerable degree, but true metals always crystallize.

The van der Waals forces are considered to be weak, but they increase with increasing number of electrons within the particles. Fluorocarbons have a higher temperature coefficient of viscosity than the analogous hydrocarbons so that some fluorocarbons can be obtained as glasses at low temperature. In this case the solidification of the liquid is due to van der Waals forces in the purest form.

Van der Waals forces are also active in the condensation and crystallization of molecules such as benzene and naphthalene, but typical glass-forming organic substances, e.g., sugar, glycerol, alkaloids, etc., contain functional groups which permit hydrogen bonding. Hydrogen bonding must participate in the glass formation of aqueous solutions.

The bonds within the molecules of an element have been called "covalent." The atoms in the chlorine molecule Cl_2 are described as being bonded by an electron pair that is shared between the two Cl atoms. This type of chemical binding is the prototype of the covalent bond which exists in its purest form only between atoms of the same kind such as the carbon atoms in a hydrocarbon.

The elements which can form glasses are oxygen, sulfur, selenium, and perhaps tellurium. These elements are unique, inasmuch as they can form paramagnetic molecules which contain two unpaired electrons. As a rule, a stable molecule contains an even number of electrons and this rule has only a few exceptions. Thus, the molecule NO contains an odd number of electrons and a molecule which contains an unpaired electron is paramagnetic and it can dimerize. As a result of its dimerization the paramagnetic molecule NO changes into the diamagnetic molecule N_2O_2 at low temperature.

The oxygen molecule, O_2, has two unpaired electrons which enables it to dimerize. Its electronic structure would make it possible for O_2 to form chains of greater length. The dimer of O_2, i.e., the molecule O_4, has been discovered in the atmosphere by O. R. Wulf (123). Applying the K. Fajans quanticule formulation to the molecule of oxygen, one can understand the reason for its polymerization. According to Fajans the O_2 molecule consists of two oxygen cores O^{6+} that are held together by ten electrons that are quantized with respect to both cores. The two unpaired electrons are quantized with respect to only one O^{6+} core each:

$$e^{-}O^{6+}(\bar{e}_{10})O^{6+}e^{-}$$

The energy gain through the pairing of two single electrons is very small so that polymerization is negligible at ordinary temperature. At low temperature, however, dimerization and polymerization seems to occur and W. Wahl (124) reports high viscosity and glass formation for elemental oxygen at low temperatures. These findings of Wahl should be checked with modern equipment that permits rapid cooling of liquid oxygen to temperatures close to absolute zero.

E. J. Shaw and T. E. Phipps (125) found that sulfur vapor is also paramagnetic, a result which was to be expected because it was known from spectroscopic data that in their ground states the molecules S_2 and O_2 are similar. At ordinary temperature the sulfur forms ring-shaped S_8 molecules in which all electrons are paired. These rings can break open and can form polymers of higher molecular weight by sharing their unpaired electrons.

The sharing of unpaired electrons and the formation of oxygen and sulfur polymers is a unique process that is distinctly different from the formation of oxide and sulfide glasses. If Wahl's observation is correct, it must be a mere coincidence that among the very few elements that can form glasses one finds oxygen, which is also the most important constituent of technical glasses.

Elemental selenium differs from sulfur only inasmuch as in

the crystalline selenium infinite chains of selenium atoms are already present so that the molecular structure of selenium does not have to undergo the drastic change during melting as does elemental sulfur. Conventional descriptions would refer to the bonds in a sulfur or selenium chain as covalent and to the forces acting between the electrically neutral chains as van der Waals forces.

The "ionic bond" is the bond type which is active between particles which differ very much in their affinity for electrons, e.g., between Na and F atoms. These atoms interact in a way that can be described as the complete removal of an electron from the sodium atoms and the completion of an octet shell of the fluorine atom. This electron transfer leads to charged particles; namely, the positive sodium ions and the negative fluorine ions. These charged particles can interact further by forming a condensed system in which they are held together primarily by coulombic attractive forces. The ionic bond in its purest form is active in fluoride glasses, e.g., in the alkali beryllium fluoride glasses which were studied by G. Heyne (126).

The glass-forming compounds discussed so far represent the different bond types in their purest form. If atoms are not identical as in glassy selenium, and are not quite as different as sodium and fluorine atoms in NaF, they are conventionally treated as forming "mixed bonds." L. Pauling (10) calls the binding forces in silica 50% ionic and 50% covalent. The degree of covalency of a bond is expressed by the "electronegativity" of the atoms. The greater the value of the electronegativity of an element, the more covalent is its bond to oxygen.

The conventional treatment of the bonds in vitreous As_2S_3 is to call them more covalent than those in SiO_2. The bonds in vitreous $ZnCl_2$, BeF_2, the complex alkali beryllium fluoride, and the alkali calcium nitrate glasses are considered to be more ionic than those in SiO_2.

J. E. Stanworth (127) introduced the electronegativity of the elements, i.e., the tendency of a neutral atom within a molecule to attract electrons, as a parameter that might be linked to glass formation. J. M. Stevels (128) suggested a subdivision of elements into four groups (Table XXII). The first group comprises the "real glass formers" and the second group the "probable glass formers." The third group is comprised of those elements whose

TABLE XXII

Electronegativity of Elements and Role in Glass Structure (128)

Glass formers		Metallic ions which participate as modifiers in:	
Real	Probable	Contracted glasses	Normal glasses
P, 2.1	Sn, 1.7	Be, 1.5	Ca, 1.0
B, 2.0	Ti, 1.6	Mg, 1.2	Sr, 1.0
As, 2.0	Zr, 1.6	Li, 1.0	Ba, 0.9
Si, 1.8	Al, 1.5		Na, 0.9
Ge, 1.8			K, 0.8
Sb, 1.8			Rb, 0.8
			Cs, 0.7

oxides cannot form glasses but whose effect upon the density of glasses reveals a stronger interaction with the oxygen ions of the network than that of the oxides of the elements of the fourth group.

The table leaves no doubt that those elements whose atoms have a low electronegativity, i.e., those which form basic oxides, are not potential glass formers. However, as far as the elements with high electronegativities are concerned, no such clearcut relation exists between their ability to form a stable glass and the value of the electronegativity of the atoms. Antimony has the same electronegativity as silicon but its oxide does not form a stable glass. The aluminum atom has a lower electronegativity than the tin atom or the zirconium atom but alkaline earth aluminate glasses are known, whereas no vitreous zirconate or stannate has been reported.

When A. G. Smekal (129) discussed his views on the conditions of glass formation he made a distinction between the large-scale stability of the random structure of the glass and the local stability of its structural units. The latter units, he wrote, "demand mixed chemical binding forces which are partly covalent and partly of ionic nature." Smekal assumed that the bonding type of a substance in a glassy state may differ fundamentally from that of the substance in its crystalline state.

This use of the "bond type" provides a convenient parameter for explaining phenomena for which no other explanation could be given. Thus, Smekal (129) explained glass formation on the basis that the liquid on cooling and supercooling assumes a bond type which is suitable for the glassy but not for the crystalline state.

Smekal (130) first published in 1942 his concept that glass formation is the result of "mixed bonds" and it must have had a certain appeal because only one year later A. Dietzel (131) used it to explain the anomaly that within a certain temperature region silica glass expands on cooling and becomes stronger on heating. Dietzel assumed that heating causes the mixed bond to change into a more ionic bond which provides greater mechanical strength.

When V. M. Goldschmidt (4) provided a new tool, namely, the crystal chemical approach to the formation and the structure of glasses, it was applied practically exclusively to silica and silicates but not to his fluoride glasses. Singling out silica as the prototype of glass-formers led to some confusion with respect to the real meaning of the chemical bond in glasses and crystals. Vitreous silica, the first glass whose structure was determined by X-ray methods, consists of two elements for which the "valency" and the "coordination number" happen to be identical. Silicon in the classical sense is tetravalent and in the modern crystal chemical sense it has the coordination number of 4. Oxygen is "divalent" and in silica it had the coordination number of 2. If structural studies in the field of glass formation would have been centered around beryllium fluoride there would have been no danger of confusing atomic and ionic descriptions. Scientists would probably not have spoken of double-bonded and single-bonded fluorine because fluorine has the valency of 1. Because of this coincidence we do not find a clearcut distinction between the two ways of describing matter but find the same author using both descriptions interchangeably. We find the term electronegativity, a property of a neutral atom, applied to elements that are treated as ions in the structure. In the same way we find the dissociation energies of compounds into neutral atoms applied to conditions where the same author uses the ionic description. For example, lead oxide in a glass is a "divalent" atom from a classical point of view. However, from a crystal chemical viewpoint, it participates in the structure as an ion which has the charge 2+ but a coordination number which is higher than 2; namely, 8 in the PbO crystal and very likely 6 in a silicate glass.

Both methods of describing matter are justified; they should be looked upon as useful approximations and the method to be preferred depends primarily on the field of research.

The role which the nature of the chemical bond is supposed to play in glass formation is rather obscure. Considering the great variety of substances which form glasses it is difficult to understand how scientists could ever consider the bond type as a factor which could determine the stability of a substance in the vitreous state.

C. Bond Strength

The concept of the bond strength or the energy of a bond between two atoms is a very useful one in discussions of the thermodynamic properties of simple molecules. The bond energies within a gaseous molecule can be derived from spectroscopic data. Thermochemical data are an additional way of obtaining values of bond energies. One can also derive the bond strength within a simple molecule by actually breaking the bond through electron impact. Using a mass spectrometer one can increase gradually the energy of the electrons and measure the energy necessary for breaking the gaseous molecule into fragments.

K. H. Sun (132) made an attempt to correlate glass formation with bond strength. He based his bond strength values on the energy of dissociation of an oxide into gaseous neutral atoms. For an oxide of the formula M_mO_n, the M-O bond strength is obtained by dividing the dissociation energy of the hypothetical oxide $MO_{m/n}$ by the coordination number of the element M. The values which were obtained by this method for the single M-O bond strength range from 119 kcal. for boron to 10 kcal. for cesium.

He shows that the oxides which form glasses have high bond energies (119 to 80 kcal.), whereas the modifiers have low values of their M-O bond (60 to 10 kcal.). Oxides with bond energies between 60 and 70 kcal. such as Al_2O_3 are grouped as "intermediates."

A closer examination of his data, however, reveals that his system lacks a rigorous scientific basis, primarily because the coordination numbers were chosen arbitrarily in order to achieve the desired result. For example, ThO_2 and ZrO_2 at high temperatures have structures (fluorite type) in which the cations are surrounded by eight oxygens. Dividing the dissociation energies of the oxides by 8 gives the value of 61 kcal. for ZrO_2 and 64 kcal. for ThO_2. An interpretation of these values in the sense of K. H. Sun should indicate that thorium oxide has a greater tendency to participate in glass formation than zirconium oxide, a conclusion which is not supported by experiments. For this reason zirconium is given a coordination number of either 6 or 8 while thorium is given the coordination number of 8 or 12. This arbitrary manipulation of the coordination numbers is used for reversing the situation and placing ZrO_2, but not ThO_2, within the group of glass formers.

Using the heats of dissociation of CaO and PbO and the actual coordination numbers of the metal atoms in their oxides, one obtains a bond strength of 45 kcal. for the Ca–O bond and 18 kcal. for the Pb–O bond. These values are in striking contrast to the known behavior of CaO and PbO in glasses. Sun (132) remedies this situation by assigning to the Ca atom the coordination number "8" (instead of 6 as in CaO) and to the Pb atom the coordination number of "2" (instead of 8 as in PbO).

The oxides ZnO and CdO have a greater tendency than CaO to form glasses in combination with SiO_2, B_2O_3 or P_2O_5. In order to bring out this difference the Zn and Cd atoms are listed as having the coordination number of "2" rather than the higher values which they assume in crystal structures.

The values of their bond strengths bring P_2O_5, Sb_2O_5, and V_2O_5 into the group of glass formers. However, only P_2O_5 forms a stable glass: V_2O_5 and Sb_2O_5 do not.

The inadequacy of this approach has been noticed by those who tried to apply it to the development of new glasses. P. L. Baynton, H. Rawson and J. E. Stanworth (133) prepared a large number of glasses based on the oxides of tellurium, vanadium, molybdenum, and tungsten. These oxides cannot form glasses by themselves. However, for reasons discussed earlier (Chapter VII,3), in combination with other compounds these oxides do not form semiconductors on melting and, therefore, can form glasses.

A paper of H. Rawson (134) gives us a good example of the difficulty facing a scientist when he tries to understand glass formation on the basis of the bond strength. Rawson discussed the properties of new glasses which offer a very interesting structural problem. He pointed out that in the past it was customary to talk about network-formers and network-modifiers. In some of these new glasses, e.g., those based on WO_3 and MoO_3, the network-modifying alkalis seem to be essential constituents because they make glass formation possible. He wrote: "It is clearly important to try to explain this behavior. It may well be that in our search for explanations for glass formation in these binary melts we may throw new light on the conditions influencing glass formation in simple compounds."

Rawson went an important step beyond K. H. Sun (132) when he recognized the importance of the absolute melting point for the ability of an oxide to form a glass. He elaborates on K. H. Sun's data and calculates constants that include both the bond strength B_{M-O} and the absolute melting temperature T_F. In spite of this improvement he arrived at the following conclusion:

"A classification of oxides along these lines does not really take one much further than Sun's slightly simpler classification, although the former does suggest a possible reason for the extreme difficulty of crystallizing B_2O_3 from the melt, the ratio of single bond strength to the melting point in °K. being particularly high for this material."

The values of the parameter "cation-oxygen bond strength/absolute melting temperature" of the oxides WO_3, MoO_3 and V_2O_5 are larger than that of SiO_2 and smaller than that of B_2O_3 as can be seen from Table XXIII.

Summarizing, we may state that no valid relation exists between the ability of an oxide to form a glass and its energy of dissociation into neutral atoms, even if this parameter is divided by the absolute melting temperature.

Dietzel makes wide use of the values of the field strength of cations (see Chapter V,2). This parameter makes it possible for him to account for many properties of glasses, e.g., their thermal expansion, but he failed to establish a simple relation between the values of z/a^2 and glass formation. In his writings A. Dietzel (135) adheres to the network theory of Zachariasen but he comments that this picture of a random nonperiodic structure of a glass cannot explain the glass formation or even the viscosity of molten com-

TABLE XXIII

Cation-Oxygen Bond Strength/Absolute Melting Temperature

Oxide	$B_{M\text{-}O}/T_F$
B_2O_3	0.164
SiO_2	0.053
V_2O_5	0.095
MoO_3	0.086
WO_3	0.059

pounds. He wrote: "We are not able to see why such an irregular network does not break down at high temperature and form a fluid melt or why a crystal of quartz or cristobalite differs from a crystal of NaCl or H_2O by not forming a fluid melt."

Dietzel plots the melting points of oxides as a function of the field strength of the cations. This plot reveals that oxides whose cations have low values of z/a^2, e.g., BaO (0.2), do not form glasses. The oxides which contain cations of the highest field strength, e.g., CO_2, CrO_3, and SO_3 (2.4 to 2.8), do not seem to form stable glasses either. The typical glass formers, e.g., SiO_2 and B_2O_3, have cations with an intermediate field strength (1.6 to 2.0). However, this intermediate group is not restricted to glass-forming oxides; it also includes oxides that cannot form glasses by themselves; e.g., V_2O_5 and MoO_3. The field strength of the cation does not lend itself to a classification of the oxides. Hence, Dietzel turns to the use of Smekal's concept of the "mixed bond type." BaO is called ionic, CO_2 and SO_3 covalent, and the glass-forming oxides are described as having a bond type somewhere in between these two extremes.

Summarizing we may state that the field strength of a cation at the distance of the nearest surrounding O^{2-} ions can be used as a measure of the bond strength, but that this value bears no more relation to the ability of an oxide to form a glass than the cation-oxygen bond strength used by K. H. Sun (132).

D. Crystal Structure Approach

There is no difference in the properties of a substance in its crystalline and its glassy state which is sufficiently characteristic for defining the glassy state. The mechanical strength of crystals and glasses are not very different; crystals can be stronger or weaker than glasses of corresponding compositions. The thermal expansion of a glass can be lower than that of the crystal (silica glass *versus* quartz) but it can also be higher than that of the crystal (cordierite *versus* a corresponding magnesia alumina silica glass). Also, as a rule glasses have lower densities than the corresponding crystals, but this rule has exceptions (eucryptite, $Li_2O \cdot Al_2O_3 \cdot 2SiO_2$).

Frequently it has been emphasized that a glass, in contrast to a crystal, softens gradually and does not have a sharp melting point. However, many crystals, e.g., silver iodide, also soften gradually and can be deformed easily below their melting points.

Albite, a crystalline sodium aluminosilicate, can be held at a temperature 50°C. above its melting point for days without losing its optical anisotropy and its crystalline outline. Hence, the "abrupt" change of properties with temperature in crystals as compared with their gradual change in glasses is rather problematic and does not provide a basis for characterizing the glassy state.

Attempts to define a glass by its energy content have been equally unsuccessful. It is true that most glasses are thermodynamically unstable, their energy content being higher than that of some crystalline phase of the same chemical composition. However, this does not seem to apply to glassy P_2O_5 which has a higher density than the stable crystalline modification, is less soluble (in $CHCl_3$), and has a lower vapor pressure than the hexagonal crystal.

The lack of major and characteristic differences between glasses and crystals with respect to their mechanical strength, density, thermal expansion, melting behavior, and their heats of formation suggests that a close structural similarity must be possible between glasses and crystals.

An evaluation of the role which the crystal structure of a substance plays with respect to its ability to form a stable glass was not possible before the development of modern crystal chemistry. Crystal structures by themselves cannot tell us why cristobalite but not magnesium oxide forms a glass when the melts of the two substances are allowed to cool. No matter how fast MgO is cooled from the molten state, one obtains periclase. No matter how slowly one cools a melt of anhydrous B_2O_3 or of potassium disilicate one obtains a glass. An explanation of the differences between these compounds with respect to glass formation requires a combination of chemical and crystallographic approaches. This combination makes the problem of glass formation a crystal-chemical problem into which dynamic considerations involving the liquid state have to be introduced.

When Goldschmidt (4) and his collaborators performed the numerous experiments which opened up the field of modern crystal chemistry it was inevitable that they should encounter the problem of glass formation. Indeed, when Goldschmidt studied his "weakened models" of feldspars he discovered an unusual example of glass formation among fluorides. He wrote: "I discovered the tendency to glass formation in such melts as $NaLiBe_3F_8$ and $KLiBe_3F_8$ when I had these melts prepared in order to synthesize the fluoride analogues of feldspars." This discovery aroused Goldschmidt's interest in structural factors which favor glass formation among simple systems.

It is interesting to go back to the original statements that Goldschmidt (4) made in order to appreciate how strongly they affected the thinking of scientists with respect to the atomic structure of glasses. In 1926, Goldschmidt wrote "My experiments demonstrate that a certain ratio of the sizes of the atoms or ions and their polarization properties must be of considerable importance for glass formation."

"We find that compounds of the type AX_2 ("A" representing a cation and "X" an anion) whose radius ratios R_A/R_X are close to 0.3 and whose anions X have a low polarizability (either O^{2-} or F^- ions) have the ability to solidify as glasses and to impart this ability of glass formation to more complex melts."

After this statement Goldschmidt elaborates on these conditions pointing out that a ratio of R_A/R_X within the limits 0.2 and 0.4 favors a tetrahedral coordination of the cation. He considers it possible that the ability of substances to form glasses may be connected with the stability of tetrahedral coordinations. He elaborates further on the role which the polarizability of the anion in the substances AX_2 seems to play in glass formation. The polarizability should be small because sulfide glasses are rare and even chlorides do not have much tendency to form glasses. Bromide and iodide glasses of the formula AX_2 were unknown.

This message had a strong impact on the thinking of the contemporary glass scientists. Firstly, Goldschmidt's findings revealed the importance of a factor which had not been stressed before, the atomic structure of the substance in its crystalline state. Secondly, Goldschmidt's findings proved that some prevailing chemical concepts were not valid. A substance did not have to be an acid in the classical sense in order to form a glass and to impart the ability of glass formation to complex melts. Before Goldschmidt, no glass scientist would have expected beryllium fluoride to resemble silica in its crystal structure or in its ability to form a glass.

In addition to the conclusions which could be drawn from Goldschmidt's findings, glass scientists learned the value of crystal chemical thinking. Goldschmidt's success did not remain a purely academic one. The very practical use which H. G. Grimm and P.

Huppert (136) made of crystal chemical thinking can be seen from the fact that they opened up a new field, the alumino-phosphate glasses. Goldschmidt taught that in addition to the classical isomorphism a new type of structural relation exists in which the couple Al^{3+}, P^{5+} can replace 2 Si^{4+} ions.

The literature on the atomic structure of glasses and on the development of new glasses reveals how fast and strongly crystal chemical thinking penetrated into structural views and into planning new glass compositions.

The next decisive step in the development of glass structures was a paper in 1932 by one of V. M. Goldschmidt's associates, W. H. Zachariasen (3), who proposed certain rules which he assumed would govern the formation of oxide glasses. Zachariasen's paper was published in journals which were more readily accessible to glass technologists than the writings of Goldschmidt. This and the fact that Zachariasen presented his ideas in the form of simple rules made the paper the basis for the structural picture that has been used by most glass technologists during the past 20 years.

Zachariasen (3) presented a picture of the atomic structure of vitreous silica in which the silicon atoms are surrounded by four oxygens in the same way as in the different structures of crystalline silica and silicates. He suggested the structure of vitreous silica to be continuous and three-dimensional, analogous to the structures of its crystalline modifications. This means that vitreous silica does not contain individual SiO_2 molecules nor polymers such as chains. Vitreous silica according to Zachariasen's picture has a continuous, random, three-dimensional structure that shows the same close range order as the crystalline modifications of silica but does not have their long range order. The only difference between glass and crystal was the absence of periodicity: a feature which required the nonequality of the structural elements in the glass. Zachariasen wrote, "Since all atoms in glass are structurally unequivalent the energy required to detach an atom from the network will be different for each individual atom." The abrupt melting of crystals and the gradual softening that can be observed when the same substance in the glassy state is heated were considered by him to be the result of this nonequality of all structural units in a glass. Thus, Zachariasen made two important contributions to the structure of glasses. He emphasized the absence of defined SiO_2 molecules and the nonequality of the building units, atoms, and polyhedra. There was a close analogy between ionic crystals and inorganic glasses inasmuch as both solids had to be treated as three-dimensional networks rather than as arrays of molecules.

For the glass-forming ability of oxides A_mO_n the following rules were derived:

1. An oxygen atom is linked to not more than two atoms, A.
2. The number of oxygen atoms around an A atom must be small.
3. The oxygen polyhedra share corners but not edges or faces.
4. If we require the network to be three-dimensional, at least three corners in each polyhedron must be shared.

The description of a silicate glass as a three-dimensional random network of tetrahedra that share all or most of their corners was simple and it had features which were very appealing. The introduction of alkali oxides into vitreous silica loosened its structure by decreasing the number of corners which each tetrahedron had to share with others. This feature could account for the lower viscosity of an alkali silicate glass as compared with pure silica. The classification of the constituents of a glass into network-forming oxides and those which modify the network was simple and useful. It is true that this picture had to be refined by introducing "intermediates," but for a long time the network concept seemed to provide a useful basis for theorizing on the structure of glasses.

As far as alkali and alkali lime silicate glasses are concerned, the rule that the stability of their random networks depended on the number of shared corners offered a satisfactory picture within a wide range of commercial glasses.

Zachariasen's rules governing glass formation did not remain without criticism. His rules were based on the findings of Goldschmidt that a certain ratio of the sizes of cation and anion in a compound of the formula AX_2 is favorable to glass formation. Zachariasen assumed that a tetrahedral or a triangular coordination can be more easily distorted than one which is octahedral or higher so that a framework of XO_3 or XO_4 polyhedra may have nearly the same energy content in the glassy as in the crystalline state.

G. W. Morey (137) in a discussion of Zachariasen's paper threw doubt on the correctness of Zachariasen's reasoning when he remarked: "Zachariasen has published an interesting paper on the structure of glass. This picture of the structure of glass seems much more probable than that of Randall, Rooksby, and Cooper but after all does it do much more than to say in the language of X-ray structure that glass is an undercooled liquid?"

"Zachariasen's further discussion is based on the assumption, also made by others, that the energy difference between crystal and glass is small, but that assumption is, as far as the writer is aware, without experimental foundation. The latent heats of melting of few crystalline silicates are known."

In the same paper, Morey (137) gives some examples. Potassium tetrasilicate is the most difficult binary silicate to crystallize, but its heat of fusion is 35 cal./g. whereas that of the readily crystallizing potassium nitrate is only 25 cal./g.

One year later, G. Hägg (53) raised an even more serious objection to Zachariasen's approach. He pointed out that glass formation is a rate phenomenon and that its explanation has to be based on the reason for the failure of a melt to crystallize and not on the structure of the crystal. Hägg emphasized that the presence of large and irregular groups in a melt must be responsible for its failure to crystallize. In the following discussion notes (138, 139) between these two scientists, it was brought out clearly that Zachariasen did not attempt to give a general explanation of glass formation but that he restricted himself to those oxide glasses which form a three-dimensional network.

In order to understand the nearly universal acceptance of Zachariasen's rules concerning glass formation, in spite of the criticism voiced by Morey and by Hägg, one has to remember two facts. Firstly, the majority of commercial glasses had compositions to which the rules of Zachariasen could be applied. The heavy lead glasses were the only exceptions known at this time. Secondly, the work of B. E. Warren and his school, who used X-ray techniques for determining the atomic structures of glasses, agreed with Zachariasen's picture.

Warren's warning that his work did not prove the validity of the network theory was ignored. Warren (140), in 1941, wrote: "It would be incorrect to say that the present random network theory of the structure of glass has been uniquely established." His statement that his results could be interpreted on the basis of Zachariasen's picture was taken for proof. Warren made some important contributions to the atomic structure of simple oxide glasses but he also cautioned about the limitations of the X-ray method. The X-ray diffraction method has developed into the most powerful single tool for studying atomic structures of crystals, but with respect to the structures of amorphous solids it has serious limitations, as has been pointed out recently by K. Grjotheim (141).

J. M. Stevels (142) found in 1954 that by proper combination of oxides, stable metasilicate glasses could be obtained. He gives the following example:

SiO_2	50.0 mole %
Na_2O	12.5 mole %
K_2O	12.5 mole %
CaO	12.5 mole %
BaO	12.5 mole %

He explained this "anomalous" case of glass formation as follows. "Choosing a batch with a great number of network modifiers the 'glue' between the chains is so irregular that crystallization is prevented."

In this explanation Stevels tries to conform with the Zachariasen three-dimensional network concept. He assumes that the metasilicate glass consists of a network of chains that are entangled in space. The chains are negatively charged and are held together by the Na^+, K^+, Ca^{2+}, and Ba^{2+} ions.

Most commercial silicate glasses (window, plate, and container glass) conform with Zachariasen's condition that at least three corners of each tetrahedron be shared so that not more than one corner is occupied by a nonbridging oxygen ion. In order to classify glasses, J. M. Stevels and his associates introduced a structural parameter Y, which denotes the average number of bridging oxygen ions per tetrahedron. The value of Y of most technical silicate glasses is of the order of 3.0 to 3.4 which means that on the average at least three, but occasionally all, of the corners of the tetrahedra are shared with other tetrahedra. A metasilicate glass has a Y value of 2.0. Glasses with a Y value of 1.0 (40 mole % silica) would contain on the average only pairs of tetrahedra, i.e., $(Si_2O_7)^{6-}$ anions. Further decrease of Y leads to the formation of single tetrahedra or orthosilicate anions $(SiO_4)^{4-}$. Orthosilicates, e.g., Na_4SiO_4, have a Y value of 0, corresponding to 33.3 mole % SiO_2. Using this structural parameter Y as a measure of the coherence of the silica network, Stevels calls glasses for which the value of Y is less than two "invert glasses."

H. J. L. Trap and J. M. Stevels (143) (1959) investigated the properties of a number of invert glasses and found that silicate glasses which contain only noble gas-type cations can be obtained for which the *Y* value is even less than 1.0. The existence of these stable glasses which have silica ratios lower than those of metasilicates means that the concept that silicate glasses must have a three-dimensional network of SiO_4 tetrahedra cannot be maintained, even if the network modifiers are cations of the noble gas-type.

We may summarize the content of the preceding chapters and draw the following conclusions. None of the four factors which we discussed need to be a prerequisite for glass formation. The shape factor would seem to be the most logical one. One should expect the shape of molecules to play a major role and, indeed, it is the decisive factor in the formation of sulfur and selenium glasses. For vitreous silica, however, it becomes artificial to assume chains or any irregular flow unit which in the molten state has sufficient permanency to be called a macromolecule whose geometry prevents nucleation and crystallization.

The nature of the chemical bond cannot account for glass formation because all classes of substances, with the exception of true metals, can form glasses. Fluoride and nitrate glasses have ionic bonds. In the selenium glass one finds covalent bonds to be active between the selenium atoms within the chains. Most commercial glasses are of the so-called "mixed bond type" and a large group of organic substances owe their ability to form glasses to hydrogen bonding. Van der Waals forces are responsible for glass formation among fluorocarbons, and are active also in low melting organic glasses and in a selenium glass.

The bond strength might be suspected of playing a role in glass formation, but it could be shown that Sun's treatment is based on arbitrary and illogical assumptions with respect to the coordination number. Dietzel's approach to the bond strength in ionic systems is sound but it reveals no relation between the bond strength as measured by the field strength of the cation and the ability of an oxide to form a glass.

With respect to the rules concerning glass formation based on the tetrahedral coordination one can only say that most commercial glasses fall within the scope of these rules but that the rules are not applicable to glass formation in a general way. Even if we limit ourselves to silicate glasses which contain only noble gas-like ions, the rules of Zachariasen are invalidated through the existence of Stevel's invert glasses.

2. Dynamic Approach to Glass Formation

Glasses are amorphous solids that have formed from a liquid on cooling in a reversible process. Among the three types of liquids the Frenkel "fissured" type is not suitable for glass formation but both the Bernal "flawless" type and the Stewart "orientable" type lend themselves to the formation of stable glasses. We use the word "stable" in the sense that the system retains its vitreous state under normal conditions, not in the sense of resistance toward corrosion. In contrast to vitreous selenium, we do not call the plastic sulfur a stable glass because it crystallizes at ordinary temperature. In our discussion of the three types of liquids we emphasized that all real liquids are intermediates and that our description of the three types refers to the idealized extremes.

Let us recall that the three extremes are very different in their rheological or their dynamic properties but that they cannot be distinguished one from the other on the basis of their thermodynamic properties. No thermodynamic treatment can distinguish between a system in which the forces acting between the individual particles correspond to the average forces modified only by the thermal motion in a statistical way (Bernal "flawless" liquid), and other systems in which the binding forces are disproportionated so that weaker and stronger forces are active simultaneously (Stewart "orientable" and Frenkel "fissured" liquids).

Let us also recall that even if there were a method available which could measure at a given moment the exact distribution of binding forces as they exist in the system, this method would enable us to identify only the flawless Bernal type liquid. Even with such a method we could not distinguish the fissured Frenkel liquid from the orientable Stewart liquid. In order to distinguish between these two structures it becomes necessary to learn how the binding forces change from one moment to the next. The distribution of binding forces in a fissured liquid at one particular instant might be the same as in an orientable liquid but for the individual particles the binding forces change rapidly in the fissured liquid but slowly in the orientable liquid. For distinguishing between these two types of liquids one has to consider time as the decisive factor. The words rapid and slow have no absolute meaning but are relative and subject to personal opinion. In this subjectivity also lies one of the fundamental difficulties in formulating the structures of liquids and the conditions of glass formation. Whether a system should be called a glass-forming liquid involves a decision that is and will always be arbitrary.

The arbitrariness in the definition of Tammann's temperature t_g, the temperature which separates the glassy state (below t_g) from that of the liquid state (above t_g), led to serious difficulties as one can see if one reads discussions on the transformation point as published around 1930 to 1940. E. Berger (144) fought valiantly for his idea that the transformation point has a real physical meaning. Other scientists showed that its temperature can be shifted considerably by varying the time scale of the experiment. Experimentally it is not easy to decrease the time scale of measurements below a few minutes and as far as increasing the scale is concerned, our life span sets a limit. In discussions on this subject, K. Endell used to refer to the transformation temperature as a property which is "Mensch gebunden," i.e., related to the human life span. From a practical point of view the situation is not serious as long as we are aware of the relativity when distinguishing glasses from liquids and of the fact that no property or measurement which does not involve time as a parameter can tell us whether we deal with a glass or a liquid.

Thermodynamics is one of the most powerful tools for the understanding of chemical reactions and equilibria. Nevertheless, the phase diagrams could not contribute to our understanding of why some substances form a glass (P_2O_5) whereas other similar substances (V_2O_5) do not. We must not expect thermodynamic treatment alone to make a major contribution to the constitution of glasses because thermodynamics does not consider time as a factor. Heterogeneous equilibria, in particular the conditions which determine the coexistence of liquid and solid phases as a function of the temperature or pressure, are based on thermodynamics.

Going from equilibria to rate phenomena leads us into fields where no such reliable tools as thermodynamics and crystal chemistry are available. Because of the tremendous importance of rate phenomena scientists tried to correlate reaction rates with parameters such as the geometry of the crystal and with thermodynamic quantities such as dissociation energies and free energy changes. Much of this effort led to fallacies.

Glass formation is a rate phenomenon that calls for a dynamic picture of the structure of glasses and for a kinetic treatment. A liquid forms a glass on cooling if the conditions do not permit its crystallization. Crystallization has two prerequisites: (1) mobility of the constituents and (2) the presence of nuclei.

The probability of nucleation is decreased by rapid cooling, high activation energy of nucleation, and low liquidus temperature. There is no generally valid relation between the activation energy of nucleation of a substance and its thermodynamic properties including the average bond strength. There is also no valid relation between the rate of nucleation and the free energy change of the process; i.e., the difference between the energy content of the compound in its crystalline and in its molten state. As far as the geometry is concerned, a glass as a supercooled liquid resembles the structure of the substance in the molten state. However, the structures of a melt may differ very much from that of the corresponding crystal (sulfur, phosphorus pentoxide) or it may bear a very close resemblance to the crystal structure (cristobalite). Glass formation is neither a function of the magnitude of the energy difference between crystal and liquid nor of the magnitude of the structural difference between crystal and liquid.

A. Rate of Cooling

The paramount importance of the cooling rate of a melt on its ability to form a glass is well understood. A melt may have a composition that would not permit its use for the manufacture of window glass or containers but would be well suited for making glass fibers or small glass beads.

G. Tammann and A. Elbrächter (145) sprayed molten salts on a cold surface and examined the droplets microscopically. By determining the sizes and the fraction of each size which crystallized and that which had solidified as a glass they studied the tendency of glass formation of salts such as thallous sulfate, lead chloride, and silver nitrate. None of these salts could be obtained as a glass in gram quantities.

Because of the importance of the cooling rate on glass formation one cannot arrive at an absolute classification of systems into those which are glass-forming and others which are not unless one standardizes the rate of cooling. The rate of cooling cannot be completely controlled because it depends upon the quantity and the shape of the sample. It is unfortunate that not all workers who report on new glass compositions mention in their papers the quantity of the substance which they were able to obtain as a glass.

When S. M. Brekhovskich (146) reported on the development of high Bi_2O_3-containing glasses he presented his observations in the form of ternary diagrams in which the fields of glass formation were plotted both for gram and for milligram quantities.

B. Liquidus Temperature

The absolute melting point of a substance or the liquidus temperature of a system is by far the most important single factor that determines its ability to form a glass. Above this temperature nuclei cannot form; therefore, a system can be kept at any temperature above its liquidus temperature indefinitely without the occurence of nucleation and crystallization. Only below this temperature can the probability of nucleation and crystallization reach finite values.

The absolute temperature enters all mathematical expressions which describe rate phenomena, usually in the form of the factor $e^{-E/T}$ in which T is the absolute temperature and E an energy term. In spite of the simplicity and the universally accepted importance of this relation the absolute liquidus temperature has been ignored by most scientists who have attempted to explain the conditions of glass formation.

The paramount importance of the liquidus temperature for glass formation accounts for the following facts:

1. The high melting carbides, nitrides, silicides, and borides do not form glasses.
2. Glass formation in the temperature region above 1500°C. is rare.
3. A large number and a great variety of organic substances melting below 200°C. are known to form glasses. Some low melting mixtures of nitrates and several hydrated salts (sodium thiosulfate), acids (sulfuric acid), and bases (potassium hydroxide) can be obtained as glasses at low temperatures.

The melting temperatures are responsible for the range of glass formation in the system Na_2O-B_2O_3. Sodium orthoborate $2Na_2O \cdot B_2O_3$ melts at 625°C. Sodium metaborate $Na_2O \cdot B_2O_3$ or $NaBO_2$ melts at 966°C. However, the latter crystallizes too fast to be obtained as a glass.

When G. W. Morey and H. E. Merwin (147) determined

the phase relationships in the system Na_2O-B_2O_3 they made the following comments: "The orthoborate is remarkable for its low melting point 625°C. and the fact that in small quantities it can be obtained as a glass. The system Na_2O-B_2O_3 is thus in marked contrast to the system Na_2O-SiO_2 in which the incongruent melting point of the ortho compound is higher than that of the meta compound and the tendency toward crystallization increases regularly with the content of Na_2O."

C. Nucleation Rate

Below its liquidus temperature a glass is in a metastable state and its rate of nucleation decides whether or not it can be molded into useful shapes and annealed so that the object is free of stresses. Earlier (see Chapter V) we described the energy barrier of reactions such as the formation of spinel from a mixture of MgO and Al_2O_3 as the "partial temporary unscreening of cations." We learned that no valid relation exists between the rates of this type of reaction and the bond energies of the compounds which are involved.

In our discussions of nucleation phenomena we learned that calcium orthosilicate nucleates faster than the metasilicate because it has the highest polarizability among calcium silicates and the formation of a nucleus becomes more probable when the new phase has a high polarizability which also means a low surface energy. These relationships dominate the behavior of a glass on cooling below the liquidus temperature. Nucleation is less likely to occur if the melt becomes supersaturated with respect to cristobalite or wollastonite than with respect to an oxide which has a polarizable cation. The oxides of tin, cerium, titanium, and zirconium can be used as opacifiers because glasses and enamels that become supersaturated on cooling with respect to SnO_2, CeO_2, TiO_2, and ZrO_2 precipitate these oxides in the form of numerous small crystals. In contrast to this, the precipitation of SiO_2, $CaSiO_3$, or devitrite $Na_2O \cdot CaO \cdot 6SiO_2$, if it occurs at all, leads to a few but relatively large crystals. The rate of nucleation is slow for these silicates because they have a low polarizability.

The formation of gold ruby or cadmium sulfide yellow glass is based upon the way in which metallic gold and CdS precipitate. The surface energy or the interfacial energy of a crystal which contains polarizable anions (S^{2-} and Se^{2-} ions or the free electrons of a noble metal) or polarizable cations (Ce^{4+}, Zr^{4+}, Cd^{2+}) is lower than that of a silicate crystal which has a low polarizability. Hence, CdS or Au crystals can form in a glass at temperatures at which the thermal energy is relatively low because for the formation of these crystal nuclei the energy barrier of nucleation is also low.

The presence of cations with a low charge (Na^+, K^+) or of high polarizability (Te^{4+} rather than Si^{4+}, V^{5+} rather than P^{5+}) enables a liquid to form fissures and to nucleate readily. The same applies to anions. The more polarizable S^{2-} ions enhance the rate of nucleation more than the less polarizable O^{2-} ions.

The fact that stable glasses can be obtained which contain a substantial concentration of highly polarizable cations (lead glasses) and highly polarizable anions (arsenic trisulfide glass) is the result of the low liquidus temperature of these glasses. A CdS crystal precipitates readily from a silicate glass when the latter becomes supersaturated with respect to CdS at 700°C. On the other hand sulfide glasses have been obtained as stable glasses because of the low liquidus temperature of these systems.

D. Heterogeneity of Complex Glasses

Whether a system is to be considered as homogeneous or as heterogeneous depends upon the yardstick one uses to describe it. An aventurine glass contains macroscopic crystals of elemental copper or Fe_2O_3 or Cr_2O_3. These glasses have compositions (high PbO content) which make these constituents compatible with the melt at high temperature but which lead to their precipitation in a temperature region in which the glass is still rather fluid (working range) so that the crystals grow to a large size and become oriented when the glass is shaped. The sparkle of a chromium aventurine glass is the result of its containing fairly large, very thin, hexagonal plates of Cr_2O_3 which are oriented nearly parallel to the surface of the blown ware. The aventurine glasses as well as these glasses that are defective because of devitrifications (tridymite, wollastonite, or devitrite) are heterogeneous in a macroscopic scale.

A group of opal glasses and enamels reveal their heterogeneity by being translucent or opaque. Under the microscope one finds that numerous small particles are embedded in the glassy matrix. These particles reflect some of the incident light because their index of refraction differs from that of the glassy matrix. The particles can be either gases (gas opacification of enamels), glasses (some phosphate opal glasses, Vycor glass), or crystals (fluoride opals).

Fluoride opals can form through the precipitation of NaF, which has a lower index of refraction than the matrix. Titania-opacified enamels precipitate rutile or anatase crystals which have higher refractive indices than the matrix.

Some glasses have been developed which contain opacifying phases that match the refractive index of the matrix only for a limited range of the optical spectrums. Such a system is colored because it is transparent for a part of the visible spectrum but scatters and reflects another part. All of these opacified glasses and enamels can be called heterogeneous on a microscopic scale.

At the beginning of this century R. Zsigmondy (148) observed that some colloidal solutions were heterogeneous. They contained particles which could be detected by their scattering of light (Faraday-Tyndall effect). In collaboration with H. Siedentopf (149), he developed an instrument which they called "slit ultra-microscope." This instrument was used for studying gold ruby glasses. A powerful beam of light issuing from a slit was focused upon the glass or the colloidal solution and was examined by a microscope. Each colloidal particle scattered some of the light and appeared in the microscope as a small diffraction disc. This instrument became a powerful tool for studying colloidal solutions including glasses. The ultra-microscope made it possible to follow the "striking" of gold ruby glasses and to explain the development of its color on heat treatment on the basis of aggregations of gold atoms (colorless) into minute particles which were pink, red or blue depending upon their sizes. Heterogeneity was thus extended into a scale in which the particles were smaller than the wave-length of light. Using the technique of "dark-field illumination" it becomes possible to study heterogeneity in glasses and fused salts (pyrosols) on an ultramicroscopic scale. Some types of colored glasses based on metallic gold, silver, and copper, as well as on solid solutions of CdS and CdSe, are heterogeneous on an ultra-microscopic scale.

The next decisive step in the exploration of the heterogeneity of glasses came with the development of electron optics. Electro-static fields and magnetic coils were introduced as "lenses" for electron beams. Theory predicted that the electron microscope should have a resolving power several hundred times that of the light microscope. In 1940 the first electron microscope picture was taken of a virus. From this time the development of commercial electron microscopes proceeded rapidly. A description of the historical development of the electron microscope, the mechanism of its image formation and the different techniques can be found in G. L. Clark's *Encyclopedia of Microscopy* (150).

The application of electron optics to glasses had a strong impact upon prevailing ideas concerning their homogeneity. In 1952, A. F. Prebus and I. W. Michener (151) were the first to discover "micelles" in apparently homogeneous silicate glasses. A few years later, in 1956, F. Oberlies (152) confirmed this discovery and was able to show that what was called a "phase separation" seemed to occur in glasses rather independent of the heat treatment. Heterogeneities of the order of 200 to 600 A. were discovered in many silicate, borate, borosilicate, and fluoride glasses. W. Vogel and K. Gerth (153–155) investigated systematically a large number of complex beryllium fluoride systems which, according to V. M. Goldschmidt, were treated as the weak models of silicates. In many of these glasses phase separations were found.

In the last few years considerable interest has developed in the phenomenon of submicroscopic heterogeneity in connection with the invention of "Pyroceram" by S. D. Stookey (100). The energy barrier of nucleating a second vitreous phase in a glass on cooling is lower than that of the formation of a crystalline phase. A nucleus of a crystal, say a cristobalite or a rutile crystal, has to have a defined structure and the stoichiometric composition of the final phase. Glasses do not have to have a constant composition in their surfaces, the surface tension or the interfacial free energy of a glass can be lower than that of crystals due to the preferential participation in the surface of those ions that lower this energy. In glasses, one distinguishes between a dynamic surface tension and a lower value for the static surface tension. For this reason nucleation of crystalline phases may be preceded by a liquid-liquid phase separation.

We are primarily interested in this phenomenon because a two-phase nature of a glass in a subcolloidal range must affect certain properties such as ionic conductivity, thermal expansivity, and thermal conductivity. When we discussed the incompatibility of MgO with SiO_2 we pointed out that with increasing polarizability of the anions and the cations, oxides become more compatible. Treating the system PbO-SiO_2 as one without a miscibility gap means only that incompatibility does not become effective in a temperature region in which macroscopic or microscopic phase separation is possible. With the advent of the electron microscope phase separations have been discovered which take place in a lower temperature, i.e., higher viscosity, region so that the particle sizes fall in the sub-ultramicroscopic range. Indeed W. Vogel (155) discovered the two phase nature of lead silicate glasses by means of the electron microscope.

Later, when we discuss the structures of the alkali silicate and borate glasses, we will return to this phenomenon.

E. Conclusions

In order to understand the vitreous state one must treat a glass as a solid that retains the essential geometrical features of the liquid from which it has formed, but which has lost the mobility of its major constituents. As far as the structures of liquids are concerned we have discussed some extreme cases. Monoatomic liquids (molten metals) do not form a glass because the mobilities of the atoms at the melting points of the metals are too high to avoid nucleation. Even the metal with the lowest melting point, mercury, has sufficient thermal energy at its melting point to allow the formation of nuclei.

The so-called normal liquids which consist of relatively small molecules, e.g., benzene, are of no particular interest to us because they will not be able to form glasses that are stable at ordinary temperature. However, if the freezing point of a normal liquid is sufficiently low, glass formation becomes possible. This is the case for some very low melting fluorine-carbon compounds that form glasses at liquid air temperature.

Among the three types of liquids which we have discussed in detail, the Frenkel or "fissured" liquid cannot form a glass. Glasses are known which have the structure of a Bernal or "flawless" liquid (SiO_2) and others which are of the Stewart "orientable" type (B_2O_3, P_2O_5). The main factor which determines glass formation is the melting point of a substance or the liquidus temperature of a system. In order to understand liquid structures one has to analyze the transitions that occur during melting. Sulfur and the hexagonal form of phosphorus pentoxide, for example, melt and form normal liquids. These liquids contain the same particles, S_8 and P_4O_{10} molecules respectively, that are present both in the crystalline and vapor phases. Neither liquid forms a glass on cooling. However, on heating further above the melting point these liquids undergo a reorganization of their atoms, which leads to complex mixtures of polymers. This transition of a normal molecular liquid into a polymer orientable type of liquid is a prerequisite for glass formation among these substances.

In silica we have another example of two liquid structures of the same chemical composition, one of which is closer to the Stewart orientable type, the other closer to the Bernal flawless type. The metastable melting of quartz leads to a liquid which contains polymers or chains and this liquid has a lower viscosity than the liquid which is obtained when cristobalite is melted and cooled to the temperature at which quartz melts in a metastable way.

These relations become important for our discussions of the constitution of vitreous silica because the heat treatment will decide whether its structure corresponds more closely to that of a Bernal flawless type or to that of a Stewart orientable type liquid.

The activation energy of flow processes and of solid state reactions is determined by the energy which is required for a partial, temporary unscreening of atomic cores and this energy is not related in a simple fashion to the bond energy of atoms or to the field strength of ions. There is no connection between bond energies and viscosity or the rate of nucleation. B_2O_3 and SiO_2 have similar bond energies but differ in their viscosities by nearly twelve orders of magnitude. Also, vitreous silica nucleates readily but vitreous B_2O_3 does not. The bond energy of the Se—Se bond is less than that of the S—S bond but elemental selenium forms a stable glass that does not nucleate easily whereas vitreous sulfur crystallizes within a few hours at ordinary temperature in spite of the great difference which exists between the structure of the glass (chains) and that of the crystal (rings). These two glasses have identical structures: they consist of S_x and Se_x chains.

The ringshaped S_8 molecule is stable up to 600°C. in the vapor phase, i.e., its S—S bond does not "break" thermally at 200°C. In the condensed state, however, S_8 molecules will undergo a requantization of their electrons and form polymers at temperatures below 200°C.

Complex glasses may undergo phase separations or nucleation on cooling because the compatibility of the constituents decreases on cooling. If a major constituent, e.g., say SiO_2 or $CaSiO_3$ precipitates from a glass in its working range, heterogeneity results on a macroscopic scale (stones, devitrification). If a constituent, say TiO_2, SnO_2, or NaF, precipitates in a temperature region in which the viscosity does not permit the nuclei to grow to a large size, opacity results; i.e., the glass develops a heterogeneity on a microscopic scale. The striking of gold ruby and of selenium ruby glasses produces a heterogeneity on a colloidal or ultramicroscopic scale. With the advent of the electron microscope phase separations have been discovered which are in a submicroscopic or subcolloidal range.

No matter in which temperature range the heterogeneity develops it is the result of an entropy effect; the compatibility or the solubility of some constituents decreases with decreasing temperature.

CHAPTER XIV

HISTORICAL REVIEW OF CONCEPTS CONCERNING THE NATURE OF THE GLASSY STATE

1. Some Early Views on the Constitution of Glasses

G. Tammann (1) worked toward establishing a description of the glassy state on the basis of thermodynamics and of reaction rates. His interest was vested primarily in the stability of a glass, its formation from a supercooled melt, and the reversible transition between glasses and crystals regardless of the chemical composition.

In the early days of glass making, technologists were interested only in glasses that contained silica as their chief constituent. From a chemical point of view, it was noteworthy that glasses did not exhibit abrupt changes in their properties when their compositions were changed gradually. M. Faraday (156), in 1830, was probably the first scientist who clearly stated that glasses cannot be called chemical compounds but must be looked upon as mutual solutions of compounds.

Some of the early views on the constitution of silicate glasses are still of interest because they were expressed by men who were thoroughly familiar with glasses, with their manufacture, and their properties. The pioneers in glass research were deeply concerned with the manufacture of glasses and their improvements. For them, the constitution of glass was by no means an abstract problem which could be treated lightly. Glass technologists needed more knowledge for predicting new glass compositions with superior properties. It is not surprising, therefore, that most thought was given to the constitution of glass in the optical industry at the time when progress depended entirely upon the success of producing a large variety of homogeneous glasses with widely different properties. The early work of H. Winkelmann and O. Schott (157) revealed that within certain narrow composition limits the properties of glasses were nearly additive.

However, F. Eckert (158) pointed out in 1923 that only some properties of glasses, e.g., their X-ray absorption, could be calculated accurately from the oxide composition. Properties involving interactions between the outer electrons are not additive. Eckert looked upon a glass as a solution of silicates, borates, and aluminates in an excess of silica.

A sound picture of the constitution of glass must include not only features which glasses as solids have in common with crystalline solids but also those which distinguish glasses from crystals. No such picture of the nature of the glassy state could be developed before the application of X-ray methods to the structure of matter because only X rays made it possible to distinguish the truly amorphous solids from substances such as red phosphorus and colloidal gold. Many substances were found to be crystalline but the size of the crystals was much too small to be recognized under the microscope.

Tammann's definition of glass as a supercooled liquid was based on the absence of abrupt changes of the properties during the solidification and glass formation. The lack of a sharp melting point has been observed for amorphous selenium as early as 1852 by W. Hittorf (159). At this time, however, the absence of a sharp melting point could not be recognized as a characteristic feature of glasses because no distinction could be made experimentally between glasses and cryptocrystalline substances.

When it became possible to measure high temperatures more accurately by means of thermocouples the techniques of taking heating and cooling curves were widely used for studying melting and crystallization processes, especially in metallic systems. As far as the phase equilibria in oxide systems were concerned, the Geophysical Laboratory of the Carnegie Institution in Washington, D.C., became the center of research. The need to develop static methods for determining phase relations in addition to the formerly used dynamic methods made these scientists conscious of the widely different melting and crystallization rates among fused oxides and their compounds. The first scientists who discovered that some similarity exists between the melting of glasses and crystals were A. L. Day and E. T. Allen (160) who, in 1905, reported their discovery as follows: "On every occasion when borax glass was heated rapidly, either powdered or in the solid block, a slight but persistent absorption of heat appeared in the same region between 490 and 500°C. and continued over some 20°C. after which the original rate of heating returned."

In 1916, K. Quasebart (161) found that the heat liberated

during the cooling of a plate glass in an industrial kiln around 530°C. resembled the liberation of the latent heat of fusion during the crystallization of a melt.

Exothermic and endothermic effects on cooling and heating were known to accompany not only crystallization and melting of substances but also phase transformations of crystals. This suggested the presence of submicroscopic crystals in the glass and it was understandable that scientists thought primarily of modifications of silica because most of the technical glasses contained an excess of silica over the most acidic silicate.

In spite of frequent references to glasses as supercooled liquids or as mutual solutions of silicates, etc., a deep rooted feeling had developed that glasses were not homogeneous on a molecular scale. Different scientists had different reasons for assuming a submicroscopic heterogeneity and without going into details it is interesting to review some of their reasons.

A "two phase" nature of glasses or their similarity to colloids has been proposed by many workers in the field of glasses. In 1912, A. V. Kroll working in the field of phosphates of high molecular weights considered glass to be a colloid, i.e., a sol, which became a true solution on heating.

In 1912, R. L. Frink connected the brittleness of glasses with their physical and chemical heterogeneity.

In 1915, G. Quincke described glasses as foams consisting of highly siliceous walls which enclose some more alkaline silicates in the cellular space.

In 1921, H. Jackson based his concept of a submicroscopic crystallinity of annealed glasses on the observation that their irradiation with X rays produced fluorescence; the same glasses did not strongly fluoresce when rapidly chilled. He interpreted his observation that chilled glasses showed little X-ray fluorescence on the assumption that a truly amorphous substance would not fluoresce when exposed to X rays. He applied the term "pyrosol" to glasses.

In 1921 M. W. Travers compared glasses with colloidal systems that contained pockets of different composition dispersed in a continuum. He based his assumption on the similarity that exists between the sol-to-gel transition of colloids and the transition of the supercooled liquid into a brittle glass.

In 1922, P. Lafon assumed modification changes of the

amorphous silica to be responsible for the change in expansivity of silicate glasses in the softening range. He postulated that the volume effects which accompany the change of low quartz into high quartz can occur also in vitreous silica, the only difference being that the two phases and, with it, the volume changes are less sharply defined in a glass than in a crystal.

In 1922, A. A. Lebedeff connected the volume changes and the heat effects in the softening range of glasses with their heterogeneity, in particular with the presence of quartz. He assumed that these crystals were so small that their modification changes were spread over a relatively wide temperature range instead of taking place at 575°C. When later studies revealed that the phenomena in the softening range were not restricted to glasses which contained silica as a major constituent, he postulated that amorphous substances may undergo modification changes in a manner similar to that undergone by crystals.

L. N. G. Filon and F. C. Harris, in 1923, explained the photoelastic properties of glasses by assuming a two phase system.

H. Le Chatelier, in 1924, interpreted the change in the viscosity of glasses with temperature on the basis of allotropic changes. In 1924, R. Liesegang spoke of glass as an emulsion; i.e., a system which consists of two liquid phases. His views were based primarily on the striking of gold ruby glasses and on devitrification phenomena.

W. E. S. Turner spoke in 1925 of a siliceous sponge, the pores of which were filled with silicates and their dissociation products. He pointed out that the low dielectric constant of silica as a solvent favored polymerization processes.

In 1925, P. Bary considered a glass to be a colloid which contains crystalline matter dispersed in a highly polymerized matrix. The alkali silicates represent the crystalline matter whereas the polymer consists primarily of polysilicates of calcium. Alumina and boric oxide are believed to participate in the polymer matrix.

W. Rosenhain, in 1927, expressed the view that certain structural configurations such as chains and aggregates are not only characteristic constituents of crystalline silicates but should also be present in glasses. Thus, the endothermic effect which occurs during the heating of a glass can be explained on the basis of a gradual solution of aggregates on heating (latent heat of fusion).

It is truly amazing to see how scientists with widely different backgrounds (physicists, chemists, colloid chemists, and metallurgists) arrived at very similar conclusions; namely, that glasses are not homogeneous but contain "aggregates" or "macromolecules" which may reach colloidal dimensions. These views, however, were wiped out with the arrival of modern crystal chemical thinking and by the study of the structure of glasses by means of the Fourier analysis of the X-ray diffraction patterns.

Only in recent years have scientists gradually returned to a structural picture that includes the concept of heterogeneity on a submicroscopic scale. With the advent of the electron microscope and its application to glasses it became possible to study vitreous systems using magnifications which revealed subultramicroscopic heterogeneities of the order of 100 A. (see Chapter XIII, 2, D).

2. Classical Work on the Vitreous State (Contributions of G. Tammann and His School)

At the beginning of this century, G. Tammann and his students began to explore systematically those phenomena that occur when different solids are subjected to a change in temperature, pressure, or both. G. Tammann's (1) books *Crystallizing and Melting*, in 1903, and *States of Matter*, in 1922, may be called the pioneering works in the physical chemistry of solids. In 1933, G. Tammann summarized in his book *The Glassy State* (*Der Glaszustand*) the results of the experimental work on glasses which was carried out in his Institute for Physical Chemistry at the University of Göttingen. He had explored the characteristic features of the glassy state and defined those properties that glasses have in common with liquids as well as with solids and those that set them apart from these two states of aggregation.

Tammann's work is that of a physical chemist but not of a glass technologist. This is important for understanding the way in which he approached the problem of the glassy state. One of Tammann's contemporaries, E. Zschimmer, a pioneer in the technology of glass, wanted to see the term "glass" restricted to inorganic substances. This attitude is understandable because, from a technological point of view, the high temperature chemistry of fused silicates is very different from other technologies. Tammann with the viewpoint of the physical chemist neither distinguished between inorganic and organic substances nor between glasses that form at high temperature and those that form at ordinary temperature or below. Tammann was interested in those features common to all amorphous solids that were obtained from a liquid by cooling under conditions which prevented crystallization.

G. Tammann started his book on the glassy state with the following sentences: "If a crystallized substance is allowed to melt and the melt is allowed to cool, the melt frequently solidifies as a glass. The rate of cooling is most important for this phenomenon. Many melts which crystallize completely on slow cooling do not crystallize at a faster cooling rate." These statements are most important for the understanding of the glassy state and they should have been chosen as guiding principles by later scientists who speculated on the conditions of glass formation. Firstly, it emphasized that glass formation is a rate phenomenon. Secondly, it calls attention to the fact that a statement concerning the glass-forming properties of substances becomes of value only when information is given about the rate of cooling or at least the quantity of the glass which can be obtained. It is most important in the scientific literature to refer to the rate of cooling which causes a certain system to produce a glass. Methods that are used for making glass fibers permit the use of compositions that could not be used for the manufacture of bottles.

The rate of nucleation and of crystal growth below the liquidus temperature determine the ability of a system to form a glass. These factors were studied most thoroughly by Tammann and his collaborators. Their experiments, carried out primarily with organic substances in a temperature range between 0°C. and 150°C., are still the basis for our present theoretical treatments of devitrification, nucleation, and glass formation.

The viscosity of a melt and its change with temperature are the keys to the understanding of glass formation. As early as 1899 Tammann concerned himself with viscosity, and published a paper on the viscosity of supercooled liquids. Conchoidal fracture and the absence of cleavage planes is characteristic of brittle glasses. Hence, efforts had to be made to determine the temperature t_g below which a supercooled melt ceased to be a liquid and became a glass. Based upon the brittle fracture of glasses, G. Tammann and A. Kohlhaas (162) standardized a simple procedure of measuring t_g. The substance was melted in a test tube and the liquid was spread over its walls so that a film of glass formed on cooling. At different temperatures a pointed glass rod was dropped upon the film from a height of 10 cm. Cracks appeared in the film if the temperature was below t_g. The primitive experiment became a powerful tool in the hands of the master. He found that regardless of the nature of the substance the glass rod fused into the melt if the temperature exceeded t_g by about 25°C. At this and at higher temperatures the supercooled liquid could be drawn into fibers. The constancy of the difference Δ between the lowest temperature at which a melt forms fibers (t_f) and the highest temperature at which it showed brittle fracture (t_g) can be seen from Table XXIV. Glasses for which the value of Δ was approximately 25°C. were called normal glasses. Some glasses, apparently those that consisted of long chain polymers behaved differently and they were called abnormal. For a certain polystyrene glass, for example, t_g was 28°C but t_f was 138°C. which makes the value of Δ 110°C., which is more than four times that of Δ of normal glasses.

Another very simple experiment, namely measuring the height of rebounce, H_R, of a sphere falling from a height H_F upon a glass provided insight into the absorption of mechanical energy by glasses. The value H_R/H_F was a measure of the energy which remained in the falling sphere, the rest had been absorbed by the glass.

These experiments, too, lend themselves to the determination of the softening range of glasses. It was found that H_R/H_F decreases above t_g and drops rapidly above t_f. At a temperature of $t_f + 20$°C., the sphere stuck to the melt.

Tammann emphasized in his writings that the definition of glasses as "supercooled liquids" refers only to their relations to the substances in the liquid and in the crystalline state. Glasses are rigid solids and not liquids. Glasses are not necessarily in internal

TABLE XXIV

Characteristic Temperatures (t_g and t_f) of Some Organic Glasses (1*c*)

Substance	Temperature, °C.		Δ
	t_g	t_f	
Salicin	43	66	23
Piperine	3	26	23
Brucine	78	104	26
Sugar	30	53	23
Polystyrene	28	138	110

equilibrium whereas a true liquid even when supercooled, e.g., water at $-10°C.$ is in internal equilibrium. All properties of a supercooled liquid, its density, refractive index, and electrical properties are uniquely defined for a given temperature and pressure. This does not apply to glasses.

Following the conventional description of the energy relations within a system a glass has to be pictured not at the bottom of an energy well but as a system which has available a variety of energy states, separated by only minor energy barriers. The energy levels which are characteristic for the glassy state, however, may be separated from that of the crystalline substance by a major energy barrier. Figure 9 illustrates this situation schematically. The height of the energy barrier which separates the glassy from the crystalline state is much greater than the thermal energy which is available at ordinary temperature. The energy levels of the glass itself are separated by minor barriers so that structural changes can take place at low temperature.

Plotting the free energy of a system as a function of its atomic structure, etc., we find the flat dell to be the location of all those glasses which exist because of their different thermal histories or because they have solidified under different hydrostatic pressures. These different energy states which a glass of a given chemical composition can assume are of interest to us because they are ex-

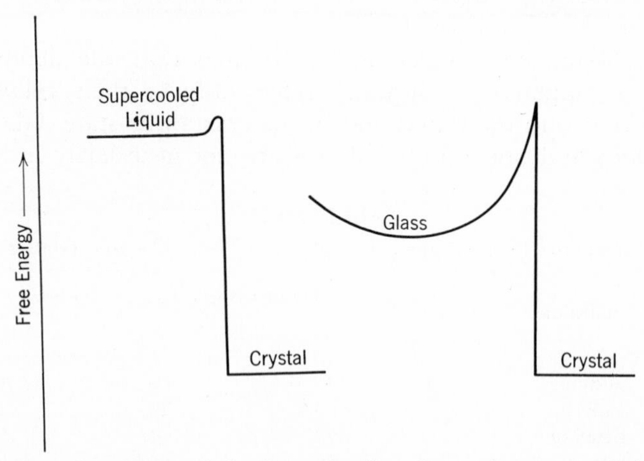

Fig. 9 Schematic picture of the free energies of crystals, supercooled liquids, and glasses

pressions of the different properties which the system can assume in its glassy state. Within a considerable range it is possible to change the properties of a glass by giving it different thermal or pressure treatments.

What lies beyond the high energy barrier that separates the glassy state from a more stable crystalline state is of no concern to us. Whether the difference between the free energies of the glass and the crystal is large or small whether it is positive or negative is of no importance for the understanding of glasses. If one day somebody finds on the basis of caloric measurements that the hexagonal form of P_2O_5 has a higher free energy than vitreous P_2O_5, this message may come as a surprise to some physical chemists but it will not change our thinking concerning the nature of vitreous phosphorus pentoxide.

Let us reflect for a moment upon the full significance of a scheme such as the one which represents the stability of glasses. If we would describe the variety of organic compounds as they occur in nature or as they are prepared in the laboratory by their compositions and their free energy relations we would find that none of them is stable in our atmosphere. For most of them, however, the energy barrier that separates their energy states in air from those of the combustion products which are essentially water and carbon dioxide is too high to be significant at ordinary temperature. Nobody who is engaged in the synthesis of new dyes or drugs would even think of relating their stabilities, their rate of fading, or what is usually called their "shelf life" with their heats of combustion.

The fact that the difference between the free energies of glasses and their stable crystalline counterparts bears no relation whatsoever to the behavior of glasses or to the characteristic features of the glassy state explains why thermodynamic approaches have not contributed much to the understanding of glasses.

The first systematic effort to explore the constitution of glasses was centered around the so-called transformation temperature, t_g. During the years 1920 to 1930 one finds a number of discussions in the glass literature concerning the justification of the "transformation point." Gradually the conclusion was reached that from a scientific point of view one should speak of a "transformation range" rather than of a "point." From a technological point of view, however, there was no doubt that most properties of glasses changed with increasing temperature in a nearly linear way up to a certain temperature. Above this temperature they change in the same direction but with a different temperature coefficient. The melting of most crystals causes the properties of the substance to change abruptly. The heating of glasses causes their properties to change gradually and continuously and only their temperature coefficients may show abrupt changes at t_g. This behavior seemed to be characteristic for the glassy state but rather independent of the chemical nature of the glass. Elemental selenium, organic substances, as well as silicate glasses of very complex composition, all behave essentially alike with respect to their property changes with temperature. On cooling, the volume decreases and if the viscosity reaches approximately 10^{13} poises at t_g the volume continues to decrease on cooling but with a smaller temperature coefficient.

The interpretation of this phenomenon was based on the assumption that the volume changes of a glass on heating and cooling is the result of two independent changes. One change of volume with temperature was considered to be a purely physical phenomenon comparable with the reversible thermal expansion of a NaCl crystal. This process dominates the volume changes as long as the glass is rigid, i.e., at temperatures below t_g. At temperatures above t_g, other "chemical" processes such as the dissociation of molecules or aggregates are superimposed over the "physical" process of expansion. In contrast to the physical part of the thermal expansion, which is an instantaneous process, the expansion resulting from chemical changes was time consuming. Chemical changes involved the inertia of masses, their diffusion and rearrangement in space and, consequently, they required some time and could be "frozen in" by cooling the melt rapidly.

On cooling a glass the viscosity increases very strongly so that the time required by the glass to reach its equilibrium structure increases rapidly with decreasing temperature. The meaning of t_g and methods for determining this temperature which seemed to be so characteristic for glasses became the main topics in the literature dealing with problems of the constitution of glasses. Europe's leading glass technologists, E. Berger (Schott und Genossen, Jena), M. Thomas (Osram Glas Werke) and W. E. S. Turner (Department of Glass Technology, Sheffield) cooperated in solving the fundamental problem of the transformation temperature. By independent experiments but using the same glasses they found that for a given rate of heating and cooling the transformation temperature of a glass was the same within a few degrees no matter whether it was determined on the basis of its thermal expansion, its electrical conductivity or its viscosity. These findings revealed the paramount importance of the rate of cooling. It was only logical to assume that an increase in the viscosity permits certain chemical or structural changes to follow the temperature changes only above a certain critical temperature. Below this temperature the structural changes or as they were called the association processes were "frozen in" but the purely physical changes continued to follow the temperature. This general description is still essentially correct. E. Berger (163) calculated the times necessary for reaching the chemical (structural) equilibrium at different temperatures around the transformation temperature. It may be interesting to see some of the figures.

Temperature 50°C. above transformation point, 20 minutes
Temperature at the transformation point, 1000 minutes
Temperature 50°C. below transformation point, 100 hours
Temperature 100°C. below transformation point, 40 days
Temperature 200°C. below transformation point, 10 years

Such a calculation, however, can be meaningful only if the changes which take place consist of one kind of reaction only. We will see later that in a glass several reactions can take place which have widely different activation energies and widely different relaxation times.

3. Modern Approach to Glasses on the Basis of Crystal Chemistry (Contributions of V. M. Goldschmidt and His School)

During the first quarter of this century scientists had to speculate on the structure of glasses and any theoretical concepts which could be proposed had to be based on similarities between glasses and other systems, colloids, crystals, and solutions. The year 1926 marks the most important milestone in the development of the constitution of glasses. At this time V. M. Goldschmidt (4) presented his ideas on modern crystal chemistry and he included glasses (Chapter VI, 4).

Goldschmidt introduced some basically new concepts into the structural chemistry of solids. These new ideas were very fruitful in relating properties of crystals with their structures. The modern approach of Goldschmidt is still the guiding principle in our discussion of the atomic structures of glasses.

A glass may resemble the crystal of the same substance with respect to the short range order but its typical glass properties, e.g., absence of a sharp melting point, optical isotropy, conchoidal fracture, are the result of the lack of long range order. V. M. Goldschmidt explained the ability of a molten ionic substance to solidify on cooling without crystallization on the basis of the geometry of the polyhedra, in particular of the ratio of the sizes of anions and cations. He assumed that substances like SiO_2 and B_2O_3 are characterized by a radius-anion to radius-cation ratio that favors polyhedra which contain a small number of anions, in this case four and three O^{2-} ions. Other oxides, e.g., SnO_2 and TiO_2, in spite of their chemical similarity, do not form glasses because the larger sizes of the Ti^{4+} and the Sn^{4+} ions call for octahedra rather than for tetrahedra or triangles. The coordination number of Ti^{4+} and Sn^{4+} ions is 6 rather than 4 as for Si^{4+} or 3 as for B^{3+} ions. These views can no longer be considered correct. Nevertheless, they have been of extreme importance for the development of later ideas. Goldschmidt's approach introduced crystal chemical thoughts into the field of glass technology.

Beryllium fluoride which from a chemical point of view has no resemblance with SiO_2 was found to form a glass. The structural elements in crystalline BeF_2 and crystalline SiO_2 are very similar. The fact that Goldschmidt was able to predict the formation of beryllium fluoride glasses analogous to vitreous silica and silicate was convincing evidence of the far reaching possibilities of his crystal chemical approach. His prediction is remarkable for two reasons, firstly because from a chemical point of view the compounds SiO_2 and BeF_2 have nothing in common, and secondly, because BeF_2 is the only known halide that forms a stable glass. Vitreous $ZnCl_2$ has been prepared but it is extremely hygroscopic and its tendency to crystallize is so strong that it is difficult to obtain and study reasonable quantities of this halide glass.

The confidence which glass scientists showed in Goldschmidt's work was further strengthened by the development of stable aluminophosphate glasses. Again the application of crystal chemistry to silica revealed a far reaching structural similarity between silica and aluminum orthophosphate $AlPO_4$. Earlier attempts to introduce P_2O_5 into glasses were failures. However, the combination of Al^{3+} and P^{5+} ions as a substitute for two Si^{4+} ions made it possible for H. Grimm and P. Huppert (136) to develop a series of valuable glasses which were free of silica and which showed superior transmissions in the short range part of the spectrums.

V. M. Goldschmidt's crystal chemical approach to the structure of glasses raised the constitution of glasses to the same scientific level as that of crystals. The energy content of a solid is vested primarily in the density of its packing and the short range order, in particular in the coordination of the cations. Density and coordination determine the volume in which electroneutrality has been established and the degree to which the cations are screened. The long range order does not have the same effect upon the stability of a solid. When Goldschmidt suggested that the same polyhedra exist both in glasses and in crystals he also explained why both solids have similar strength, densities, and energy contents.

The next decisive step in the development of a picture of the constitution of glass was a paper by W. H. Zachariasen (3), one of V. M. Goldschmidt's associates, who in 1932 proposed certain ideas concerning the formation of oxide glasses. Zachariasen presented his ideas in the form of simple rules which soon became the basis for the structural picture that has been used by most glass technologists during the past 25 years (see Chapter XIII, 1, D).

4. Application of X-ray Diffraction Methods to Glass (Contributions of B. E. Warren and His School)

The application of X rays to crystals opened a new era and made modern crystal chemistry possible. When the method was first introduced by M. von Laue it provided a new and very powerful tool for studying crystals and the first results of this method had a strong impact on our thinking. Concepts which seemed to be well established were shaken in their very fundaments. We have seen (in Chapter VIII) that the concept of what constitutes an amorphous solid had to be revised. The concept of the monovalency of sodium and chlorine atoms had no place in the description of a sodium chloride crystal. The established idea of molecules as the constituents of silicates, crystalline or glassy, had to be abandoned.

For the determination of the atomic structure of crystals the X-ray diffraction method is the method par excellence. G. W. Morey (6) and his collegues in the Geophysical Laboratory in

Washington who studied the phase relations in the system Na_2O-CaO-SiO_2 and determined some optical properties of representative ternary glasses extended their work to the X-ray examination of glasses.

In 1925 R. W. G. Wyckoff and G. W. Morey (164) made an attempt to answer the question whether or not a similarity existed between the broad, diffuse X-ray patterns of the ternary glasses and the possible crystalline constituents which formed the primary phase; e.g., the compound $Na_2O \cdot 2CaO \cdot 3SiO_2$. No definite conclusions could be drawn. Some glasses showed only very diffuse halos corresponding to the diffraction patterns of liquids but others showed a band which for highly siliceous glasses coincided roughly with the main line of cristobalite. Later, however, Morey showed that the devitrification of these glasses did not gradually sharpen the broad bands but rather superimposed over the diffuse pattern of the glass the new diffraction pattern which is characteristic for the crystal.

C. W. Parmelee, G. L. Clark and A. E. Badger (165) as well as G. L. Clark and C. R. Amberg (166) in 1929 made some attempts to interpret the diffuse X-ray patterns of glasses in terms of SiO_2 molecules arranged in chains. They thought of bundles of silica chains because it was the general opinion at this time that even diffuse X-ray patterns would be indicative of an incipient crystallization.

A few years later J. T. Randall, H. P. Rooksby, and B. S. Cooper (167) applied X rays to different glasses and they thought that they could go considerably further than the earlier workers. They stated that it is reasonable to assume that vitreous silica consists approximately of 80% cristobalite.

In the meantime, physicists had discovered that crystallinity is not an essential prerequisite for the formation of X-ray diffraction patterns. P. Debye, P. Ehrenfest, F. Zernicke, and J. A. N. Prins had developed a mathematical approach which could account for the interaction of X rays with liquids. P. Debye and H. Menke (8) carried out experiments with liquids and they interpreted the diffuse liquid diffraction patterns in terms of interatomic distances. They proved that a broad diffuse X-ray pattern can be the result of certain self-repeating distances between atoms which occur in a monoatomic liquid. Earlier it was assumed that a broad diffuse X-ray pattern indicated the presence of a large number of extremely small crystals. It was well established that crystals showed a broadening of their lines when they were ground to a very fine particle size. As a matter of fact, this broadening could be used for estimating small particle sizes.

On the basis of the new theoretical knowledge of liquid diffraction patterns, B. E. Warren (5) and his school were the first to launch a systematic attack upon the problem of the atomic structures of simple oxide glasses, vitreous silica, vitreous boric oxide, alkali silicates, and borates as well as vitreous calcium phosphates. The conclusion was reached that the picture which Zachariasen presented was the simplest scheme in agreement with the experimental data. Silica glass does not contain individual SiO_2 molecules, it can not be reasonably described as a heapwork of submicroscopic crystals of cristobalite. The absence of a strong, small-angle scattering distinguishes vitreous silica from the other amorphous forms of SiO_2, silica gel. Silica gel consists of discrete particles separated by voids, it resembles a pailful of pebbles, as Warren described it, but the glass is a continuum in its structure, it resembles a pailful of water.

B. E. Warren took a definite stand against the views of those who interpreted the X-ray diffraction patterns of vitreous silica as the result of an array of extremely small crystals of the high temperature crystalline form of silica, cristobalite. In 1937 he wrote: "The strongest ring in the cristobalite pattern comes at very nearly the position of the first broad peak in the vitreous silica pattern. Since the breadth of the lines on a powdered crystalline pattern increases continuously with decreasing size of crystalline particles, it is evident that if one postulates in vitreous silica cristobalite crystals sufficiently small, the strong peak of cristobalite would broaden out to give the appearance of the vitreous pattern. From a formal point of view this interpretation is perfectly sound, and since cristobalite is the stable form of silica through the temperature range in which the glassy SiO_2 stiffens up, it is not at all unreasonable to expect cristobalite crystals in the glass."

"Let us assume tentatively that the X-ray pattern of vitreous silica is actually due to small cristobalite crystals, and see what conclusions can be drawn. Changing the microphotometer records to intensity curves, and measuring the half intensity breadth of the peak, we can calculate the average particle dimension by the Bragg particle size equation."

Carrying out the calculation, Warren obtains a particle size of 7.7 A. "Since the edge of the unit cell of cristobalite is about 7.0 A. we are forced to postulate cristobalite crystals comprising scarcely more than one unit cell in order to explain the observed peak width. Since the essence of the idea of crystallinity is regular repetition it becomes decidedly artificial and formal to extend the term crystal to cover so small an aggregation of atoms."

The work of Warren showed that it is unreasonable to speak of submicroscopic crystals as the constituents of vitreous silica and that vitreous silica should be described as a continuum rather than a heapwork of particles.

In spite of the warnings of Warren that neither the X-ray method nor any other single method can provide a proof of Zachariasen's picture, the work carried out in Warren's laboratory was considered by many scientists as proof of Zachariasen's concept of the constitution of glasses.

The picture of Zachariasen's continuous three-dimensional random network became the starting point of most later discussions on the constitution of glasses, including glasses of much greater complexity than silica.

CHAPTER XV

SOME PROBLEMS CONCERNING THE CONSTITUTION OF GLASSES

Before we can evaluate the contributions which can be made by different experimental approaches toward solving the problem of the constitution of glasses we should examine the nature of the problems which the vitreous state offers to physical chemists and to glass technologists.

1. Similarity of Unrelated Substances in the Glassy State in the Transformation Region

Our primary interest is the constitution of and the characteristic features of inorganic glasses. Nevertheless, we call the work of G. Tammann the pioneering work in the physical chemistry of the glassy state. This seems paradoxical and calls for an explanation because most of Tammann's work was carried out with organic substances. Tammann's interest was very broad: he included elemental selenium as well as technical silicates in his experimental program but his fundamental work on glass formation (studies concerning the softening range of glasses and their nucleation and crystallization) was carried out with organic materials. This poses an important problem because the similarity of otherwise unrelated substances in their glassy states makes it impossible to correlate the characteristic features of the glassy state with a certain type of substance. It forces us to provide an explanation for the characteristic features of glasses, e.g., their behavior in the softening range, that is applicable to all types of solids regardless of whether they consist of individual molecules or whether they are three-dimensional ionic structures.

Whatever happens in the transformation range is a time-consuming process which involves a change in the geometry of the particles. Also, this change must be of such a general nature that it can take place in ionic substances such as BeF_2, in elements such as selenium, in organic materials such as phenolphthalein and, finally, in all commercial glasses.

This similarity of a large variety of substances when in their glassy state presents one of the major physical-chemical problems in any attempt to catalogue glasses within the different groups of compounds and within the known states of aggregation.

2. Effect of the Thermal History of Glasses on Their Properties

In contrast to the properties of a supercooled liquid, the properties of glasses are not uniquely defined by their chemical composition, temperature, and pressure. The properties of all glasses depend upon the way they have been cooled.

For two reasons the energy of a chilled glass is higher than that of the same glass in annealed condition. Firstly, the chilled glass has some mechanical energy in a stressed condition stored in its system: tensile stresses in the interior and compressional stresses in an outer layer. This energy can be compared with that of a watch spring. Secondly, the chilled glass has a different chemical constitution. It has a higher energy content than the annealed glass and it can be called an unstable modification of the annealed glass.

Chilling freezes in an atomic arrangement which is similar to that arrangement stable at high temperature. The thermal history of a glass determines its properties, e.g., the density, but the thermal history is not limited to those changes which take place above t_g or in the softening range. Some glasses show volume effects at ordinary temperature. The icepoint depression of a thermometer reveals that the volume changes of some glasses are not strictly reversible when the temperature is varied between 0°C. and 100°C.; i.e., in a region in which the glass represents a completely rigid and brittle solid. The aging of a thermometer and the secular shift of the icepoint indicates volume changes which take place over a period of years at ordinary temperature. How is it possible that a rigid glass far below t_g undergoes volume changes at constant temperature?

3. Boric Acid Anomaly

The nonstoichiometric composition of glasses offers a technological advantage over materials that are well-defined compounds: one can change the properties of a glass gradually and continuously by changing their chemical composition. Glass technologists have determined empirically for a certain composition field how certain additions or substitutions affect the different properties of a representative glass. The changes of properties with composition were measured and expressed in terms of "factors." Since the end of the last century, when the major development of glass technology began, "factors" have been used in the formulation of new glasses. Glass technologists are well aware of the fact that no property is strictly additive. However, the use of "factors" has become an important tool in planning composition changes of a glass. For a five-component glass containing the oxides A, B, C, D, and E a property X is determined by an equation such as the following:

$$X = P_A \cdot a + P_B \cdot b + P_C \cdot c + P_D \cdot d + P_E \cdot e$$

in which P_A, P_B, etc., are the weight per cents of the oxides A, B, etc., and a, b, etc., are the "factors" for the different constituents. For some properties such as the specific heat this equation gives results that are valid over a wide composition range. For other properties the field in which a factor can be used is more limited. Hence "factors" have been developed for soda-lime glasses and other factors for enamels, etc.

This method of calculating a property of a glass on the basis of additivity cannot be applied to glasses which contain boric oxide. The addition of B_2O_3 to soda lime silicate glasses changes the properties of the glass in a direction opposite to that expected from the properties of vitreous B_2O_3 alone. Among the factors for oxides, e.g., for the thermal expansion of glass, B_2O_3 had to be given a factor with a negative sign. This feature is referred to as the "boric acid anomaly."

The phenomenon of the boric acid anomaly is the classical problem as far as the constitution of glass is concerned and it is still subject to speculation. E. Zschimmer coined this phrase in 1905 when he discovered that the beneficial effect which B_2O_3 has upon the properties of an alkali silicate glass reaches a maximum for additions of 10 to 15%. This maximum of beneficial action results because small additions of B_2O_3 change most properties of an alkali silicate glass in a direction which is exactly opposite to that expected from the properties of B_2O_3 alone. In spite of its own high coefficient of thermal expansion the addition of B_2O_3 lowers the thermal expansivity of an alkali silicate glass. In spite of being water-soluble itself, B_2O_3 increases the chemical resistivity of an alkali silicate glass.

4. Mixed Alkali Effects

The boric acid anomaly is of considerable historical interest and from a scientific point of view it has received unusually great attention. From a purely chemical point of view it really is not so unusual that the combination of two acidic oxides such as B_2O_3 and SiO_2 produces a product, the properties of which are very different from those expected on the basis of additivity. The fact that a heteropolyacid can have properties that deviate fundamentally from those of the constituent acids is too well established in aqueous chemistry to create a sensation.

From a chemical point of view the "mixed alkali effect" is far more spectacular. Firstly, we do not expect a sodium salt to differ drastically in its properties from a potassium salt, possible exceptions being its hygroscopicity or solubility. Certainly a mixture of the two salts should have properties which are close to being additive. Some properties of mixed alkali glasses show deviations from additivity that can be attributed to and have been explained on the basis of the greater efficiency of packing a mixture of ions rather than ions of one size.

Density measurements reveal that the substitutions of K_2O for Na_2O in soda lime silica glasses changes this property in a way which deviates from linearity. Viscosity measurements also reveal deviations from additivity, especially in the low temperature or high viscosity region. The viscosity of mixed alkali glasses goes through a slight minimum and their indentation hardness goes through a maximum.

The electrical conductivity of mixed alkali glasses, however, goes through a minimum that is both unexpected and spectacular. The electrical (ionic) conductivity of a glass in the low temperature region is the result of the mobility of its alkali ions. Due to the larger size of the K^+ ion a potassium silicate has a higher specific resistivity than a sodium silicate glass of corresponding composition. For example, the specific conductivity of a sodium disilicate glass is of the order of 10^8 ohms/cm. and that of the potassium disilicate at the same temperature is of the order of 10^9 ohms/cm. Replacing a part of the sodium by an equivalent amount of potassium produces a glass whose resistivity is of the order of 10^{12} to 10^{13} ohms/cm.

5. Interdependence of Physical and Chemical Properties

The fundamental work of Abbe and Schott aimed at the development of glasses in which the refractive index and the dispersion could be varied independently. Glasses were available with a high value of n_D (the heavy lead silicate glasses) and others with a fairly low value of n_D. However, the dispersive powers of these glasses were nearly proportional to their refractive powers. It became essential for the development of an optical industry to have glasses which have low dispersions in spite of having high refractive indices and vice versa.

We are interested in the need to alter properties of glasses in an independent fashion. We want to be able to free ourselves from existing interdependences. Some of these interdependences are far from being obvious. For example, the chemical resistivity of a silicate glass can be varied very widely. The water soluble alkali silicate can be changed into a very resistant glass by introducing B_2O_3 and Al_2O_3 into the glass. However, any change which improves the chemical resistivity also causes the glass to become more difficult to melt. Silicate glasses that have low melting ranges have been developed, but these glasses, as a rule, have high coefficients of expansions and consequently they are very poor with respect to their resistance to thermal shock. It is, of course, highly desirable to be able to overcome this interdependence between the melting range of a glass, its chemical durability, and its resistance to thermal shock. Vitreous silica is outstanding with respect to its resistance to thermal shock but among all glasses it is also the one that is most difficult to melt. The relationship is not obvious between the high viscosity of vitreous silica, on the one side, and its high chemical resistivity toward acid attack or its low coefficient of thermal expansion on the other. Also, why is the low melting B_2O_3 soluble in water and why does it have such a very high coefficient of thermal expansivity?

This interdependence of those properties which are of importance presents one of the major problems in the consitution of glasses. From a technological view point it may be called the "number one" problem which demands a better understanding of the constitution of glasses and their fundamental properties; i.e., viscosity, thermal expansivity, and chemical resistivity.

6. Properties of Glasses and Phase Relationships

Our present approach in teaching students the fundamentals of glass technology and ceramic technology is based on the phase diagrams. The phase diagrams tell us the exact temperature above which a liquid phase is stable indefinitely. Below this temperature the liquid is metastable and the precipitation of crystals is merely a matter of time. Every glass technologist is aware of the paramount importance of the liquidus temperature. Even the recent developments in modern crystal chemistry have not helped to clarify phase relationships. Our modern approach to structures has made us lose ground in the field of phase relations. The systems Li_2O-SiO_2, Na_2O-SiO_2, and K_2O-SiO_2 are very different with respect to the number of their compounds, the melting points of corresponding compounds, and what has been called their "dissociation" in the liquid state. When G. W. Morey and N. L. Bowen (6) reported their work concerning the phase relationships in alkali silicate systems, they called attention to the different tendencies of the alkali disilicates to dissociate in the molten state. They found that this tendency to dissociate in the molten state increases with decreasing atomic weight of the alkalies. The disilicate of lithium melts incongruently. At the time when this work was done the constitution of silicates was discussed on a molecular basis. Equilibria were introduced of the type:

$$Na_2Si_2O_5 \rightleftarrows Na_2SiO_3 + SiO_2$$

Such an equilibrium between different molecular species could account for the widely different shapes of the liquidus curve. As our knowledge of the structures of silicates advanced, we were forced to abandon the molecular description of crystalline or fused silicates. The facts, however, remain and we still find discussions of phase diagrams in which the authors refer to the tendencies of binary and ternary silicates to dissociate in the molten state.

We may ask more specifically: How can one describe the structural difference which must exist between the melt of sodium disilicate and that of potassium disilicate at those temperatures at which these liquids are in equilibrium with the solid phases? This problem is of immediate interest to the glass technologist because a relationship seems to exist between the structures of the liquids and the tendencies of the alkali silicates to form glasses.

CHAPTER XVI

USEFUL EXPERIMENTAL METHODS FOR STUDYING THE CONSTITUTION OF GLASSES

The variety of problems confronting a scientist who wants to explore the constitution of glasses makes it obvious that the development of a consistent picture of the vitreous state has to be based upon a combination of several experimental methods. For determining the atomic structure of crystalline matter the X-ray diffraction method can stand alone in most cases; it is only in special cases that the X-ray method requires support by other methods. The diffuse X-ray diffraction pattern of glasses and other amorphous solids is not as useful in the determination of their structures because these solids do not consist of those self-repeating unit cells that provide the constancy of distances in crystals. However, for glasses of very simple compositions, such as vitreous SiO_2, GeO_2, TeO_2, and BeF_2, the X-ray method has given us valuable information concerning the average cation-anion distance and the approximate coordination number of the cations. It was the X-ray method which revealed that vitreous TeO_2 contains the tellurium atoms in sixfold coordination, an important discovery which called for a revision of the concepts of Goldschmidt and Zachariasen who assumed that three- or fourfold coordination of the major cations is the prerequisite for glass formation in oxide or halide systems.

The determination of the infrared spectrum of a substance has become one of the most important tools in structural research and in the identification of organic compounds. Infrared absorption spectra can give direct information concerning the strength of the binding forces between the atoms. As these methods are developed they will no doubt give us valuable information concerning the atomic structures of glasses. Improved techniques and systematic work on simple glasses of widely varied composition are needed to make this method a major approach to the solution of structural problems. Infrared spectroscopy is the ideal supplement to the X-ray method, one providing information about binding forces the other about the geometry.

Among the great variety of experimental approaches the

interpretation of absorption spectra of colored glasses proved to be of particular interest. Absorption spectra make it possible to follow oxidation-reduction processes of elements of the transition group as a function of the glass composition, which in turn can give us information concerning the "acidity" of glasses. The introduction of NiO into a silicate glass leads to an equilibrium between structural elements which contain Ni^{2+} ions in fourfold and in sixfold coordination. This is a most important feature because it reveals that these ions participate in the glass structure in the form of well defined and highly symmetrical polyhedra. Light absorption reveals that the Ni^{2+} ions are not randomly distributed in an ill-defined three-dimensional random network. According to our views, symmetry of the environment of a cation, especially of a cation that has a charge greater than 1, is important for achieving a maximum degree of screening. For this reason a cation tends to assume a symmetry of its environment in glasses that is similar to or, in some cases, even higher than that found in some crystals. The fact that Pb^{2+} ions in a silicate glass have no visible absorption, whereas PbO is brown reveals that the Pb^{2+} ion in a glass must be surrounded by O^{2-} ions in a much more symmetrical fashion than in the crystalline oxides. Only at higher temperature will lead glasses assume the brown color of PbO. Glasses in their absorption spectra resemble aqueous solutions in which the cations find themselves in zero force fields; i.e., in highly symmetrical environments.

The important relation helps us in bridging the existing gap between the chemistry of glasses and that of the better known aqueous solutions. Therefore, considerable space will be devoted to the mechanism of color and fluorescence indicators. Examples will be cited that indicate how the indicators can be used for solving structural problems. It might be interesting to learn that long before the electron microscope discovered subultramicroscopic heterogeneities in lithium silicate glasses, W. A. Weyl (168) predicted them on the basis of the blurred absorption spectra of lithium glasses containing Nd^{3+} ions as color indicators.

Most methods now used for exploring the structure of glasses are indirect methods. The thermal expansion of glasses from room temperature into the softening range has been used for many years in order to determine the transformation temperatures. In spite of the fact that this property is not yet well understood, it proved to be most useful. Its wide use stems primarily from its practical importance and from the possibility of measuring it fairly accurately over a wide temperature range. Much of the early work on the constitution of glasses, especially the effects of their thermal history, is based on measurements of those volume changes which occur during heating and cooling at different rates.

The same applies to the viscosity of glasses. The viscosity is one of the most important properties of a glass, and governs the whole manufacturing process. Viscosity is a unique property inasmuch as it changes with the temperature over many orders of magnitude. Nevertheless, even today the widely different viscosities of B_2O_3 and SiO_2 are not yet generally understood.

The viscosity in binary systems has been used widely for finding out whether compounds exist in the molten state. However, an analysis of numerous systems, especially by N. S. Kurnakov (169) as well as by G. Tammann and M. E. Pillsbury (170) revealed that no rigorous relation exists between the phase diagram of a binary system and the maxima and minima in the viscosity of the liquids. The same applied to the ionic conductivity of fused salts and of glasses. Therefore, we shall deal with these two important properties when we discuss specific cases.

In contrast to the ionic conductivity of glasses which cannot be used to distinguish between the basically different structures of B_2O_3 and SiO_2 (both are insulators), the formation of electrical potentials in systems which involve glasses seems to be a promising tool. We shall, therefore, discuss in detail the use of the oxygen electrode in determining the constitution of glasses.

In order to arrive at a consistent picture of the constitution of simple glasses a vast amount of experimental data has to be accumulated.

We mentioned in the preface of this book that it is not our intention to give a complete picture ot the structure of all glasses but to stimulate scientists engaged in glass research and to show the methods of research that we think can best be used to approach this research on structure.

1. X-ray Diffraction Method

The work of B. E. Warren (5) and his collaborators, H. Krutter and O. Morningstar (171), oı the structure of vitreous silica can be truly called a milestone in the exploration of the constitution of glass. Three pertinent fundamental facts were established. Firstly, contrary to earlier ideas, vitreous silica does not consist of molecules. Secondly, the concept of vitreous silica as consisting of submicroscopic cristobalite "crystals" is just as artificial as the concept of individual SiO_2 molecules or chain polymers. Thirdly, vitreous silica differs fundamentally from silica gel, which also is amorphous, by having a continuous structure. The gel shows discontinuities or pores on a submicroscopic scale.

This successful solution of one of the major problems of the constitution of glasses, namely, the establishment of the atomic structure of vitreous silica, agreed very well with the one presented by W. H. Zachariasen. It is unfortunate that this agreement was interpreted by many workers in this field as a proof of the validity of the general concept of glass formation in oxide systems as presented by Zachariasen.

Most scientists interested in the constitution of glasses ignored the warnings of Warren and placed too much confidence in Zachariasen's concept. They were not aware of the fact that the evaluation of the X-ray diffraction patterns can give only a static picture of the average geometry. Such a picture can be fairly reliable with respect to the close range order if the glasses are of very simple composition.

W. A. Weyl (172) in a paper "Thoughts on the Constitution of Glass" pointed out the unavoidable difficulty that arises when a scientist interested in the constitution of glasses has to depend upon the judgment of others who are experts in the use of certain research tools. Warren's warning was based on his expert judgment. He was fully aware of the shortcomings of the X-ray method but those who were interested in glass were not.

J. A. Prins (37) is one of the pioneers in the theory of the X-ray analysis of the structure of amorphous substances. He also was deeply interested in the atomic structure of amorphous sulfur. He is an example of the unusual case of one man combining a strong interest in the structure of a material with the expert knowledge of limitations of the X-ray method. Sulfur in the liquid state undergoes a major structural change on heating. Between 120 and 160°C. the liquid consists of ring shaped S_8 molecules. Above 160°C. it changes into a highly viscous liquid containing chainlike high polymers. This liquid on cooling can form a glass. Prins studied this drastic structural change by means of X rays, but he declined to interpret the diffraction patterns and he made the following comment: "The change in the diffraction pattern from 120 to 250°C. is, however, too gradual and too weak to give conclusive evidence for this molecular change, although later it may be looked upon as compatible with it." Only when sulfur is stretched and oriented does its pattern reveal clearly the orientation of chains and of rings.

The X-ray diffraction method provides a picture of the atomic structure of crystals because this geometry can be derived from the interatomic distances and the coordination numbers of the atoms. In order to do the same for a glass the number of constituents has to be small and the symmetry of their short range order has to be very high. For vitreous silica, this method gives a fair picture of the short range order because of the simplicity of the system (only two kinds of atoms) and the very small deviation of the glass structure from that of a perfect crystal (high symmetry of the polyhedra). B. E. Warren, H. Krutter and O. Morningstar (171) interpreted the diffuse maxima of vitreous SiO_2 as follows:

The position of the first maximum reveals that the Si-O distance is 1.62 A. The area under this peak gives the coordination number of approximately 4 for silicon. Both values are in good agreement with the values found for the crystalline forms of silica.

The second maximum, at 2.65 A., corresponds to the closest distance between two O^{2-} ions. This value can be obtained from a calculation of the O-O distance if one can assume (1) that all four oxygens are equidistant from the central silicon atom and (2) that all oxygens are located at the corners of tetrahedra.

Making these two assumptions one can derive the O-O distance from the Si-O distance by using the geometry of the regular tetrahedron.

$$\text{O-O distance, } 1.62 \times \sqrt{8/3} = 2.65$$

The agreement between this calculated distance and the experimental value confirms the fact that the two assumptions must be essentially correct. Hence, the first two peaks of the radial distribution curve establish the regular tetrahedral structure of vitreous SiO_2.

The absence of a major intensity of small angle scattering reveals that the structure of vitreous silica does not have a high concentration of cracks and voids, a feature which is characteristic for the atomic structure of a silica gel.

Later when we discuss the structure of vitreous silica we will see that Warren's picture is essentially correct but that it represents the idealized structure and that refinements which cannot be obtained by means of the X-ray method, have to be added.

The successful evaluation of the radial distribution curve derived from the Fourier analysis of the diffuse X-ray diffraction pattern of vitreous silica was possible because, as a first approximation, one can assume that the distance between the Si-O, Si-Si, and O-O atoms are nearly the same. If an alkali such as K_2O is introduced into vitreous silica the situation becomes much more complex. Instead of three dominating atom pairs one now has to consider six major distances. In addition to the Si-O, Si-Si, and O-O distances three more distances have to be taken into consideration; namely, the K-O, K-Si, and K-K distances.

J. Biscoe, M. A. A. Druesne, and B. E. Warren (173) evaluated the complex radial distribution curve of K_2O-SiO_2 glasses in the same way as had been done earlier by B. E. Warren and J. Biscoe (174) for Na_2O-SiO_2 glasses. G. Hartleif (175), however, approached this problem in a different way. He subtracted the contribution of the three atom pairs of pure silica from the distribution curves of the alkali silicate glasses, assuming that the presence of the alkali did not seriously affect the average coordination of silicon or the Si-O distances. This method, however, can only be used as a first approximation for alkali-silicate glasses. We will see later that the structure of the alkali silicates deviates considerably from those pictures which had been developed on the basis of X-ray analysis.

We do not enter into a detailed discussion of the atomic structures of alkali silicates and borates because these glasses are too complex for a rigorous analysis. Even for a pure SiO_2 glass we will have to modify the picture based upon constant Si-O distances because we have to assume some fissures in order to explain the increase in strength of vitreous silica on heating as well as its solvent power for certain gases.

In alkali silicates, however, the constancy of the Si-O distance is impossible, even in principle, because the electron density distribution between the cores of silicon and oxygen is very different for bridging and nonbridging O^{2-} ions.

What applies to the alkali silicate glasses should also apply to a certain extent to pure GeO_2 because the low melting point of the quartz-like GeO_2 suggests the simultaneous presence of weaker and stronger forces. The variation of forces can be the result of very small variations in distances, but the X-ray method does not reveal whether one deals with a distribution of distances or with a single Ge-O distance in a glass.

The establishment of silicon, germanium, and beryllium in fourfold coordination in vitreous SiO_2, GeO_2, and BeF_2 should be essentially correct. However, it is unfortunate that it established an incorrect pattern because it apparently proved the concept of Zachariasen that tetrahedral structures are essential for glass formation.

The structural aspects of oxide glasses would have developed very differently if vitreous TeO_2 had been studied at the same time as vitreous SiO_2 or BeF_2. The structure determination of a TeO_2 glass which contained less than 2% Li_2O by G. W. Brady (176) is of special interest to us. It is the first structure determination which reveals that a glass can be based upon cations in octahedral coordination. The Te^{4+} ion resembles the Ti^{4+} ion with respect to its coordination in the crystal structure. TeO_2 is isostructural with rutile and brookite (TiO_2). The Te^{4+} ion also resembles the Pb^{2+} ion because it has a high polarizability and can be described as a Te^{6+} core (Ag^+ configuration) with an electron pair quantized with respect to its core; namely:

$$[Te^{6+}(e_2^-)]^{4+}$$

analogous to

$$[Pb^{4+}(e_2^-)]^{2+}$$

According to T. Ito and H. Sawada (177) the Te^{4+} ion in the TeO_2 crystal is surrounded by six O^{2-} ions at distances which vary between 2.05 A. and 2.79 A. The Pb^{2+} ion in PbO is screened by eight O^{2-} ions, four of them at a distance of 2.30 A. but the other four more remote, 4.29 A.

Neither the pure PbO nor the pure TeO_2 can form a glass by itself but glasses of very high TeO_2 and high PbO content can be obtained, primarily because the liquidus temperatures of these systems are low.

The evaluation of the diffraction pattern of the TeO_2 glass gave a radial distribution function with four peaks at 1.95, 2.75, 3.63, and 4.38 A. The first two peaks are well resolved and could be attributed to the Te-O distances. The area of the first peak gives 4.3 and that of the second peak 1.9 nearest oxygens. This means that the glass has basically the same coordination scheme as TeO_2 in its brookite form. The Te^{4+} ion is surrounded by six O^{2-} ions, four of which are located at an average distance of 1.95 A. and two at an average distance of 2.75 A.

G. W. Brady (176) arrives at the conclusion that it is very likely the TeO_6 octahedra are preserved relatively unchanged when the crystalline TeO_6 is transformed into a glass. As far as the evaluation of the third and the fourth peak is concerned, Brady was not quite as certain and he wrote:

"The two peaks at 3.63 A. and 4.38 A. overlap and we cannot be as definite about their maxima as we can about the inner well-resolved peaks. Also because a variety of distances occur in this range in the crystalline system, it is not safe to attempt to resolve them into discrete peaks and compute their areas. However, it may be said that as in the crystalline system, there are on the average two preferred sets of Te-Te distances."

A TeO_2 crystal which is isostructural with brookite consists of strongly deformed octahedra that form ribbons along the c-axis. The ribbons are connected to neighboring TeO_6 octahedra by the sharing of edges in the direction of the a-axis and by the sharing of corners in the direction of the b-axis.

Brady's work established the fact that the TeO_2 glass has essentially an octahedral structure, and that a close similarity must exist between the structure of the glass and that of the crystal. The crystal structure suggests the formation of ribbons in the molten state so that one may expect a TeO_2 glass to have a structure somewhere between that of a flawless Bernal liquid and that of an orientable Stewart liquid. Further work on TeO_2 fibers is needed before a decision can be reached as to whether the glass contains orientable polymers consisting of chainlike TeO_6 octahedra.

We consider it of paramount importance that this work disproves the idea that the cations must be in fourfold coordination in order for an oxide to form a glass. Very likely more octahedral structures will be discovered when the X-ray analysis is extended to lead orthosilicate glasses or to G. W. Morey's high TiO_2-Ta_2O_5 glasses.

The presence of chainlike polymers might be studied by measuring the diamagnetic anisotropy of vitreous TeO_2 after stretching. However, chainlike structures were discovered by G. W. Brady (178) for vitreous sodium phosphate.

G. W. Brady (178) studied a Na-metaphosphate glass and calculated its radial distribution function. The first peak at 1.55 A. could be attributed to the P–O distance. The area under this peak gives the value of 4.2 as the number of the nearest O^{2-} ions. He postulated that each PO_4 tetrahedron is linked to two other PO_4 tetrahedra so that chains are formed. The second peak, at 2.48 A., had to be attributed to a combination of the O-O, the Na-O, and the P-P distances.

On the assumption that the PO_4 groups are regular tetrahedra one can calculate the contribution of the O-O distances to a second peak. Subtracting the contribution leaves a peak at 2.35 A. that could be attributed to the Na-O distance and one at 2.67 A. that could be attributed to the P-P distance. The peak at 2.35 A. gives a value of 2.4 for the number of oxygens which are in close proximity to the Na^+ ions. The peak at 2.67 A. for the P-P distance indicates that the PO_4 tetrahedra are joined in such a way that the P—O—P bond has an angle of 115°C.

The analysis of the X-ray diffraction patterns of the Na-metaphosphate glass reveals the existence of long linked chains of PO_4 tetrahedra. Each tetrahedron is joined to two others by the sharing of corners and the chains are crosslinked by O—Na—O bonds.

The X-ray method as applied to glass did provide some very important information. The first glasses which were examined were found to have structures which agreed with the concept of glass formation as proposed by Zachariasen. This agreement was taken as a proof of the correctness of this picture and the random continuous three-dimensional network theory was widely accepted as "the" structure of oxide glasses. Warren's warnings were ignored, and so was the criticism of E. A. Porai-Koshits (179) who stressed the fact that X rays provide only an average picture. Hence, the X-ray method as applied to glasses has to be supplemented by other methods.

The shortcomings of the X-ray method as applied to glass have been discussed by several scientists. S. Urnes (180) recently published an excellent critical review of the X-ray diffraction method and its variations as a tool for studying glasses. We agree in principle with the treatment of S. Urnes, but we still prefer to base our lamentation on the sequence of the X-ray studies rather than on the inherent limitations of the method which were realized by B. E. Warren and his associates. The idea of tetrahedral structure as a prerequisite of glass formation would never have developed if the TeO_2 glass had been studied prior to or at the same time as vitreous silica. Also, the idea of a continuous three-dimensional network would never have been regarded as the only possible structure of an oxide glass if the structure of vitreous $NaPO_3$ had been studied earlier.

In spite of all the shortcomings of X-ray methods when applied to glass, if we were given the problem even today of exploring the structure of one of Morey's glasses in the system TiO_2—Ta_2O_5 we would still start out by examining its X-ray patterns.

2. Infrared Spectra

When a system is exposed to radiant energy, let us say to a spectrum which ranges continuously from the ultraviolet over the visible and into the infrared and radio microwave region, some parts of the continuous spectrum are selectively absorbed. The system, whether it is a gaseous molecule or a glass, absorbs only those parts of the spectrum which can raise its energy level. The latter can be accomplished either by the excitation of electrons or by changing the vibrational or rotational energy of the atoms or molecules. The energy necessary for exciting electrons is usually high as compared with that which can increase the amplitudes of the vibrations of the atoms or ions around their equilibrium positions. We are particularly interested in the quantized vibrations of atomic nuclei. The energies affecting these vibrations are related to the potential energy of the vibrating system, which means that they can tell us something about the interaction of an atom or ion with its environment. The absorption bands that affect atomic vibrations range from about 1 to 25 μ; i.e., from 1000 to 25,000 mμ. These wavelengths are much longer or the frequencies are much smaller than those of the visible spectrum which extends from about 400 to 800 mμ. Infrared spectra of simple and highly symmetrical molecules can be interpreted rigorously. At the present time efforts are being made to extend this method to more complex systems including glasses.

Organic chemistry benefited most from the applications of infrared methods. Organic chemistry deals with molecules of a highly complex nature, but chemists learned to associate certain absorption bands with the presence of certain functional groups and thus developed infrared spectroscopy into a powerful analytical tool.

Infrared spectroscopy can give us some information concerning the binding forces that are active within a molecule. Some of the absorption bands indicate the resistance offered by a certain bond between two atoms to a small change in their equilibrium distance. The "stretching force constants" which can be derived from the infrared spectrum are useful in determining the interaction of the atoms within a given molecule. The force constant is proportional to the force tending to restore the equilibrium configuration of a molecule after it has undergone a minute displacement of its atoms from this equilibrium configuration. The dimension of the force constant is, therefore, force per unit displacement. The force constant and the masses of the atoms that are involved in the displacement determine the frequency of the stretching vibration. If one can assume that the system is a harmonic oscillator the force would be proportional to the displacement and the potential energy would be proportional to the square of the displacement.

The difficulty in giving a rigorous interpretation of the infrared spectra lies in the fact that no molecule is strictly a harmonic oscillator and the absorption spectra include other effects besides simple bond-stretching operations.

The rapid increase in the repulsive forces acting between two atoms or ions when the distance is decreased makes it obvious that the particles in their vibrations move together less readily and move apart more readily than one would expect for a harmonic oscillator. This anharmonicity of vibrations makes it very difficult to interpret force constants obtained from infrared spectra on an absolute scale. However, one can compare variations in the force constants for the same type of bond in analogous systems.

Let us examine briefly the interactions in a very simple molecule. In the molecule CO_2, the C^{4+} core is screened by two O^{2-} ions which are strongly deformed as can be seen from the small C-O distance of 1.15 A. The screening of the C^{4+} core by three O^{2-} ions in the $(CO_3)^{2-}$ anion does not require such strong interaction and hence the C-O distance in the carbonate ion is 1.31 A. The C-O distance of 1.15 A. in CO_2 can be lengthened if one of the two O^{2-} ions is replaced by two NH_2^- groups. The C-O distance in urea $(NH_2)_2CO$ is larger (1.25 A) than that in CO_2.

The Raman spectra and the infrared spectra can provide information just as valuable as the length of the C—O bond in different molecules.

Let us compare the molecules Cl_2CO and $(NH_2)_2CO$. In the former, phosgene, the carbon core interacts more strongly with its oxygen than in the latter, urea, because the NH_2^- group is a better screener than the Cl^- ion. The C-O vibrational frequency in phosgene, Cl_2CO is 1810 cm.$^{-1}$. Replacing the two Cl^- ions by NH_2^- groups results in a lower frequency of 1655 cm^{-1} for the C-O vibrations in $(NH_2)_2CO$. This can be interpreted as stronger binding forces between C and O atoms in phosgene than in urea. As a result of the stronger electronic interaction between the C^{4+} core and its O^{2-} ion in the phosgene molecule, the O^{2-} ion is more strongly deformed and the frequency of the vibration is increased. The following values for the C-O stretching frequencies reveal that the screening power is highest for the NH_2 group, lower for H atoms and phenyl groups, and lowest for the Cl atoms.

Urea	$(NH_2)_2CO$	1655 cm.$^{-1}$
Formamide	$H(NH_2)CO$	1671 cm.$^{-1}$
Benzamide	$C_6H_5(NH_2)CO$	1696 cm.$^{-1}$
Phosgene	Cl_2CO	1810 cm.$^{-1}$

Using these simple molecules we can observe how the interaction of a carbon core with one O^{2-} ion undergoes a change when its screening by other ligands is changed. Essentially the same changes must take place when an Si^{4+} core interacts with oxygen ions of different screening power. We assume that the introduction of K_2O into vitreous silica not only provides nonbridging, more polarizable and therefore better screening O^{2-} ions, but that those Si^{4+} cores which are screened by one of these nonbridging O^{2-} ions will interact less with their other three bridging O^{2-} ions. This in turn increases the polarizability of all O^{2-} ions. We postulate on this basis that among the more common alkalies the introduction of K_2O lengthens the Si-O-Si distances most. These changes in distances might be small but the changes in forces or polarizabilities can still be large. We shall return to this view later when we discuss the constitution of the alkali silicate glasses.

Our assumption can never be investigated easily by means of X-ray diffraction studies even if the experimental methods were to become improved. The fundamental difference between the infrared method and the X-ray diffraction method lies in the fact that the latter integrates over atomic distances and provides one value for the Si—O distance not only in vitreous SiO_2 but also in a sodium silicate glass. The infrared method, however, can give more details.

When quartz is melted at 1450 to 1500°C. the resulting metastable liquid contains residues of the original quartz structure. The metastable melting of a quartz crystal, more than 200°C. below the melting point of the stable form of silica, is the result of the different forces acting within the chains (parallel to the c-axis) and between the chains (perpendicular to the c-axis). This difference in forces is quite substantial as can be seen from the difference in the thermal conductivities measured parallel and perpendicular to the c-axis of a quartz crystal. This difference, however, is vested in very small differences in the Si—O distances.

H. Z. Brugel (181) found that in some samples of fused silica the fine structure of a quartz band at 8.93 μ is preserved. This means that the melting of quartz produces a glass which is not completely randomized. Technologists appreciate that silica glasses from different manufacturers have slightly but distinctly different properties which can become important for some special uses. These differences cannot be found by X-ray methods but they are revealed by the infrared spectra.

Some samples of fused silica have a band at 10.8 μ which has been attributed to the presence of OH^- ions. This band is absent in powdered quartz but can be developed when finely powdered quartz (grain size about 1.0 μ) is brought into contact with water. Water itself does not have this band.

There has been considerable interest in the last ten years in the development of glasses which do not absorb in the near infrared range; i.e., which have a high transmission from the visible region to approximately 5.0 to 6.0 μ. The demand for infrared-transmitting windows has resulted in an effort to extend the fields of glass formation. This effort can be compared with that of Abbe and Schott when they had to extend the narrow region of optical glasses which were available prior to their work. Oxides such as GeO_2 which formerly were not particularly interesting in the field of optical glasses were introduced to make infrared-transmitting glasses. Also, known but instable glass compositions, such as the calcium aluminates, were modified in order to produce useful glasses of sufficient stability. Later, when we discuss glasses containing OH^- ions, we will learn more about these aspects of infrared spectroscopy.

The early work of W. W. Coblentz in 1906, T. Dreisch in 1927, and of F. Matossi and associates in 1937 is primarily of historical interest and can be found in W. Eitel's book (107)

The Physical Chemistry of Silicates. As far as the constitution of glasses is concerned, the modern application of infrared spectroscopy starts around 1952 with the work of V. A. Florinskaya and R. S. Pechenkina (182) and that of I. Simon and H. O. McMahon (183).

B. E. Warren used the Bragg formula for estimating the particle size of possible crystals of cristobalite within vitreous silica and arrived at a size that was not much more than that of the unit cell of cristobalite. On this basis Warren took a strong stand against the description of glasses as containing "crystallites," i.e., particles which show a degree of order which goes considerably beyond the first coordination sphere (see Chapter XIV).

On the basis of infrared spectra, Florinskaya and Pechenkina reach a somewhat different conclusion. They found a similarity between glasses and crystals which did not seem to agree with the concept of randomness of the glass structure. According to the views of Florinskaya and Pechenkina, the similarity of the spectra indicates that the bonds characteristic for a defined chemical compound are inherent to the glass. Groups with regular positions of the atoms exist in the glass. They assume that these ordered regions must have larger diameters than those derived from X-ray structure analysis because with diameters of only 10 to 12 A, the maxima of the absorption bands of the glass and of crystalline silicates could scarcely coincide so accurately. These ordered regions are pictured as bonded to one another by an interlayer which has a much less regular structure. The crystallites, together with the peripheral film of higher distortion, represent an area of local heterogeneity. The diameters of such areas must be considerably larger than the diameters of the crystallites themselves.

From this point of view the structure of even a binary silicate glass such as a sodium disilicate glass is complex and heterogeneous. They assume further that in glass formation silica can participate in different modifications, together with silicates, some of which may not yet have been found in the pure crystalline state.

Crystalline sodium disilicate occurs in two modifications stable below and above 680°C., respectively. Crystallization below the inversion temperature, at 620°C., causes both modifications to appear. Crystallization at 700°C. causes primarily the α-form to appear. Both forms can be distinguished by their own characteristic infrared bands and bands of both forms were found in the glass.

On the basis of their extensive infrared measurements Florinskaya and Pechenkina (182) draw the following conclusions:

1. The thermal history of a glass from its melt to the rigid state, as well as its crystallization, can be studied by infrared methods.

2. The microstructure of glass is complex and heterogeneous; silica, in different modifications, and silicates participate in its formation, the latter appearing as distinct chemical compounds and also as crystalline solutions.

3. There are zones with a regular structure in the glass; i.e., crystallites exist with atomic positions similar to those in the crystals of the silica modifications and corresponding silicates. There is a continuous transition from the most regular parts of these zones to irregular portions, and vice versa. The formation of groups from which crystallites are formed in the cooling glass begins very early, even in a glass melt above the liquidus temperature. The diameters of the crystallites must be considered to be somewhat larger than those derived from X-ray analysis.

4. The SiO_4 tetrahedra in the glass are discussed as structural elements that have variable distances between the silicon and oxygen atoms. The average distances are smallest in silica glass, and largest in glasses with isle structures.

The conclusions drawn by Florinskaya and Pechenkina (182) on the basis of their infrared work have not been generally accepted but the method is still very new and one can never tell how much of the disagreement between different scientists is real and how much results from different meanings attached to the terminology. The usefulness of the Bragg formula for estimating particle sizes from the broadening of lines is well established. However, is this formula valid over such a wide range of sizes that it can be used for deriving that a particle has the dimensions of one unit cell?

When we discussed liquid structures (see Chapter IX) we arrived at the conclusion that the orientable liquid (Stewart type) can be treated as consisting of molecules. The fissured liquid (Frenkel type), however, was described as containing "clusters" of ions separated by fluctuating fissures. We did not call these clusters molecules because of their short lifetimes. We assume that gradual transitions exist between the three types of liquids that we selected as the extreme models. We have no unambiguous definition for molecules and compounds and certain groupings might appear as "clusters" when examined by one method but as "compounds" when examined by a different method.

When I. Simon and H. O. McMahon (183) studied the infrared spectra of quartz, cristobalite and vitreous silica they assigned the most prominent band at 1055 to 1065 $cm.^{-1}$ in quartz and the corresponding band at 1085 $cm.^{-1}$ in cristobalite to the Si—O—Si stretching frequency. For vitreous silica this band is shifted to 1100 $cm.^{-1}$ Most amazing, however, is the sharpness of this band in vitreous silica. At a temperature of $-195°C.$ the width of the infrared band at 1100 $cm.^{-1}$ is only 10% larger than the corresponding band in perfectly crystalline quartz. This fact lends strong support to our description of vitreous silica as being a flawless liquid of the Bernal type.

It is also significant that any addition to vitreous silica broadens the Si—O—Si stretching frequency band. The wave number changes from 22 mole % K_2O from 1100 to 1050 and for 40 mole % K_2O to approximately 1000 $cm.^{-1}$. This shift of the Si—O—Si frequency reveals that K_2O not only introduces nonbridging O^{2-} ions but that it weakens the binding forces of the Si—O—Si bridges or that it makes all O^{2-} ions more polarizable.

Simon and McMahon (183) studied a large number of sodium silicate glasses and found that the change of the spectra is by no means monotonic. If the Na_2O content exceeds 30% the single peak which is attributed to the Si—O—Si stretching frequency is split into two peaks. This can only mean that in addition to the general weakening with increasing alkali content a disproportionation of the average Si—O—Si bond strength occurs which produces stronger and weaker bonds.

Simon and McMahon (183) comment on this phenomenon as follows: "No satisfactory quantitative explanation for this abrupt change at a definite critical concentration of the added oxide has yet been found. It may be significant, however, that at a molar concentration of 33.3% Na_2O the number of added oxygen atoms is just high enough to make one of each four oxygens surrounding each silicon 'nonbridging,' i.e., not bonded to the next neighboring silicon."

We prefer to describe similar phenomena as the result of the formation of a "superstructure" or of the appearance of a new ordering principle. This description is the least committing one because superstructures may form in systems that do not form compounds. However, there is no reason why this ordering principle should not be related to similar orders in crystalline silicates as has been done by Florinskaya and Pechenkina (182). In this case the use of the term "molecules" would be perfectly sound.

The next decisive step in the development of infrared spectroscopy as a tool for exploring the constitution of glasses was made by B. I. Stepanov and A. M. Prima (184) who calculated the vibrational spectra of SiO_4 tetrahedra in different lattices. Crystals such as enstatite, $MgSiO_3$, and diopside, $CaMg(SiO_3)_2$, form lattices in which the SiO_4 groups share only two corners with other SiO_4 tetrahedra. This interlinkage leads to infinitely extending $(SiO_3)_x$ chains which are held together by Mg^{2+} and Ca^{2+} ions. In other lattices such as those of some clay minerals and micas, the SiO_4 tetrahedra share three of their four corners and form infinitely extending sheets. In vitreous silica, as well as in the crystalline modifications quartz and cristobalite, all oxygens are shared. Stepanov and Prima calculated the spectra for these types of structures and thus developed the theoretical basis for a quantitative interpretation of the infrared spectra as well as for the Raman spectra of silicate glasses.

On the basis of this work of Stepanov and Prima (185), J. Zarzycki and F. Naudin (185) were able to give us some valuable information on the structure of vitreous SiO_2, GeO_2, and BeF_2. They also examined glasses of the compositions $2SiO_2,X_2O$; $2GeO_2,X_2O$ and $2BeF_2,XF$ in which X is an alkali ion. Their work represents another milestone in the development of a consistent picture of the constitution of glasses.

Melting a BeF_2 glass under ordinary atmospheric conditions produces some BeO through a partial hydrolysis according to

$$BeF_2 + x\,H_2O \rightarrow BeF_{2-2x}\,O_x^{2-} + 2x\,HF$$

The resulting glass contains an occasional O^{2-} ion which replaces two F^- ions. The O^{2-} ions and the F^- ions have approximately the same internuclear distances in the tetrahedron which means that X-ray methods cannot respond to such a substitution. The infrared spectra, however, indicate the presence of some oxygens because the forces between the Be^{2+} ion and the doubly charged O^{2-} ions are approximately twice as great as those between the Be^{2+} ion and the singly charged F^- ion. Zarzycki and Naudin (185) discovered such an oxygen contamination in their BeF_2 glass and they could correlate the intensity of the Be—O bond with the time the glass melt had been exposed to air.

For the alkali-free glasses, SiO_2, GeO_2, and BeF_2, the following force constants were obtained:

$$K_{Si-O} = 4.0 \times 10^5 \text{ dynes/cm.}$$
$$K_{Ge-O} = 3.3 \times 10^5 \text{ dynes/cm.}$$
$$K_{Be-F} = 1.1 \times 10^5 \text{ dynes/cm.}$$

Going from SiO_2 to GeO_2 and BeF_2 weakens the structure because the Ge^{4+} ion is larger than the Si^{4+} ion and the Be^{2+} ion has a lower charge. The ratios of the force constants give the following degree of weakening:

$$K_{Ge-O}/K_{Si-O} = 0.83$$
$$K_{Be-F}/K_{Si-O} = 0.28$$

These ratios can be calculated on the basis of the charges of the ions and the internuclear distances. The internuclear distances are:

$$\text{Si-O} = 1.60 \text{ A.}$$
$$\text{Ge-O} = 1.70 \text{ A.}$$
$$\text{Be-F} = 1.60 \text{ A.}$$

The coulombic attractive forces between Si^{4+} and O^{2-} ions are given by the formula

$$\frac{z_{Si^{4+}} \cdot z_{O^{2-}}}{(r_{Si-O})^2}$$

Using the coulombic forces leads to the following values for the weakening of the glass structure:

$$K_{Ge-O}/K_{Si-O} = \frac{4 \times 2}{4 \times 2}\left(\frac{r_{Si-O}}{r_{Ge-O}}\right)^2 = 0.88$$

$$K_{Be-F}/K_{Si-O} = \frac{2 \times 1}{4 \times 2}\left(\frac{r_{Si-O}}{r_{Be-F}}\right)^2 = 0.25$$

The calculated values agree very well with those obtained experimentally from the infrared bands.

X-ray methods average over all Si-O distances within the SiO_4 tetrahedra and they cannot reveal the distribution of distances in a glass of the composition $Na_2O,2SiO_2$. Such a glass consists of SiO_4 tetrahedra which as an average share only three of their four O^{2-} ions with adjacent tetrahedra. As an average each SiO_4

tetrahedron contains three bridging O^{2-} ions which are contrapolarized by other Si^{4+} cores and one nonbridging O^{2-} ion which is contrapolarized by the weaker fields of sodium ions. As a result the electron density distribution between the nonbridging O^{2-} ions and their Si^{4+} ion is less symmetrical and the silicon nonbridging oxygen bond is stronger than the silicon bridging oxygen bond. This increase of the electron density between the nuclei of oxygen and silicon must lead to a smaller internuclear distance but the X-ray diffraction method does not respond to this difference but averages over all Si-O distances.

In layer structures one must distinguish between the force constants Si-bridging O and Si-nonbridging O. The ratio between the two units is 3:1 for an infinitely extending layer of SiO_4 tetrahedra. This ratio corresponds to that of a disilicate glass; e.g., $Na_2O,2SiO_2$.

The force constant Si-nonbridging O was found to be larger than that for Si-bridging O. This means that the SiO_4 tetrahedra are deformed not only in layer lattices but also in alkali silicate glasses. The magnitude (20%) of the increase of the force constant reveals that the Si-nonbridging O distances must be $\sim$10% smaller than the Si-bridging O distance.

The deformation of the BeF_4 groups in the fluoride glasses is less pronounced than that in the silicates, due to the lower polarizability of the F^- ions.

The infrared spectroscopy of glasses is still very young. The method also does not as yet have available the factual information concerning crystal structures which was so helpful in the application of X rays to glasses. Nevertheless, the method has already provided some badly needed information concerning the structure of glasses. Our dynamic approach to the structures of glasses is based on the distribution of forces and only the Raman spectra and the infrared spectra can provide direct information concerning the forces acting within the structural units.

The most important facts concerning the constitution of glasses as revealed by infrared spectroscopy may be summarized as follows:

1. Vitreous silica represents a highly ordered structure which differs only little from a "perfect" crystal. This result strongly supports our description of vitreous SiO_2 as having a structure of the "flawless" type Bernal liquid.

2. The addition of any other oxide to vitreous silica produces a disturbance of its structure. The broadening of the Si—O—Si stretching frequency indicates a disproportionation of the Si—O—Si bonds; i.e., some are weakened but others are strengthened.

3. The singly bonded O^{2-} ions are more strongly bonded to their Si^{4+} ion than the bridging O^{2-} ions. Only the K. Fajans' approach to chemical binding based on the deformation of the electron clouds of the O^{2-} ions can account for this phenomenon.

4. Measurements of the force constants Si—O, Ge—O, and Be—F give the same ratios as those calculated on the basis of electrostatic forces acting between the respective ions. This means that the electrostatic description of forces and the ionic description of the structures of glasses are satisfactory and that no need exists for introducing the concept of a "partial covalency."

3. Color and Fluorescence Indicators

A. Introductory Remarks

During the years 1930 to 1937, W. A. Weyl and his collaborators, E. Kreidl, H. Pfeilschifter, H. Rudow, and E. Thümen, developed optical indicators for following those changes in the constitution of glasses that occur when their compositions or the temperature or their heat treatment are changed. This work is presented in detail in Weyl's book (29) *Coloured Glasses*.

In spite of the numerous efforts of physicists, the light absorption of inorganic solids is not yet understood because it involves changes within electronic systems of great complexity. Thus, one finds no explanation in the literature of some of the simple problems. Why is CdO brown? Also, the fact that ZnO and ZnS are white and CdS is yellow would not let one expect CdO to be darker than CdS. Usually the sulfides are more deeply colored than the oxides.

All rare earth oxide ions have absorption spectra which show fine structure in aqueous solutions, in the solid state, including glasses. This can be attributed to their excitation of electrons in an inner, well protected shell. The Pr^{4+} ion, however, is yellow and has no fine structure in its absorption. Why does Pr^{4+} form readily but Nd^{4+} is not known? Why does the Pr^{3+} ion but not the Pr^{4+} ion have a fine structure in its absorption.

We must admit that our knowledge concerning the colors of inorganic substances is strictly empirical. Nevertheless, color has been used widely for obtaining information on chemical changes when other methods have failed. When G. Tammann (1) and J. A. Hedvall (186) opened up the field of solid state chemistry by their systematic studies of reactions between solids they frequently took advantage of color changes as indications of the beginning of a solid state reaction. At this time X-ray methods had not yet been developed to such an extent that they could be used for identifying reaction products, and purely chemical methods failed in many cases to reveal whether a reaction had taken place.

G. F. Hüttig (34), who made major contributions to solid state reactions, took advantage of color changes in order to identify his "active intermediate states."

When F. Weidert (187) studied the absorption spectra of neodymium and praseodymium in glasses and aqueous solutions he noticed that there was not only a difference between aqueous solutions and glasses but also that the parent glass had a considerable influence upon the fine structure of these spectra. As early as 1922, Weidert suggested using these optical indicators to study the constitution of glasses.

The first definite suggestion of how to use color indicators for learning more about the structures of solids was made by R. Hill and O. R. Howell (188). They found that the color produced by cobaltous ions in different crystals could be used for deriving the coordination number. They found that most pink and red compounds of cobalt contain the Co^{2+} ion in sixfold coordination. Blue and green cobalt compounds were found to contain the Co^{2+} ion in fourfold coordination. However, W. Feitknecht (189) analyzed the existing information on the color of cobaltous compounds and arrived at the conclusion that no such simple relation exists between their colors and the coordination number of the Co^{2+} ion or the nature of the binding forces.

B. A Classification of Color and Fluorescence Centers and Their Uses as Indicators in Structural Problems of Glasses

Organic chemists are in the fortunate position of being able to consider certain groups of atoms such as the azo group —N=N— or the nitro group $—NO_2$ as the origin of the light absorption of very complex dye molecules. They are fully aware that the molecule as a whole contributes to the light absorption and that other functional groups modify it considerably. Nevertheless, the selection of a small group of atoms as the color center gives the organic chemist the opportunity to systematize and to catalogue his dyestuffs. Nitrophenol, for example, is catalogued as a nitro-dye. We are well aware of the fact that the colors of solid $LiO \cdot C_6H_4 \cdot NO_2$ is different from the analogous Na, K, and Cs compounds because the fields of the cations affect the electron density distribution in the solid. We face a similar situation in inorganic solids. It is well known that iron oxide, Fe_2O_3, one of the most widely used mineral pigments, can assume very different hues depending on the manner in which it has been prepared. We know that the nature of the defects and their concentration and the mechanical stress introduced by excessive milling of a pigment can strongly change its color. Hence, it is impossible to attribute the light absorption of a solid to one particular ion or to a small atomic group. Nevertheless we shall make an attempt to catalogue colored solids, such as minerals, synthetic crystals and glasses, according to groups which we think are primarily responsible for their light absorption.

It goes without saying that a solid can have a color which is the result of the simultaneous presence of color centers of the several types. Table XXV lists those color centers which cover almost all possibilities of producing visible absorption in inorganic solids.

TABLE XXV

Classification of Chromophors in Inorganic Systems

Chromophor	Mineral	Synthetic products
1. Atoms, molecules	Lazurite	Blue sulfur glass, selenium pink glass
2. Ions of the transition elements	Rhodonite, malachite	Cobalt and nickel ions in glasses
3. Mutual deformation of colorless ions	Greenockite, orpiment	Selenium ruby glass
4. Valency interaction	Vivianite, magnetite, mica	Blue iron glasses
5. Induced valency	Red feldspar	Praseodymium yellow
6. Symmetrical and asymmetrical units	Clay, flint	Leached vycor
7. Electron transfer by radiation	Blue rock salt, hackmanite	Solarized glasses
8. Metals	Copper, gold	Gold ruby glass, silver yellow stain

In the last few years physicists and theoretical chemists have developed new interest in the structural interpretation of the color of inorganic substances. An attempt is being made at the present time to develop a quantitative approach to the interpretation of absorption spectra: the ligand-field theory.

L. E. Orgel (190) in a recent book on the chemistry of the transition elements, covers the new approach to the colored compounds of the transition elements. This group is by far the most important group for glasses and it provides the most useful color indicators. One can hope that a better understanding of the spectra of the ions of the transition elements will be of benefit for a better understanding of the constitution of glasses.

(*1*) *Atoms and Molecules*

Single atoms or neutral molecules of an element represent the simplest chromophors. The absence of an electrical excess charge prevents a strong interaction between these chromophors and the environment. Such a chromophor is relatively independent of the composition of the matrix. The purple color of iodine vapor (I_2 molecules) is characteristic for all solutions that contain I_2 molecules in nonpolar solvents, for example, in hexane or carbon tetrachloride. The absorption peak of such a solution is shifted to shorter wavelengths when polar or more polarizable molecules are added.

Lazurite, a natural mineral, and ultramarine, its synthetic counterpart, owe their blue color to the molecule S_2. A slight influence of the environment upon the absorption spectrum of this chromophor may be seen by the changes of the hue either toward purple or greenish blue.

It is possible to develop the neutral molecule S_2 as a chromophor in glasses. The addition of elemental sulfur to fused sodium borate or sodium phosphate produces a deep brown melt that owes its color to the polysulfide ion $(S_x)^{2-}$. Addition of B_2O_3 or P_2O_5 to such a melt leads to elemental sulfur which produces a blue color. This chromophor has an absorption spectrum that is approximately the same in borate, phosphate, or silicate glasses as it is in the natural or synthetic mineral.

The chromophors of the pink selenium glass and of the purple tellurium glass are the Se and Te atoms, respectively.

Atomic silver and atomic gold are essentially colorless. When exposed to ultraviolet radiation, a glass which contains these metal atoms can fluoresce. These metal atoms are fluorescence centers that can change into metallic color centers through an aggregation process which produces metallicity.

(2) *Ions of the Transition Elements*

Many minerals owe their color to the presence of ions of the transition elements as major or minor constituents. Chemists are familiar with these chromophors because they are characteristic for crystals and aqueous solutions. Analytical chemistry takes advantage of some characteristic colors of ions and of complexes in aqueous solutions as well as in glasses (borax bead, microcosmic salt bead).

The valency of the element or the charge of the cation determines its electronic configuration. This factor is of utmost importance but there is no simple relation between the absorption spectra of two states of valency of the same element. They have to be treated as different individuals. Some Cu^{+} compounds are colorless, but most Cu^{2+} compounds are strongly colored. The element chromium (greek *chromos*, color) owes its name to the variety of colors which this element assumes in different compounds (chromates: yellow-orange red; chromic: green, purple; chromous: red).

The role the nature of the anion plays in determining the light absorption is rather complex. In combination with the least polarizable anions, F^{-} and OH^{-} ions, most transition elements show only weak light absorption. CuF_2 is colorless, the hydroxides of Cu^{2+}, Co^{2+}, and Ni^{2+} are faint blue, pink, and green. As a rule, the probability of absorption increases with increasing polarizability of the anions.

If we want to define the atomic group representing the chromophor it is not sufficient to refer to a Cu^{2+} ion or to a Cu^{2+} $(O^{2-})_4$ group; one has to include the second coordination sphere as the latter determines the polarizability of the O^{2-} ions. If the anion has a fairly high polarizability, even the replacement of one alkali atom by another may change the color drastically.

The absorption spectra of Co^{2+} and Ni^{2+} ions can be very useful for following the changes which occur in the coordination number. The Mn^{2+} ion reveals similar changes in their environment by its characteristic fluorescence. Before we discuss some structural phenomena which can be explored by means of color and fluorescence indicators we will analyze the ways in which the environmental conditions affect the properties of an ion of the transition group. We will restrict ourselves to a discussion of those features which are essential for the understanding of optical indicators.

If a transition element is introduced into a system, e.g., a glass or a solution, its light absorption is determined by the interaction of its electrons with the surrounding anions. This interaction depends upon several factors; namely:

1. The symmetry of the environment
2. The nature of the anion
3. The cation-anion distance
4. The thermal motion of the anion with respect to the cation
5. The polarizability of the anion as determined by its own coordination
6. The long range order of the system (heterogeneity in a sub-colloidal range)

In order to understand the color of a system which contains one type of colored cation, say Cu^{2+} or Co^{2+} ions, all of these factors have to be considered.

The *symmetry of the environment* of the indicator ion determines the electrical field to which it is exposed. The more this field deviates from spherical symmetry the greater will be the distortion of its electronic system. Crystals of low symmetry which contain colored ions show pleochroism; i.e., the light absorption has become a function of the direction. For example, crystals of Egyptian Blue, a calcium cupric silicate of the formula $CaO \cdot CuO \cdot 4SiO_2$, are deep blue in one direction and faint purple in another. Pleochroism cannot occur in solutions or in glasses even if the color center were to have a planar configuration because the absorption spectrum integrates over many color centers which have different positions.

Lead oxide is yellow or brown because the Pb^{2+} ion finds itself in an asymmetrical field in which it behaves as a dipole or a Pb^{4+} ion plus a pair of electrons: $[Pb^{4+}(e_2^-)]^{2+}$ Bringing this ion into a symmetrical environment of O^{2-} ions causes the color to disappear. A solid solution of PbO in SrO is colorless.

The *nature of the anion* determines the degree of mutual interaction. As a rule, fluorides are less strongly colored than iodides.

The absorption in some sulfides or selenides is so strong that it leads to metallic reflectance.

The *cation-anion distance* is a function of the degree of mutual deformation. The cation-anion distance is a very important parameter with respect to color. This distance depends on the symmetry, the nature of the anion, and on the second coordination sphere of the central cation.

The *thermal motion of anions with respect to the cations* is another important factor. The absorption and emission process is fast as compared with the vibration of ions. For electronic processes, therefore, the average cation-anion distance is not the only decisive factor. As pointed out earlier (see Chapter III), the optical properties of ions are determined by the maximum and not by the average deformation of the electron clouds.

Thermal motion blurs the absorption spectrum because it causes a rapid change of the electrical field. Color centers, in which the distance between anion and cation is small so that the cation forms a "complex," are least affected by thermal motion. Aqueous solutions containing CrO_4^{2-}, MnO_4^-, $CoCl_4^{2-}$, etc., ions have absorption spectra which consist of several well defined bands. These spectra are less influenced by temperature changes than those of cations surrounded by a larger number of O^{2-} ions at greater distances.

The *polarizability of the anion is determined by its own coordination*, a factor which reveals the importance of the nature of the alkali ions in glasses. This is brought out strikingly by the variety of colors of the alkali platinum cyanides.

$Na_2Pt(CN_4) \cdot 3H_2O$, *colorless*
$NaKPt(CN_4) \cdot 3H_2O$, *orange*
$LiKPt(CN)_4 \cdot 3H_2O$, *red*
$LiRbPt(CN)_4 \cdot 3H_2O$, *yellow with green fluorescence*

Also, sensitive organic systems such as violuric acid show a similar color change when its protons are replaced by different alkalies (halochromy). The color of the lithium salt resembles closely that of the free acid which is orange-red. The potassium salt is blue and the cesium salt is green.

The *long-range order of the system.* It is not possible to measure the light absorption and emission of single indicator ions. Absorption and emission spectra integrate over a large number of absorption and emission processes. In systems which lack long range order, e.g., in glasses, the indicator ions find themselves in environments which deviate from the average. As a result, the spectra of glasses show less structural details than those of crystals. Elimination of the thermal motion by cooling the system close to absolute zero cannot bring out fine structures in the spectra of glasses but it can do so in those of crystalline solids.

A system without long range order, i.e., a glass or a solution, permits the establishment of equilibria between optical indicator ions in different states of coordination. This feature makes it possible for us to investigate those factors that influence the coordination requirements of cations.

In order to illustrate the roles played by the different factors, the color of cobaltous ions in different environments will be discussed in some detail. This element has received the greatest attention by chemists interested in the color of inorganic substances. Traces of cobalt can be detected by the blue color which it imparts to a borax bead. Cobaltous nitrate is used in analytical chemistry to distinguish between $Al(OH)_3$ and $Zn(OH)_2$. Addition of a drop of a solution of cobaltous nitrate and calcination produces Thenard's Blue with the former and Rinmann's Green with the latter. The absorption spectra of glasses and solutions containing Co^{2+} ions have greatly contributed to the understanding of those factors which determine the coordination number of a cation.

The Co^{2+} ion occurs in fourfold and in sixfold coordination. In fourfold coordination its spectrum shows five distinct bands and the intensity of the light absorption of the $Co^{2+}X_4^-$ complexes is very high. The position of these bands depends on the nature and polarizability of the anion so that its color can vary from blue to green:

$(CoCl_4)^{2-}$ in HCl, *blue*
Rb_2CoCl_4 crystals, *green*
$(CoBr_4)^{2-}$ in HBr, *green*

W. R. Brode (191) found that for the grouping $(CoX_4)^{2-}$ the absorption shifts to longer wavelengths as the atomic weight of the anion increases. With increasing weight, the size and the polarizability increases and the latter determines the degree of mutual deformation and, with it, the light absorption. The stronger deformation in the $(CoI_4)^{2-}$ anion as compared with the $(CoCl_4)^{2-}$ group makes excitation by smaller light quanta possible: $(CoCl_4)^{2-}$ is blue; $(CoI_4)^{2-}$ is green.

We prefer to shift the emphasis from the atomic weight of the anion to its polarizability. This approach can account for the fact that the second coordination sphere around the Co^{2+} ion is nearly as important as the nature of the anion. There are two ways in which the blue color of the $(CoCl_4)^{2-}$ group in an HCl solution can be changed into green; namely, (1) by replacing the Cl^- ions by the more polarizable Br^- ions, and (2) by increasing the polarizability of the Cl^- ions. The latter can be accomplished by replacing the strong field of the proton by the weaker field of a Rb^+ ion: Rb_2CoCl_4 is green. For use as structural indicators we are primarily interested in the color of cobaltous ions surrounded by O^{2-} ions. It is important, therefore, to remember that the polarizability of O^{2-} ions can vary over a wide range (see Chapter V). When tightened by a proton, the oxygen ion has a low polarizability and the colors of cobaltous compounds in which the Co^{2+} ion is completely surrounded by OH^- ions are pink like that of the fluoride. CoF_2 has a rutile structure which means that the Co^{2+} ions are surrounded and screened by six weakly polarizable anions. The absorption process requires that one or more electrons be raised into a higher energy level. This excitation brings electrons of the Co^{2+} ion closer to the surrounding anions. A fairly rigid electronic system, i.e., one which contains a weakly polarizable anion, makes excitation difficult. Therefore, CoF_2 is only weakly colored. It has an absorption band in the green part of the spectrum between 500 and 550 mμ which does not show any structure.

W. Feitknecht (189) in a critical review of older theories on the color of cobalt compounds wrote: "The undeformed or weakly deformed cobaltous ion is pink. Increasing deformation shifts the absorption band to longer wavelengths, the color deepens, first to purple then blue and finally green."

Cobaltous salts are pink if the anions have low polarizability. Cobaltous carbonate, sulfate, acetate, etc., are pink. A solid solution of CoO in MgO is pink. The pink color is associated, therefore, with Co^{2+} ions in sixfold coordination. Sixfold coordination is characteristic for those compounds of cobalt that contain ligands of low polarizability, e.g., H_2O molecules and F^- or OH^- ions. The excitation of the Co^{2+} ion can be achieved by smaller light quanta if its environment becomes more polarizable. The absorption band shifts to longer wavelengths and the color shifts from pink to blue and green: CoF_2 pink, $CoCl_2$ blue, $CoBr_2$ green.

The confusion in the interpretation of the color of cobalt compounds is caused by two structurally different color centers containing Co^{2+} ions in different states of coordination and having different absorption spectra but producing the same hue. Both groupings, however, produce green and blue colors. For example:

Green: CoO_4 groups in CoO—ZnO solid solution (Rinmann's Green)
$CoBr_6$ groups in crystalline anhydrous $CoBr_2$
Blue: CoO_4 groups in $CoAl_2O_4$ (Thenard's Blue)
$CoCl_6$ groups in crystalline anhydrous $CoCl_2$

An additional complication arises when the first coordination sphere of the Co^{2+} ion contains two kinds of anions. For obvious reasons combinations of either two kinds of anions around a cation or one kind of anion around a cation in different distances cannot be described by one parameter. The use of a coordination number in these cases can be very misleading. In basic salts an additional factor, the asymmetry of the electrical field, enters the picture. As a result of such an asymmetrical group of anions which leads to greater distortion, hydrated basic sulfates can be blue and green. For this reason we should emphasize that the pink color indicates Co^{2+} ions in sixfold coordination, but Co^{2+} ions in sixfold coordination are not necessarily pink. This relation is not sufficiently understood. W. Feitknecht (189) examined a large number of basic salts of cobalt and came to the conclusion that no general, simple relation exists between color and coordination number or between color and bond type.

In order to demonstrate the way in which a Co^{2+} ion signals its change from sixfold coordination into fourfold coordination, let us follow the color change of a cobaltous chloride solution upon the addition of magnesium chloride. An aqueous solution of cobaltous chloride is pink and has an absorption peak at 512 mμ. If a larger number of ions are introduced into the solution through the addition of $MgCl_2$, two changes are produced. The first additions (up to 5 N $MgCl_2$) increase the intensity of the peak and causes a slight shift to longer wavelength. This change can be attributed to a structural change of the water resulting from the fields of the Mg^{2+} and Cl^- ions. This particular change can be produced by many salts (calcium nitrate, strontium chloride) and compounds (glycerol) which are soluble in water. Beyond a certain concentration of $MgCl_2$, however, (approximately 5 M at ordinary temperature) a new color center appears which consists of four bands in the yellow and orange part of the spectrum. The intensity

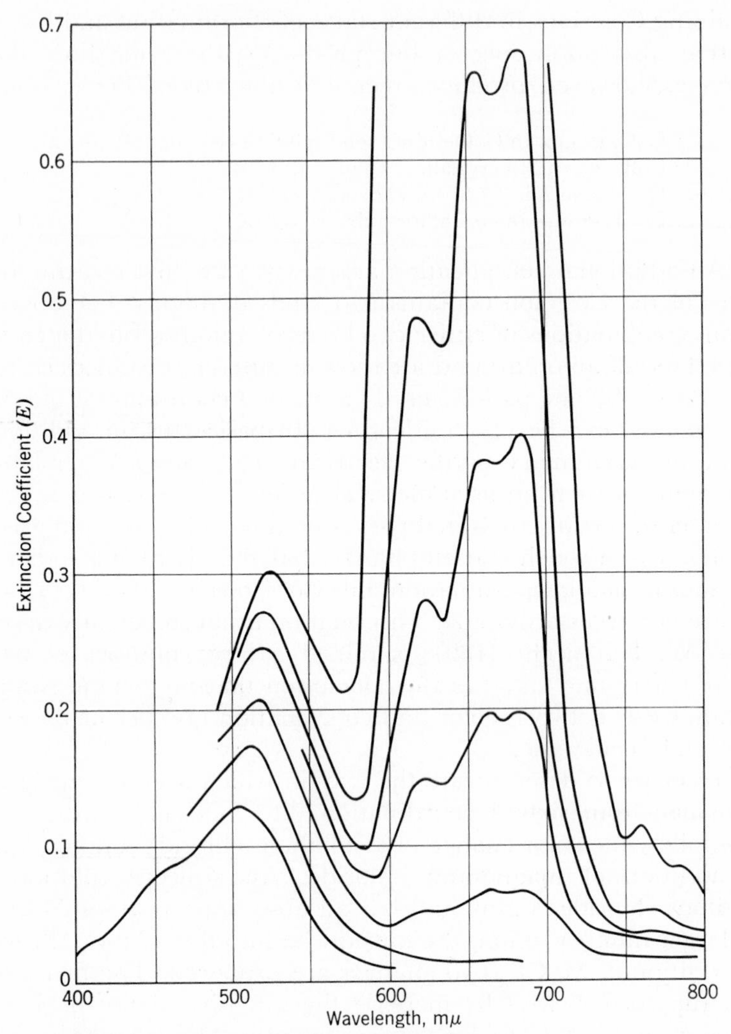

FIG. 10. Absorption spectra of aqueous solutions of $CoCl_2$ containing increasing amounts of $MgCl_2$. (From (29).)

of the light absorption of this color center is approximately 50 times that of the first one (Fig. 10).

A similar color change can be produced by the addition of HCl or $CaCl_2$, but not of $ZnCl_2$. The Zn^{2+} ion in an aqueous solution of $ZnCl_2$ retains an environment of Cl^- ions and does not make them available to the Co^{2+} ion. This is in contrast to the Mg^{2+} ion which seems to exchange its Cl^- ions for an environment of less polarizable water. It is a characteristic feature of many systems that the non-noble gas cation combines with the most polarizable anion leaving the less polarizable screeners, in our case the H_2O molecules for the cations of the noble gas-type.

Glasses behave like aqueous solutions and allow the establishment of an equilibrium between the two color centers. This equilibrium depends upon the composition of the glass and upon the temperature. If the temperature of the solution is raised, fewer Cl^- ions are required for the formation of the blue CoX_4 group. Water, a solvent of relatively low polarizability, can be replaced by an alkali fluoberyllate, metaphosphoric acid, or fused B_2O_3. In these media Co^{2+} ions produce pink colors and we can assume that they surround themselves with six O^{2-} ions.

Any increase in the polarizability of the O^{2-} ions, through the addition of alkali to B_2O_3 or to H_3PO_3, for example, causes the formation of blue color centers.

A very similar change in absorption spectra can be accomplished if a pink cobalt glass is heated (Fig. 11). A borosilicate glass which is purple when cold shows the characteristic maximum at 550 mμ which we attribute to the presence of CoO_6 groups. At higher temperatures the three maxima of the CoO_4 groups appear.

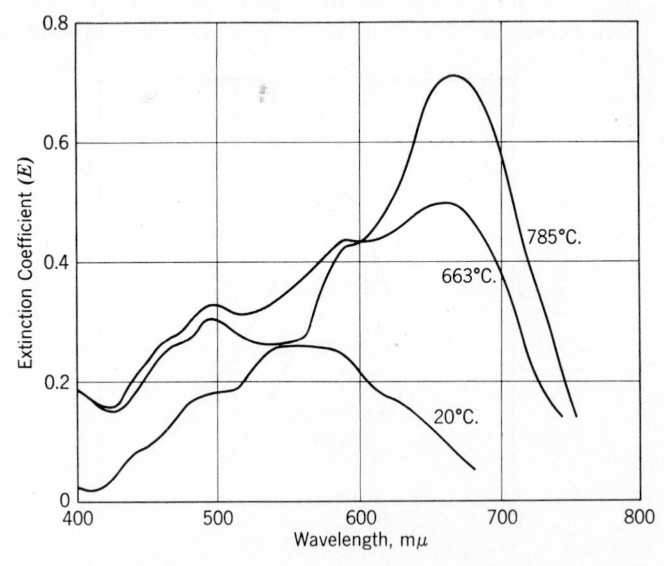

FIG. 11. Effect of temperature upon the light absorption of a purple borosilicate glass containing Co^{2+} ions. (From (29).)

The behavior of Ni^{2+} ions in glasses is very much the same as that of Co^{2+} ions. Nickel as an optical indicator offers an advantage over cobalt because the intensities of the light absorption of the two nickel color centers are not as different as those for the cobalt color centers. In glasses which contain an equilibrium of CoO_4 and CoO_6 groups, the intense absorption of the CoO_4 group obscures that of the CoO_6 group. This is not the case for nickel.

In glasses whose O^{2-} ions have only a low polarizability (H_3PO_3, B_2O_3, and lithium silicate glasses), the Ni^{2+} ion produces a yellow color which is the result of a single band with a maximum at 420 to 440 mμ (Fig. 12). The exact position of the maximum depends upon the nature of the glass. This yellow color center corresponds to the pink cobalt center so that it is very likely an NiO_6 group. Glasses whose O^{2-} ions have a greater polarizability develop a purple color when NiO is introduced. We may assume that the Ni^{2+} ion participates in their structures as NiO_4 groups (Fig. 13). The absorption spectrum of the purple nickel glass shows some resemblance to bands. When NiO is introduced into a series of corresponding alkali silicate glasses, the following colors are produced: the lithium silicate glass will be yellow, the rubidium silicate will be purple. The sodium silicate glass will be gray and its spectrum indicates the simultaneous presence of both color centers in approximately equal concentrations. A potassium silicate

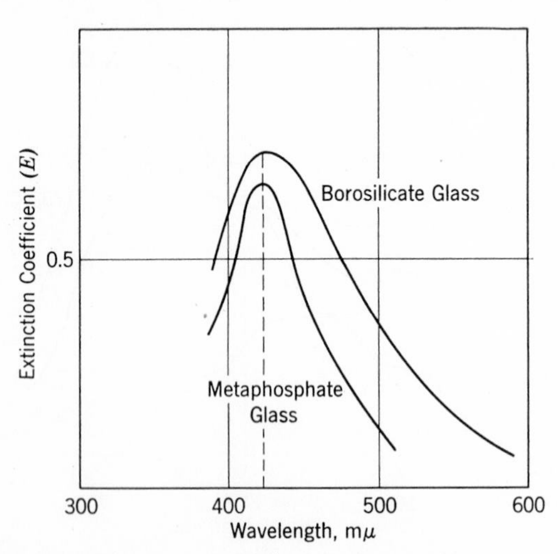

FIG. 12. Absorption spectrum of Ni^{2+} ions in sixfold coordination (yellow color center). (From (29).)

glass will be grayish-purple because the concentration of the NiO_4 groups exceeds that of the NiO_6 groups.

As a rule, one may say that any metal ion that can form either octahedral or tetrahedral coordination enters preferentially the lower, tetrahedral coordination when it is screened by polarizable anions; e.g., Br^- ions. High temperatures also favor low coordinations. The higher, octahedral coordination is preferred in combination with poorly screening anions; e.g., F^- ions.

Fig. 14 shows the effect of temperature upon the absorption spectrum of a gray sodium silicate glass. Upon heating, the absorption band of the yellow centers decreases and that of the purple band increases. This shift from NiO_6 to NiO_4 groups has its analogue in the effect of temperature upon the equilibrium between the pink and blue color centers of Co^{2+} ions in glasses (Fig. 11) as well as in some aqueous solutions. If a glass containing the two color centers of Ni^{2+} ions is cooled very rapidly, the equilibrium characteristic for a higher temperature is "frozen in" and the glass is more purple than it would be if it had been cooled slowly (Fig. 15).

The fluorescence of Mn^{2+} ions in glasses of widely different compositions was studied by S. H. Linwood and W. A. Weyl (192). The Mn^{2+} ion can develop two fluorescence centers: one is responsible for the emission of green light and the other for the

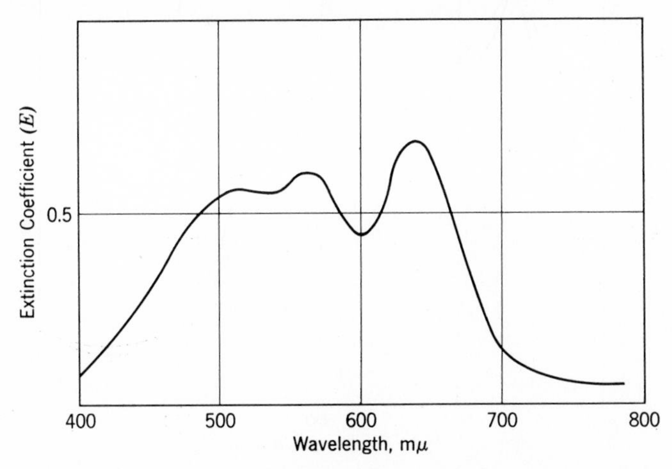

FIG. 13. Absorption spectrum of Ni^{2+} ions in fourfold coordination (purple color center). (From (29).)

emission of red light. Both fluorescence centers respond to excitation by near ultraviolet (3650 A. mercury line). Glasses which have compositions favoring the formation of the pink CoO_6 group or the yellow NiO_6 group also favor the red fluorescence center of

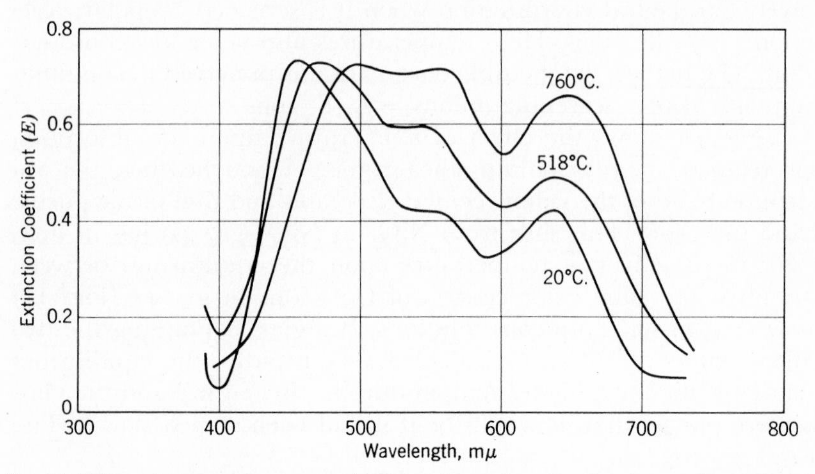

FIG. 14. Effect of temperature upon the light absorption of a nickel glass. (From (29).)

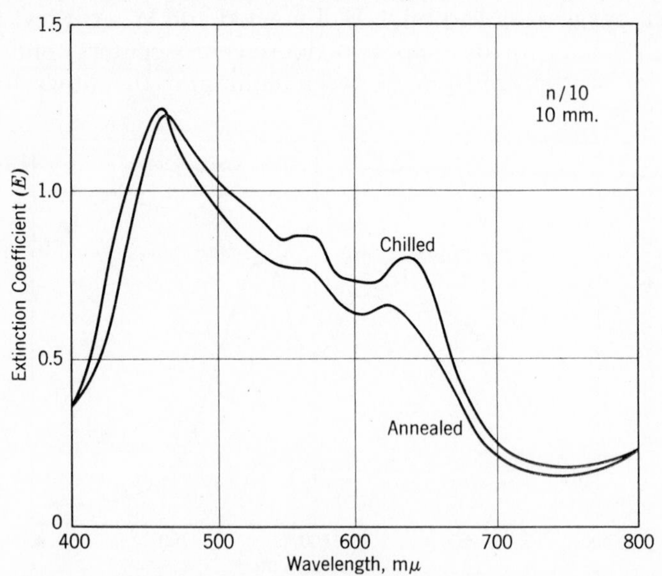

FIG. 15. Effect of the thermal history upon the light absorption of a nickel glass. (From (29).)

the Mn^{2+} ion. Compositions which favor the formation of the blue CoO_4 group or the purple NiO_4 group also favor the green fluorescence center of the Mn^{2+}. By analogy, the conclusion was drawn that Mn^{2+} ions in sixfold coordination, i.e., surrounded by six O^{2-} ions of low polarizability, fluoresce red. Likewise, the green fluorescence was attributed to Mn^{2+} ions in fourfold coordination. Again, we want to call attention to the fact that a number, i.e., four or six, can describe only those environments in which the anions are at the same distance and are of the same kind. Crystals of low symmetry will not fall under this rule.

The absorption spectra of XO_4 groups, e.g., of $KMnO_4$, are relatively little affected by temperature. This seems to apply to the green Mn^{2+} fluorescence center whose emission did not change much when the glass was cooled to liquid air temperature. Its fluorescence began to disappear only above 200°C. Red fluorescing Mn^{2+} glasses, however, showed a stronger increase in fluorescence intensity when the temperature was lowered to liquid air temperature. Their fluorescence faded above 100°C. This different response to temperature agrees with the interpretation that the green fluorescence is due to manganese in fourfold coordination.

For using the Mn^{2+} ion as a fluorescence indicator one has to work under neutral or weakly reducing conditions because the Mn^{2+} ion can easily lose an electron and change into the deeply colored purple Mn^{3+} ion. This phenomenon can be used for studying the rate of oxygen diffusion into a glass at elevated temperatures. An alkali manganese silicate glass melted under strongly reducing conditions will not permit manganese to form the highly colored, purple Mn^{3+} ions. Such a glass is light brown due to Mn^{2+} ions. Exposure of such a glass to oxygen at elevated temperature permits the oxygen to diffuse into the glass as can be seen from the formation of purple color centers.

The use of Ni^{2+} and Co^{2+} ions as color indicators has the advantage of being able to work rather independent of the ambient atmosphere over a wide range of glass compositions. Only recently A. Dietzel and M. Coenen (193) found that in highly alkaline silicate glasses the Co^{2+} ion can be oxidized and form Co^{3+} ions which participate in the glass as $Co^{3+}(O^{2-})_4$ tetrahedra.

Ions of the transition elements which change their quantum state more easily in different environments can be used as indicators for determining the acidity-basicity relationships in glasses.

If an oxide such as Cr_2O_3 is introduced into a molten glass an equilibrium will be established between two states of oxidation; namely, the Cr^{3+} ion and the Cr^{6+} ion. This equilibrium can be measured easily by determining the absorption spectrum in the visible region. The Cr^{3+} ion produces a maximum at 6500 A., i.e., in a region of the spectrum where the Cr^{6+} ion does not absorb. The equilibrium depends upon the ambient atmosphere, the temperature and the polarizability of the O^{2-} ions. For acidic glasses (e.g., H_3PO_3) the equilibrium lies entirely on the side of the Cr^{3+} ion, whereas basic glasses (e.g., K_2O, $3SiO_2$) favor the formation of chromates and shift the equilibrium toward Cr^{6+} ions. The exact position of the equilibrium depends upon the partial pressure of oxygen and the temperature of the melt. Additions, such as B_2O_3, MgO, and CaO, which polarize the nonbridging O^{2-} ion in an alkali silicate glass shift the equilibrium toward the side of the Cr^{3+} ion.

Other oxides such as V_2O_5, Fe_2O_3, and MnO behave in a manner similar to that of Cr_2O_3. W. Stegmaier and A. Dietzel (194) used these color indicators for systematic experiments to determine the acidity-basicity relationships in simple glasses of widely different compositions. This method provides valuable information concerning the concentration of O^{2-} ions which are exposed to only one cation of high charge (nonbridging O^{2-} ions) because they are the ones which are available for the formation of chromate ions, i.e., the equilibrium is shifted toward the Cr^{6+} side. The same can be said about the behavior of the other oxides. Increasing basicity shifts the equilibrium toward the higher state of oxidation if the partial pressure of oxygen and the melting temperature are kept constant.

In using color indicators for determining the acidity or basicity of glasses we have to remember that no single parameter exists for glasses which corresponds to the pH of an aqueous system.

As mentioned before, the Co^{2+} ion in sixfold coordination is pink and the same ion in fourfold coordination is deep blue. The extent to which a Co^{2+} ion is able to form a CoO_4 group depends upon the availability of O^{2-} ions of sufficiently high polarizability. If one tries to introduce CoO into pure B_2O_3 glass one finds that this oxide is not compatible with the melt, the melt remains turbid and gray because the CoO does not go into solution. Small additions of alkali, however, can make the two oxides compatible and now the melt on cooling forms a transparent pink glass. Additions of more alkali provide O^{2-} ions which are sufficiently polarizable to permit the formation of CoO_4 groups so that the glass becomes blue. Formally, the change from pink to blue can be attributed to an increase in basicity of the borate glass that occurs when alkali is added. However, such a generalization may be misleading as one can see from the following example: P_2O_5 is a very strong acid, nevertheless, a P_2O_5 glass can produce CoO_4 groups because of its favorable anion to cation ratio of 2.5 as compared with that of 1.5 for vitreous B_2O_3. We consider vitreous P_2O_5 a Stewart liquid which contains a high concentration of nonbridging O^{2-} ions. These ions are available to the Co^{2+} ion for the formation of tetrahedral CoO_4 groups. Alumino-phosphate glasses have structures which come close to that of a Bernal liquid; i.e., the number of nonbridging O^{2-} ions approaches zero. Hence, CoO produces more CoO_6 groups in an alumino-phosphate glass than in a high P_2O_5 glass. A. A. Kefeli (195) in a discussion remark pointed out that according to an unpublished observation of T. I. Veinberg, alumino-phosphates of different Al_2O_3–P_2O_5 ratios behave unexpectedly differently from other glasses when alkali is added. Using Co^{2+} ions as an indicator it was found that glasses with 30 to 40% P_2O_5 conform to the general rule that alkali shifts the equilibrium from CoO_6 to CoO_4 groups. The same color indicator in glasses with 60 to 70% P_2O_5, however, responds to the addition of alkali in the opposite way. We describe a pure P_2O_5 glass as having a structure which contains two kinds of O^{2-} ions which are characterized by extremely different polarizabilities. For this reason a pure P_2O_5 glass can behave as if it were a strongly basic glass and regardless of the nature of the oxide added, the basicity is decreased. For structural problems of this type, the use of color indicators can reveal information which cannot be obtained by other methods.

W. A. Weyl and E. Thümen (29,113) by introducing Co^{2+} and Ni^{2+} ions as color indicators were able to give a definite structural explanation for the effect of the thermal history on the properties of glasses. They found that the average coordination number of Ni^{2+} ions decreases with increasing temperature and that a chilled glass of a given composition contains its Ni^{2+} ions in a lower average coordination than the same glass in annealed condition. This means that increasing temperature shifts the equilibrium between NiO_4 and NiO_6 groups toward the NiO_4 groups and rapid cooling freezes in an equilibrium which is characteristic for the high temperature. This finding is important for an understanding of structural changes in glasses as a function of the temperature and of their previous thermal history. Assuming an analogous behavior of cations other than Ni^{2+} ions one can explain the fact that replacement of SiO_2 by GeO_2 decreases the viscosity of some glasses at high temperature but increases the viscosity at low temperature (N. M. Parikh and H. E. Simpson (196)). It is possible that a temperature dependent equilibrium between GeO_6 groups (low temperature) and GeO_4 groups (high temperature) is established which affects the viscosity of the germanate glasses differently than it does that of the silicates where the coordination remains unchanged.

The color of a glass containing Ni^{2+} ions when allowed to solidify under hydrostatic pressure was used by T. Förland in our laboratory for demonstrating that high pressure modifications of a silicate glass are characterized by O^{2-} ions which have a lower polarizability than those of the same glass formed under normal pressure. This decrease in polarizability shifts the coordination number of Ni^{2+} ions from 4 (purple) toward 6 (yellow).

(3) Mutual Deformation of Colorless Ions

Many ions, e.g., Hg^{2+}, Cd^{2+}, and Pb^{2+} ions, which in an aqueous solution do not absorb within the visible region can produce intensely colored crystals when combined with anions of relatively high polarizability, e.g., S^{2-}, I^-, etc. I. J. Piccard and E. Thomas (197) have coined the term "latently colored" for those ions that are colorless when hydrated or when combined with anions of low polarizability (perchlorates, nitrates, sulfates, carbonates), but produce colored sulfides, iodides, etc. Examples are the red cinnabar (HgS) and the yellow minerals greenockite and orpiment (CdS and As_2S_3).

This type of color centers has been related to the "co-valency" of the bond but it can be explained better on the basis of a mutual deformation of the electron clouds of ions. When K. Fajans developed his ideas of the mutual interaction of ions, J. Meisenheimer (198) used this concept for explaining the colors of PbI_2 and HgI_2 as resulting from the high polarizability of the I^- ion. The following series is an excellent example for the progressive intensity by which the electron cloud of the anion is pulled over by the Cu^{2+} ion as the size of the anion increases:

CuF_2	$CuCl_2$	$CuBr_2$	CuI_2
white	yellow	brown	nonexistent

In combination with the most polarizable I^- ion, the Cu^{2+} ion (17 outer electrons) succeeds in removing an electron from the anion and the gradual deformation leads to a change in the quantum configuration: formation of Cu^+ ions (18 outer electrons) and I_2 molecules.

$$Cu^{2+}\ I_2^- \rightarrow Cu^+\ I^- + I$$

The concept that the color of PbI_2 is a characteristic feature of a "Pb—I bond" is very misleading. We found that a solid solution of PbI_2 in SrI_2 is colorless in spite of the fact that it contains Pb^{2+} ions surrounded by I^- ions. The intensive yellow color of PbI_2 is the result of the deformation of the ions in a layer lattice, the asymmetry of which favors their mutual deformation.

In many cases a combination of ions leading to strong mutual deformation gives rise to light absorption in a glass if the latter is allowed to cool slowly. A soda-lime silicate glass to which some cadmium sulfide has been added remains colorless when it is cooled rapidly. It contains the colorless ions Si^{4+}, Ca^{2+}, Cd^{2+}, Na^+, O^{2-}, and S^{2-}. In the melt and in the rapidly cooled glass the O^{2-} and S^{2-} ions can be assumed to be more or less randomly distributed. If the concentration of S^{2-} ions is kept well under 1%, the probability of Cd^{2+} and S^{2-} becoming direct neighbors is low. Reheating to a temperature at which rearrangement of the ions can take place leads to a regrouping. The sulfur ions are the largest and, therefore, the most polarizable anions in this glass. The cadmium ions are the only cations present which are not of the inert gas type and, consequently, the Cd^{2+} ions exert the strongest polarizing action upon the anions. Energy of deformation can be gained if the glass structure loses some of its entropy and rearranges itself so that the Cd^{2+} ions become surrounded by S^{2-} ions. The mutual deformation of the outer electronic shells of these two ions produces the yellow color characteristic of CdS crystals.

The relationship between color and lattice energy is exemplified in a comparison between Ag^+ and Na^+ compounds. Silver compounds containing fairly polarizable anions are colored whereas the corresponding sodium compounds are colorless. The Ag^+ ion has a greater electron affinity than the Na^+ ion. According to K. Fajans (199), the greater mutual deformation may be seen from the difference between lattice energies of Na and Ag compounds (Table XXVI).

TABLE XXVI
Relationship between Color and Ionic Deformation

Ion	Difference between lattice energies $U_{AgX} - U_{NaX}$ (kcal.)	Molar refractivity of the anion (cc.)	Color of Ag compound
Cl^-	25.6	9.0	White
Br^-	31.4	12.7	Yellow
I^-	39.1	19.2	Yellow
½ S^{2-}	49.8	20.0	Black
½ Se^{2-}	63.6	25.0	Black

From the molar refractivity values it can be seen that there is a strong increase in the polarizabilities of the anions from Cl^- to I^-. Light absorption increases from AgCl to AgI. In the same series the lattice energy of the Ag salt exceeds that of the Na salt. The lattice energy of the sodium halides can be described as the coulombic energy gained by bringing the positively and negatively charged ions from infinity into the crystal lattice. For the corresponding silver compounds, to this energy term, another term has to be added which accounts for the energy of deformation of the ions.

(4) Valency Interaction

The interaction of two states of valencies of the same element, of iron for example, offers one of the most interesting problems in the field of color of inorganic substances. The facts are well known and have been summarized by G. R. McCarthy (200). In some minerals (magnetite) the simultaneous presence of Fe^{2+} and Fe^{3+} ions produces gray to black colors, whereas in others (vivianite), blue to green colors are produced. The mineral vivianite, a ferrous phosphate, can appear colorless when freshly mined but exposure to the air causes partial oxidation and formation of blue color centers. This interaction between Fe^{2+} and Fe^{3+} ions is of considerable practical importance in glass technology. In contrast to the chromophors in HgS and As_2S_3 where the colors result from an interaction of a cation with its immediate neighbors, the blue to green iron colors in glasses and crystals containing both Fe^{2+} and Fe^{3+} ions must involve an interaction between cations which may be separated by an order of magnitude of around ten ionic distances.

W. A. Weyl (47) and R. R. Shively, Jr. (201) prepared coprecipitations of $Fe(OH)_2$ with colorless hydroxides and oxidized the Fe^{2+} to Fe^{3+} ions in order to estimate the distance at which this mechanism begins to operate. Oxidation of the white precipitate leads to tan and brown colors in all mixtures in which the resulting Fe^{3+} ions are too remote for interacting with the Fe^{2+} ions. When a certain concentration of $Fe(OH)_2$ is exceeded, the mutual interaction between Fe^{3+} and Fe^{2+} ions becomes significant and the white precipitate assumes a bluish or green color on oxidation. In this case the brown color which is characteristic for $Fe(OH)_3$ develops only after all Fe^{2+} ions have been oxidized. Whereas 12 mole % $Fe(OH)_2$ is required for producing this interaction in $Al(OH)_3$, 0.5 mole % is sufficient to produce it in $Cd(OH)_2$ and 3 mole % in $Zn(OH)_2$.

An atomistic theory of this interaction could be advanced which correlates the probability of an electron transfer process over a given distance with the polarizability of the anion. When we discuss the semiconducting glasses based on sulfides and related compounds we will return to this phenomenon.

(5) *Induced Valency*

A crystal can force an impurity atom to assume an otherwise unknown quantum configuration. This phenomenon was discovered at the same time by three groups of workers, P. W. Selwood (202) at Northwestern University, E. J. W. Verwey, P. W. Haayman, and F. C. Romeyn (203) in Holland, and W. A. Weyl, G. H. Johnson, W. Capps and T. Förland (204) at the Pennsylvania State University. It is interesting to see that this phenomenon was discovered by three groups who not only worked independently but whose primary interests were in different fields; namely, magnetism, electrical conductivity, and color of inorganic substances.

If an impurity ion does not have the same charge as the normal ion which it replaces, the lattice can induce the foreign ion to assume the same charge as the normal cation which it replaces.

When a small amount of iron oxide is introduced into silica (J. A. Hedvall and P. Sjöman (205)) relatively strong pink to red colors are observed. Certain varieties of feldspar are deep red in spite of a very low iron content. We assume that these colors are the result of Fe^{4+} ions which take the place of Si^{4+} ions.

Pure CeO_2 is white but a trace of Pr_2O_3, which in itself is only faint green, produces a deep brown color. The lattice of CeO_2

stabilizes the quantum state Pr^{4+} which is unknown in aqueous solution and in glasses.

Many of the important ceramic pigments are oxides, some of them simple oxides such as SnO_2 or TiO_2, others more complex compounds, e.g., $MgAl_2O_4$, spinel, and its derivatives. In order to produce absorption in the visible region, elements of the transition group are introduced. In an idealized form we can write the following formulae for some of the commercial pigments.

$Zr^{4+}_{1-x}Pr^{4+}_{x}Si^{4+}O^{2-}_{4}$, Praseodymium yellow
$Sn^{4+}_{1-2x}Al^{3+}_{x}V^{5+}_{x}O^{2-}_{2}$, Tin-vanadium yellow
$Ti^{4+}_{1-2x}Ni^{3+}_{x}Sb^{5+}_{x}O^{2-}_{2}$, Nickel-titanium yellow
$Al^{3+}_{2-x}Mn^{3+}_{x}O^{2-}_{3}$, Alumina-manganese pink

The development of this type of chromophor is based upon the periodicity of crystals and it is, therefore, the only chromophor that has no counterpart in the vitreous state.

The principle of induced valency is not limited to oxides but may also be applied to metals.

The red-colored metallic copper has a high coefficient of absorption in the long wave portion of the spectrum. Systems which have high coefficients of light absorption, such as the tungsten bronze or organic dyes, show metallic luster to a certain extent. Crystals of the green-absorbing red dye eosine have a green metallic luster. The crystalline red-absorbing malachite green has a dark red metallic luster. From the red color of copper we may conclude, therefore, that the metallic phase is not an array of Cu^+ ions (18 outer electrons) with "free" electrons but contains Cu^{2+} ions (17 outer electrons) as well. These ions impart blue to green colors to many compounds.

Alloying the metallic copper with those elements which exhibit a tendency to produce both divalent and trivalent ions (for example, Ni or Mn) should affect the Cu^+-Cu^{2+} equilibrium in the metal. Indeed, addition of manganese or nickel causes the red color of copper to disappear.

The association of the red color of copper with the presence of Cu^{2+} ions and their red absorption raises an interesting question. Can one induce other ions with 18 outer electrons to assume the electron configuration of the Cu^{2+} ion and thus produce a red metal by alloying white metals?

Zn^{2+} and Cd^{2+} ions have the same outer electron configuration as the Cu^+ ion. If one brings Zn or Cd atoms into positions that demand more than two valence electrons, they would have to assume the electron configuration of the Cu^{2+} ion. This seems to be the case for the intermetallic compounds LiZn and LiCd. They have the diamond-like NaTl structure and show the same red reflectance color as metallic copper. In these structures the Cd^{2+} or Zn^{2+} ions are induced to imitate the charge of the Tl^{3+} ion. This induced valency leads to Cd^{3+} and Zn^{3+} ions whose electron configurations resemble Cu^{2+} ions. Hence, the alloys LiCd and LiZn have the red color of metallic copper.

(6) *Symmetrical and Asymmetrical Units*

Saturated hydrocarbons are colorless, no matter how large their molecules are. In contrast to molecules with double bonds, their excitation energy lies at such a high value that only ultraviolet radiation can raise an electron into a higher orbital. The same applies to those oxides which contain only noble gas-type cations.

Quartz is one of the best examples. Its absorption lies in the short ultraviolet because its electrons are tightened by the strong fields of the small Si^{4+} ions (neon structure). Oxygen atoms with two electrons, i.e., O^{2-} ions, are not stable in the free state nor in the hydrated state. They are unstable with respect to O^{-} ions and electrons. The stability in quartz of O^{2-} ions and other anions with a charge greater than 1, is the result of the two adjacent Si^{4+} ions. This, of course, applies only for the bulk of the crystal and not for its surface.

The surface of a crystal contains ions that have incomplete coordination. This can lead to strong distortions and may even lead to an electron transfer, e.g., the formation of O^{-} and chemisorbed $(O_2)^{-}$ ions. W. A. Weyl and T. Förland (204) pointed out that the surface of a crystal may absorb radiation which is transmitted by its bulk. As long as one deals with a single quartz crystal, the light absorption of its distorted surface cannot produce a visible effect. However, an aggregate of very small quartz crystals must contain a substantial concentration of distorted SiO_4 tetrahedra and, therefore, such a microcrystalline solid may have optical properties which deviate noticeably from those of a single crystal.

J. H. Weymouth and W. O. Williamson (206) discuss this subject very thoroughly. They show that certain brown English flints cannot be bleached by oxidation with concentrated hydrogen peroxide or by treating them with chlorine at elevated temperatures. If the brown color of this finely subdivided quartz were due to impurities, in particular carbonaceous material or iron, it would bleach under these conditions. The deviation of density and refractive index from the normal values are in agreement with our concept. The color center may be a strongly distorted SiO_4 tetrahedron or even a group which contains a singly charged O^- ion.

$$Si^{4+}\left(\frac{O^{2-}}{2}\right)_3 O^-$$

This type of color center, a strongly distorted asymmetrical unit containing a central cation of the noble gas-type, occurs in surfaces and becomes significant in porous media. Silica gel, silica alumina catalyst, and the leached out, dried but unshrunken Vycor brand glass, are typical examples.

The same asymmetrical unit may form in the interior of a quartz crystal as a metastable color center under the influence of radiation. High energy radiation will affect those parts of a quartz crystal which contain Li^+ or Na^+ ions. They attract electrons from O^{2-} ions changing the latter into O^- ions and thus producing asymmetrical units. The difference between the brown color of flint and that of smoky quartz or irradiated quartz lies in the instability of the color centers which form under radiation. The brown color of irradiated quartz bleaches on heating, that of the flint does not.

It goes without saying that the chromophors described as asymmetrical units can be superimposed upon any one of the previously described color centers. W. O. Milligan (207), for example, observed that the yellow pigment CdS (greenockite) turns red upon grinding in a mortar. Mechanical disturbance produces the same effect as increased lattice vibration. At 300 to 400°C the greenockite is red because its absorption edge has shifted from the blue to the green part of the spectrum.

Repeatedly we pointed out that the lack of visible absorption of silicate, borate, and phosphate glasses which contain a major concentration of lead oxide must mean that the Pb^{2+} ions participate in these glasses in the form of highly symmetrical polyhedra. The fact that lead orthosilicate, Pb_2SiO_4, forms a stable glass has been a major problem in the constitution of glasses ever since the Zachariasen concept was used. The absence of color reveals that due to the polarizability of the Pb^{2+} and O^{2-} ions the two oxides PbO and SiO_2 become compatible at high temperature because both the Si^{4+} and the Pb^{2+} ion can form stable symmetrical polyhedra.

G. O. Bagdykyants and A. G. Alekseev (208) studied the structures of a number of lead silicate glasses by means of electron diffraction patterns. Using the trial and error method, they assumed that the true atomic arrangement in a glass was the one for which the calculated scattering intensity curve gave the best agreement with the experimental curve. The silicon ion was assumed to form in these glasses the normal regular SiO_4 tetrahedron. As far as the Pb polyhedra were concerned closest agreement corresponded to Pb^{2+} ions surrounded by six O^{2-} ions. Each O^{2-} ion is linked to three Pb^{2+} ions and one Si^{4+} ion. This structural picture showed especially good agreement in the electron diffraction patterns of high lead silicate glasses.

The lack of visible absorption of lead glasses suggests that the PbO_6 groups become fairly regular octahedra on cooling of the melt. Distorted polyhedra would produce visible absorption analogous to crystalline PbO. Indeed, heavy lead glasses turn brown on heating because the fluctuation of symmetry with increasing temperature shifts the absorption band into the visible region.

At the present time a strong interest exists in the subcolloidal phase separation which has been observed in many glasses when they were examined with the electron microscope. We explained earlier (see Chapter XII) why the compatibility of oxides increases with increasing temperature and why combinations of oxides that are compatible at high temperature may become incompatible at low temperature. Glasses which are homogeneous in a microscopic and even on an ultramicroscopic scale may develop heterogeneity in a subultramicroscopic scale (lithium silicates and borates). With the advent of the electron microscope it became possible to detect subultramicroscopic heterogeneities (see Chapter XIII). According to K. Rosenhauer and F. Weidert (209) the absorption spectrum of the Nd^{3+} ion in glasses signals any change of the structure which affects the stability of the glassy state. Composition changes which increase the tendency of a glass to divitrify also blur the normally sharp absorption bands of the Nd^{3+} ions. The absorption indicators can be used therefore for studying the compatibility of oxide systems.

Color and fluorescence centers will respond differently when participating in a crystal or in a glass of corresponding composition. Fluorescence in particular has been used for studying the formation of glasses and their devitrification.

For many technical processes that involve sintering, etc. it becomes of interest to determine the temperatures at which the first glassy phase will form in a system. Uranium oxide or sodium uranate do not fluoresce but $(UO_2)^{2+}$ ions in glasses show strong green fluorescence when they are exposed to ultraviolet radiation. C. Kühl, H. Rudow, and W. A. Weyl (210) used this phenomenon as a basis for determining the beginning of glass formation in different glass batches. W. Büssem and C. Schusterius (211) applied this fluorescence indicator method to studies concerning the effects of fluxing agents in ceramic bodies. The beginning of glass formation in steatite bodies which contained fluxing oxides and their disappearance on heat treatment could be followed easily using some uranium oxide as a fluorescence indicator. The formation of a vitreous phase in such a ceramic body caused it to fluoresce under ultraviolet light and the fluorescence disappeared when the glassy phase changed into crystals.

Whether a color or fluorescence center is symmetrical or not depends to a large extent upon the temperature. Due to the asymmetry of thermal vibrations the color center may undergo strong changes with the temperature.

The change of a fluorescence center from its excited state into its ground state, i.e., the dissipation of the absorbed energy, depends upon the temperature of the glass because it is accelerated by collisions of the fluorescence center with the surrounding ions. Most condensed systems show a measurable afterglow which increases with decreasing temperature.

The organic dye dimethylnaphtheurodine is particularly sensitive to its environment. This dye fluoresces in colors ranging from a blue-green in hexane to orange in amyl alcohol. Its fluorescence in the monomer methylmethacrylate changes into phosphorescence when the solvent polymerizes because the large polymer molecules are less suitable for dissipating the energy than the small, highly mobile monomer molecules.

S. H. Linwood and W. A. Weyl (192) found that the green fluorescence of the Mn^{2+} ion (Mn^{2+} in fourfold coordination) is less sensitive to temperature changes than its red fluorescence

(Mn^{2+} in sixfold coordination). E. V. Anufrieva and M. V. Volkenstein (212) studied the temperature dependence of the fluorescence of auramine and other dyestuff molecules in organic glasses and found that the intensity versus temperature curve shows a break at t_g (Fig. 16). The formation of defects or asymmetries in the glass permits new modes of vibrations which accelerate the dissipation of the energy and which change the absorbed light directly into heat. Hence all fluorescence intensities were found to decrease with increasing temperature.

W. D. Smiley and W. A. Weyl (213) studied the duration of the afterglow of glasses of different compositions at ordinary temperature. The uranyl group $(UO_2)^{2+}$ was used as fluorescence indicator. The $(UO_2)^{2+}$ group represents a relatively shielded fluorescence center as compared with Mn^{2+}, Tl^+, or Cu^+ ions. It is the only inorganic cation that fluoresces in aqueous solution. In glasses the fluorescence of the $(UO_2)^{2+}$ group is much stronger than in water and the fluorescence color varies between blue-green

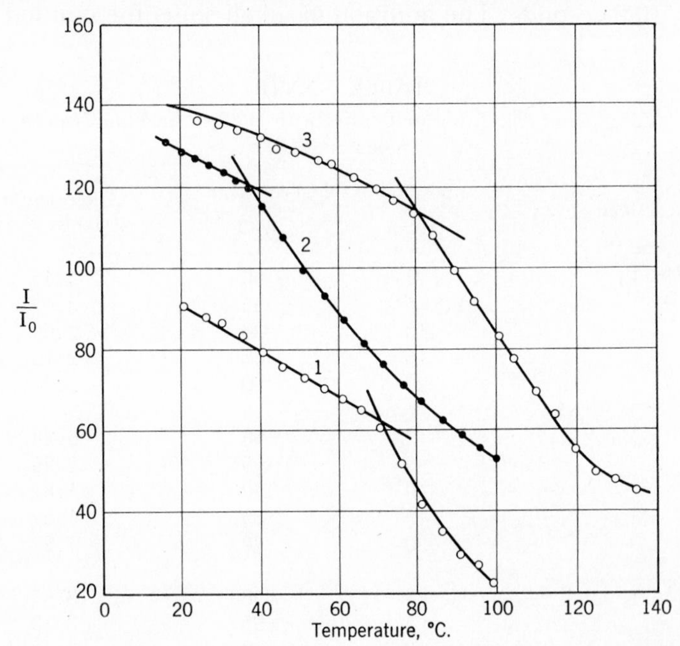

FIG. 16. Fluorescence of auramine in organic glasses as a function of the temperature. (1), in polyvinyl butyral; (2) in polyvinyl acetate; (3), in polyvinyl chloride. (From (212).)

and yellow-green depending upon the composition of the base glass. The blue-green color indicates a minimum of interaction (largest light quanta) and the yellow-green fluorescence (smallest light quanta) a strong interaction or a maximum dissipation of the excitation energy. Generally speaking, the addition of alkali to a glass shifts the fluorescence of the uranyl groups from blue-green to yellow-green. This intensified interaction of the $(UO_2)^{2+}$ group with the surrounding O^{2-} ions leads finally to the formation of the uranate group $(UO_4)^{2-}$ which does not fluoresce. Hence, glasses with highly polarizable O^{2-} ions (lead orthosilicate) do not strongly fluoresce when uranium is introduced.

Uranium oxide UO_3 is not compatible with B_2O_3, but if 2 mole % Na_2O are introduced into the melt some uranium oxide can be dissolved. The resulting glass shows a strong blue-green fluorescence indicating that little interaction exists between the molecular liquid of the Stewart orientable type and the uranyl group. Such a glass has an afterglow which lasts approximately 3.5×10^{-2} seconds. The addition of alkali shifts the emitted light

TABLE XXVII

Afterglow of Alkali Borate Glasses with $(UO_2)^{2+}$ as Fluorescence Indicator (213)

Alkali	Composition of the glass (mole %)		Afterglow in seconds, $\times 10^2$
	Alkali	B_2O_3	
Li	2	98	3.45
	5	95	3.07
	10	90	2.60
	15	85	2.23
	20	80	2.06
Na	2	98	3.23
	5	95	2.25
	10	90	1.81
	15	85	1.52
	20	80	1.22
K	2	98	3.67
	5	95	3.13
	10	90	2.60
	15	85	2.13
	20	80	1.62

TABLE XXVIII
Effect of Heat Treatment on the Afterglow of Sodium Borate Glasses (213)

Composition (mole %)	Afterglow of glass in seconds, $\times 10^2$		Increase of the afterglow (%)
	Chilled	Annealed	
$2Na_2O$, $98B_2O_3$	3.23	3.57	10
$5Na_2O$, $95B_2O_3$	2.25	2.86	27
$10Na_2O$, $90B_2O_3$	1.81	2.40	33
$15Na_2O$, $85B_2O_3$	1.52	2.08	36
$20Na_2O$, $80B_2O_3$	1.22	1.70	42

toward longer wave lengths or smaller light quanta and decreases the duration of the afterglow because O^{2-} ions of greater polarizability are available and the thermal vibrations become more intense. We describe this change by saying that the molecular structure of the glass changes in the direction toward a point of our ternary diagram which lies somewhere on the line between the Bernal flawless type and the Frenkel fissured-type liquid.

The effects of the different alkalies upon the duration of the afterglow can be seen in Table XXVII. The glasses were chilled and examined in unannealed condition because some scientists expressed the opinion that phosphorescence is a property which is characteristic of the crystalline state. Annealing the glass increases the duration of the afterglow. We interpret this increase (Table XXVIII) as the result of a structural change of the glass in the direction away from the corner which represents the Frenkel fissured type liquid and we do not attribute it to an incipient crystallization.

No matter what the structure of a given glass is, it changes toward that of a Frenkel fissured liquid on heating. Hence, a chilled glass has a structure which resembles that of a Frenkel fissured liquid more than does the structure of the annealed glass.

(7) *Electron Transfer by Radiation*

Many minerals, e.g., blue rocksalt and varieties of quartz and zircon, probably did not form as the colored variety but developed their particular hue under the influence of nuclear radiation (radioactive material, cosmic showers). In this case, the resulting color center may be metastable and change under the influence of light (hackmanite) or heat (zircon). Frequently, heating to relatively low temperature (300°C) causes the color of a mineral to change, sometimes with emission of light (thermoluminescence). Because even traces of foreign elements may cause this phenomenon, little exact information is available. Color centers of this type have been examined in the alkali halides.

In glasses several combinations of ions undergo an electron transfer and produce "metastable centers" under the influence of radiation. One of the most spectacular changes in the visible region results from an electron transfer from a Ce^{3+} ion to a V^{3+} ion. A soda-lime silicate glass to which 0.5% V_2O_5 and 0.5% CeO_2 have been added develops a green color due to the formation of V^{3+} ions. After exposure of this glass to sunlight the green color changes to purple. The V^{3+} ion (green) traps an electron donated by an excited Ce^{3+} ion and changes into a V^{2+} ion (purple).

$$Ce^{3+} + V^{3+} \rightarrow Ce^{4+} + V^{2+}$$

The V^{2+} ion, or more correctly, the V^{3+} ion plus its trapped electron, is the metastable color center of the solarized glass. On heating to 250 to 300°C the original green color is restored with emission of light. A similar phenomenon occurs in glasses containing manganese which assumes a purple color due to the transition Mn^{2+} into Mn^{3+}.

It is important to realize that these metastable color centers which have formed through an electron transfer process have absorption spectra which may differ considerably from normal V^{2+} or Mn^{3+} ions. The normal color centers in a glass have had the opportunity to form their own suitable environments. The metastable color centers, e.g., V^{2+} or Mn^{3+} ions, have formed in the glass at room temperature and, therefore, find themselves in environments (coordination number) which are suitable for the original V^{3+} or Mn^{2+} ions but not for the ones which have trapped or donated electrons.

Recent interest in dosimeters and indicators for high energy radiation led to the development of several glasses which change their absorption in the visible or in the ultraviolet part of the spectrum when they are exposed to gamma radiation. In most of these dosimeters the nature of the color centers that form in the glass is still obscure. We shall discuss herein only two examples for which the structural changes upon irradiation is fairly well established.

Silver ions can be introduced into some complex phosphate glasses in fairly high concentrations (15% Ag_2O). These ions are colorless and they do not fluoresce. However, when such a glass is exposed to high energy radiation, electrons are liberated from O^{2-} ions and trapped by Ag^+ ions. This electron transfer produces fluorescent silver atoms according to

$$O^{2-} + Ag^+ \xrightarrow{h\gamma} O^- + Ag^0$$

The fluorescence intensity can be used for estimating the energy of the radiation to which the glass has been exposed. W. A. Weyl, J. H. Schulman, R. J. Ginther, and L. W. Evans (214) developed a radiation-indicating phosphate glass on this basis.

The introduction of elemental sulfur into some acidic glasses gives rise to a blue color (boro-ultramarine of H. Knapp, 1879) as the result of the formation of S_2 molecules. Elemental sulfur in the form of S_2 molecules has a characteristic light absorption because of the presence of unpaired electrons. The addition of electrons to this color center changes it into a colorless anion according to

$$2O^{2-} + S_2 \xrightarrow{h\gamma} 2O^- + (S_2)^{2-}$$

This reaction has been used by K. O. Otley and W. A. Weyl (215) for developing a direct reading indicator for high energy radiation; namely, a blue glass that fades when it is exposed to gamma radiation.

The formation of radiation centers in a glass involves electronic conductivity over limited distances. The electronic conductivity of oxide glasses is too small to be measured, but it is sufficient to influence the stability of radiation centers.

By far the most comprehensive study of radiation centers (solarization) and their stability as a functon of the composition of the base glass has been made by G. E. Rindone (216). Glasses containing small quantities of the oxides of cerium and arsenic were exposed to sunlight and the loss of transmission was measured. Solar radiation caused an electron transfer and produced an electronic system which in its excited state absorbs visible light. The degree to which a glass solarizes depends upon the rate at which the electrons can return to their original quantum states. This rate depends upon what would be called "electronic conductivity" in a macroscopic description. In atomic dimensions the rate of the return of the electrons is determined by the degree to which the anions are tightened by their environment. This means that the number of color centers formed depends on the firmness with which the electron is held in the trapped position which ultimately determines the change in transmission. If the energy required for the return of the electron is very low, little or no color change will occur.

The fact that the energy needed for restoring the electron into its original position is lower in glasses where the oxygen ions are less polarized is substantiated by observations of the temperatures required for restoring the original transmission. Heating samples of the solarized glasses for one hour at various temperatures reveals that the original transmission is restored at lower temperatures for those glasses in which the oxygen is less polarized. For example, fading begins at 100°C for potash glasses containing barium oxide and is complete at 300°C. For the soda-magnesia glasses fading begins at 200°C. and temperatures above 400°C. are needed for restoring the original transmission. This means, in terms of the activation energy needed for the return of the trapped electrons, that if the soda-magnesia glass mentioned above is exposed to solar radiation while it is heated between 200 and 400°C., its solarization would be comparable to that of the potash-barium oxide glass solarized at room temperature.

Soda glasses containing alkaline earth oxides solarize in the order BaO < SrO < CaO < MgO. This is represented in Figure 17 in which the loss in transmittance, i.e., the transmittance of the unsolarized glass minus the transmittance of the solarized glass, is plotted against wavelength. The presence of PbO prevents solarization in most cases.

Lithia glasses containing alkaline earth oxides solarize in the order CaO < BaO < SrO < MgO. There is no solarization in the lithia glasses containing PbO.

In the potash glasses MgO causes considerably more solarization than the other divalent oxides. Solarization increases in the order PbO < BaO < SrO < CaO < MgO, although the differences between BaO, SrO, and CaO are small.

Solarization increases with increasing SiO_2 content in the soda-magnesia glasses.

The measurement of the stability of color centers provides a valuable and most interesting method for studying the localized

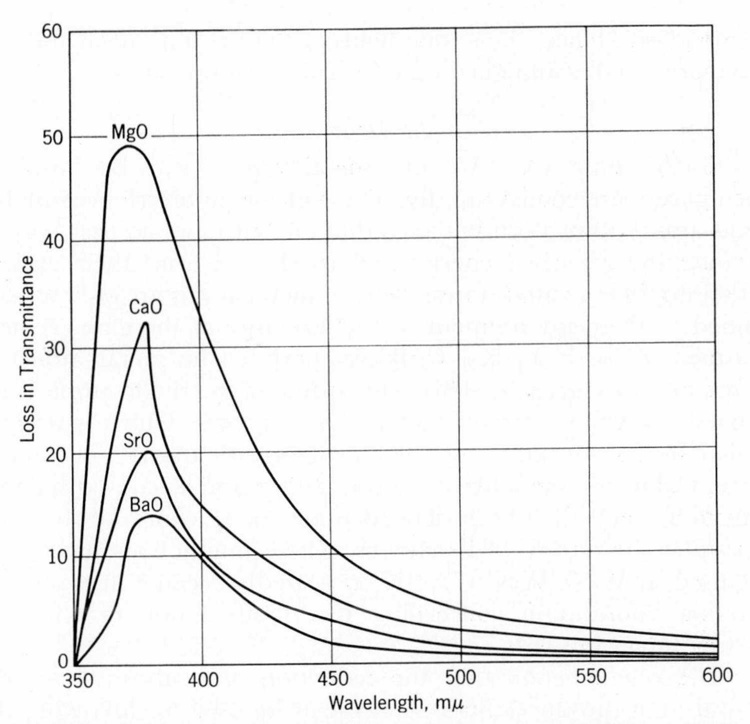

FIG. 17. Solarization (loss in transmittance) of sodium-alkaline earth-silicate glasses activated with cerium-arsenic. Solarized 1200 hours. (From (216).)

electronic conductivity in oxide glasses. The constitution of the glass enters this picture as can be seen from the role played by the alkalies.

For glasses containing Na_2O and K_2O, the effect of the different alkaline earth oxides is exactly as expected. The order of increased concentration of color centers, Ba < Sr < Ca < Mg, is the order of decreasing size, decreasing polarizability, and increasing polarizing power. The barium glasses have, so to speak, the highest electronic conductivity. The behavior of the lithia glasses shows the simultaneous presence of two antagonistic effects. Increasing the polarizability of the O^{2-} ions, e.g., through the replacing of MgO by BaO, should lower the solarization because it should enable the electrons to return faster to their original position. This change, however, enables the Li^+ ions to remain more uniformly distributed in the glass so that they do not form subcolloidal micelles to the same extent as in the corresponding Li-Mg-silicate glass. Hence, the strong fields of the Li^+ ions affect the O^{2-} ions more in a barium glass than in a magnesium glass.

(*8*) *Metals*

Single atoms (Ag, Au) or "metal vapors" can be frozen in when glasses are cooled rapidly. These glasses fluoresce because the metal atoms absorb ultraviolet radiation but have no easy way to dissipate the absorbed energy and to change from their excited states into their ground states. Neutral metal atoms are only weakly bonded to their environment in the structure of the glass. A heat treatment of such a glass (striking) permits the metal atoms to diffuse and to aggregate. This aggregation of the single atoms leads to particles which develop metallicity, a process which is accompanied by the formation of color centers with the loss of fluorescence. Color and metallicity are intimately connected and for thin films of a metal they both depend upon the thickness of the films and upon the nature of its carrier. These interactions have been discussed by W. A. Weyl (77, 217) repeatedly because they provide valuable information concerning the depth action of chemical binding forces in solids.

The phenomenon that the reduction of a silver ion to the neutral atom produces fluorescence can be used for following the diffusion of hydrogen molecules into a glass which contains Ag^+ ions as indicators. As the H_2 molecules diffuse into the glass they reduce the silver ions to atoms and make the glass fluorescent.

Heating the fluorescent glass causes the silver atoms to aggregate. The fluorescence disappears and the glass assumes a yellow to brown color which is the result of particles of metallic silver (silver stain).

The silver stain and the copper stain have been widely used for decorations on glass and for producing colors. These techniques are based on the substitution of a Ag^+ ion for a Na^+ ion or a Cu^+ ion for a K^+ ion and subsequent reduction of these ions to the metals.

H. S. Williams (218) studied the reactions of a soda lime silicate glass with the vapor of CuCl. The Cu^+ ions introduced by by a treatment with CuCl vapor produce a strong greenish fluorescence when irradiated with the 2537 A. line and a weak orange fluorescence when exposed to 3650 A. radiation. Exposure of the glass to CuCl vapor at 500°C and higher causes the Cu^+ ion to disproportionate into Cu-atoms and Cu^{2+} ions and the latter produce blue color.

The distribution of the Cu^{+} ion, i.e., their concentration gradient as a function of time and temperature, can be studied by treating the glass with hydrogen and allowing the metal atoms to aggregate and develop color centers (copper ruby).

The rate of aggregation of gold atoms and the formation of metallic color centers is a function of the temperature and of the binding forces which are active between the gold atoms and their carrier. If the binding forces are weak the color centers are formed at a lower temperature than if these forces are strong. This relation has been used by E. C. Marboe and W. A. Weyl (219) for studying the forces between gold atoms and ionic solids.

If an oxide such as Sb_2O_5, Sb_2O_3, Bi_2O_3 or PbO is introduced into a glass, the O^{2-} ions participate in the screening of all cations. Exposure of such a glass to hydrogen gas can produce metallic

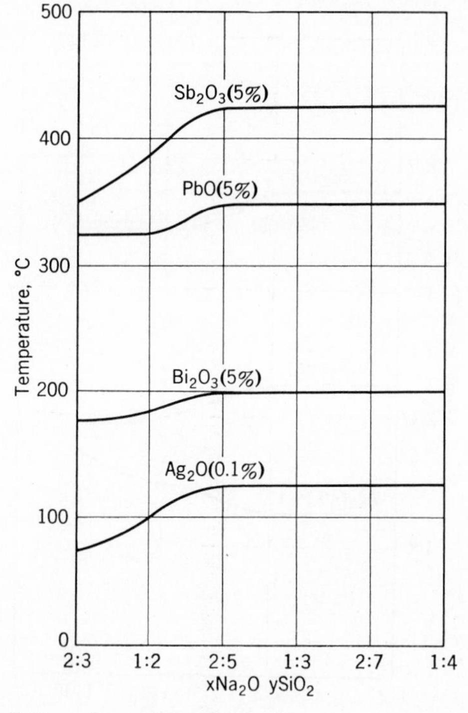

FIG. 18. Reducibility of metal ions by hydrogen in sodium silicate glasses. (From (220).)

color centers by a reaction of the type

$$2Bi_2^{3+}O_3^{2-} + 3H_2 \rightarrow 4Bi + 6OH^-$$

This reaction changes some of the O^{2-} ions of the glass into lesser screening OH^- ions. As the O^{2-} ions are shared with Si^{4+} or B^{3+} ions the constitution of the glass determines the temperature at which metallic color centers can form. Experiments of this type have been performed by A. W. Bastress (220) who used borates, silicates and boro-silicates of different alkalinity (Figs. 18–20). The data given in Table XXIX reveal that the addition of more than 15% TiO_2 to a sodium disilicate glass makes it increasingly difficult to form metallic color centers of Pb.

It is not likely that this strong increase in the temperature of formation of metallic lead is the result of the increased difficulty of reducing the lead ion to the atom. Very likely the participation of such a high concentration of titania in the glass structure makes it difficult for the Pb atoms to diffuse and to form metallic color

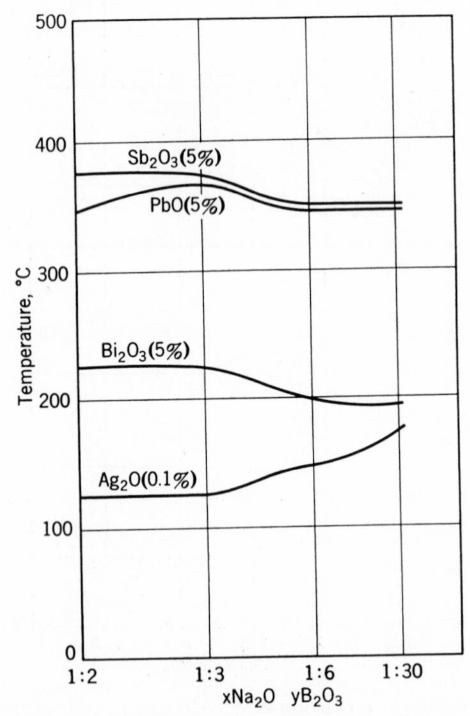

FIG. 19. Reducibility of metal ions by hydrogen in sodium borate glasses. (From (220).)

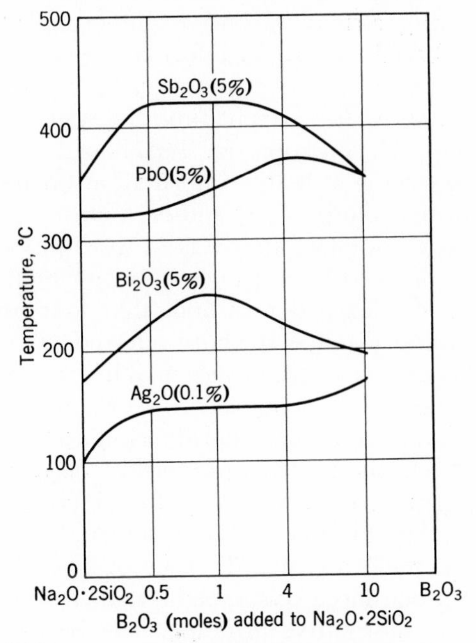

FIG. 20. Reducibility of metal ions by hydrogen in sodium borosilicate glasses. (From (220).)

TABLE XXIX

Effect of Additions to Sodium Disilicate Glass

Glass composition	Temperature of color center formation, °C.
Na_2O, $2SiO_2$	350
Na_2O, $2SiO_2$ + 5% TiO_2 + 5% PbO	350
Na_2O, $2SiO_2$ + 15% TiO_2 + 5% PbO	375
Na_2O, $2SiO_2$ + 25% TiO_2 + 5% PbO	525
Na_2O, $2SiO_2$ + 35% TiO_2 + 5% PbO	550

centers. Ti^{4+} ions act as "metallophilic" ions which delay the diffusion of metal atoms in a glass. For more detailed information on the role of metallophilic groups in controlling the rate of diffusion of metal atoms the paper of E. C. Marboe and W. A. Weyl (214) and the book *Coloured Glasses* (29) should be consulted.

C. CONCLUSIONS

The application of color and fluorescence indicators which have been described in this chapter reveals the versatility of the method for solving structural and technological problems. The method itself is based largely on information obtained from color studies using crystals of known structures as the hosts for ions of the transition elements. At the present time the systematic work of O. Schmitz-DuMont, H. Brokopf, K. Burkhardt, and H. Gossling (221,222) is producing valuable information on the effect of the environment on the color of Co^{2+} and Ni^{2+} ions.

This might be the place to extend a word of warning to those who apply the color and fluorescence indicator methods to crystalline substances. We learned in school that four apples and four pears cannot be added unless they are referred to as eight pieces of fruit, which of course is less informative. The same logic applies to the screening of cations. It is not useful to describe an asymmetrical environment of a cation by one coordination number. The figure 8 in the description of the coordination of Pb^{2+} ions in PbO does not have the same significance as the figure 4 in describing the coordination of Si^{4+} ions. The Pb^{2} ion in PbO is screened by eight O^{2-} ions: however, four of them are at a distance of 2.30 A. and the other four are at the much larger distance of 4.29 A. from the Pb^{2+} ion. It is much more informative to emphasize the asymmetry of the Pb^{2+} ion in PbO than to give its coordination number.

Very likely the Pb^{2+} ion in glasses is in sixfold coordination, in some lead fluoride glasses maybe even in eightfold coordination, but this is not of primary importance for the constitution of these glasses. Important is the fact that the lead ion assumes a highly symmetrical coordination in a glass so that colorless glasses can be made which contain 90% PbO from an oxide which in itself is brown.

Color indicators give us information about the symmetry of the polyhedra and the way it is affected by substitutions and additions. Color indicators can make visible the thermal history of glasses whereas all other methods reveal changes of properties which do not permit an unambiguous interpretation.

Color indicators can be used for studying the interaction of glasses with their environment. The diffusion of hydrogen and oxygen into a rigid glass can be made visible by selecting the proper color and fluorescence indicator. The diffusion of water into a glass changes some O^{2-} ions into the less polarizable OH^{-} ion, a change which causes a cation such as the Co^{2+} ion to increase its coordination from 4 to 6 and to signal its different environment by changing from a deep blue into a pink color.

The rate of diffusion of metal atoms within a glass or on surfaces can be made visible by the development of metallic color centers.

Color and fluorescence indicators can be used in cases where other methods fail to provide information. This method, more than any other, has been elaborated upon because little information on it is available in the literature and it can be used to help solve problems in addition to those encountered in glasses. An exploration of the behavior of fused salts and of the chemistry of surfaces would certainly gain by the use of optical indicators. Later, when we discuss the chemistry of surfaces, we will learn about another group of optical indicators which can give us useful information concerning the force fields of surfaces.

4. Magnetism

The introduction of "magnetic indicators" to a glass should provide information similar to that obtained from optical indicators. However, the experimental work in this field has not been extended to include systematically varied simple glasses that would permit an unambiguous interpretation of their paramagnetic susceptibilities. One of the first efforts made in this field is the work of C. Andresen-Kraft (223) who compared the magnetic susceptibilities of silicate glasses of different states of oxidation. These glasses contained both Fe^{2+} and Fe^{3+} ions and their equilibria were followed by a combination of magnetic and optical measurements. The main target of this work was the development of a method that would permit a rapid determination of the state of oxidation of the iron in technical glasses. At the time this work was done, structural questions could not be attacked by these methods. The interaction of Fe^{2+} and Fe^{3+} ions is of such complexity that iron glasses do not provide a suitable basis for a structural interpretation of a new property.

K. Breit and R. Juza (224) introduced Co^{2+} and Ni^{2+} ions as magnetic indicators into various alkali borate glasses. These indicators are much simpler than the oxidation equilibrium between the ions of iron and, indeed, these authors were able to correlate magnetic susceptibilities with the color of the glasses. Glasses which produced the red CoO_6 groups gave a magnetic susceptibility of 163×10^{-6} for the Co^{2+} ion and the blue glasses gave lower values (152×10^{-6}).

P. W. Selwood (225) in his book on magnetochemistry reviews

earlier work on glasses that contained paramagnetic ions. He reached the conclusion that more systematic work, especially in the low temperature region, was needed before the determination of the susceptibility of paramagnetic ions in glasses could be used as a structural tool. There is no obvious reason why such a systematic study could not be made but we believe that it is doubtful that the paramagnetic indicator method will yield information about the constitution of glasses which could not be obtained otherwise, e.g., by color indicators.

According to our views, the value of magnetic measurements lies primarily in its adaptability to the study of orientation in glass fibers. For obvious reasons it would be very difficult to determine a small distortion or an orientation of CoO_4 or CoO_6 polyhedra in glasses by means of absorption measurements. However, glass fibers or bundles of fibers lend themselves readily to the determination of the paramagnetic and diamagnetic anisotropy.

E. Weir Toor (226) measured the magnetic anisotropy of two types of glasses, one a diamagnetic sodium magnesium silicate (Na_2O, MgO, $4SiO_2$) and the other a paramagnetic glass of the composition Na_2O, NiO, $4SiO_2$. The magnetic moment of the Ni^{2+} ion in this glass was 3.6 Bohr magnetons.

Drawing these glasses into fibers and measuring the magnetic anisotropy revealed that the magnesium glass remained isotropic within the limits of experimental error but the nickel glass became anisotropic. The paramagnetic anisotropy of the nickel glass was weak for fibers thicker than 0.2 mm. in diameter but it increased rapidly with decreasing thickness of the fibers or with increasing rate of drawing. Annealing the fibers of the nickel glass restored its magnetic isotropy.

Without going into experimental details one can readily see that the measurement of the magnetic anisotropy provides a method for studying orientation effects under conditions (fibers) in which the corresponding indicator method based on light absorption would encounter experimental difficulties.

Glasses that do not contain paramagnetic ions are diamagnetic. P. W. Selwood, J. A. Parodi and A. Pace, Jr. (227) studied the orientation of essentially vitreous organic high polymers by measuring the diamagnetic anisotropy as a function of the rate of drawing. Polyethylene terephthalate fibers revealed an anisotropy which increased with increasing drawing ratio.

B. K. Banerjee (65) applied this method to inorganic glasses and found that vitreous B_2O_3 developed a strong anisotropy when drawn into fibers. In contrast to vitreous B_2O_3, the diamagnetic anisotropy of vitreous SiO_2, and some borosilicate glasses was zero. We consider this experiment of Banerjee to be of paramount importance for the understanding of the vitreous state. We used this information for the classification of glasses, in particular, for the part which the orientable liquid of the Stewart type plays in glass formation. Banerjee's measurements reveal that pure B_2O_3 is an orientable liquid (Stewart type) and that the addition of alkali changes it into a Bernal type liquid. The diamagnetic anisotropy of a sodium borate glass with 10% Na_2O was only one tenth the value of that of the pure B_2O_3 glass.

5. Refractive Index, Molar Refractivity, and Density

When we discussed the molar refractivity of the O^{2-} ions we saw that K. Fajans and N. J. Kreidl (26) used this value for interpreting the interactions between cations and anions in silicates. The value of $R_{O^{2-}}$ of the orthosilicates varies between 3.35 for the orthosilicate of beryllium and 4.97 for that of barium. K. Fajans and his school have used the molar and ionic refractivities, in particular, their deviations from additivity to learn more about the intricate electrical interactions in molecules and compounds.

W. Biltz, F. Weibke, and L. Schrader-Traeger (228) claim that the molar refractivities of certain simple glasses are strictly additive and that their calculation from the oxide-increments leads to fairly accurate results. These relations have been examined many times. In particular, E. Kordes (27) and Kordes and H. Becker (229) made numerous measurements and calculated the molar refractivities of binary glasses and found distinct deviations from additivity.

The refractive index of a glass and its change with the composition and heat treatment are of primary importance for optical glasses but it cannot be related directly to structural changes because the refractive index n_D depends upon two properties, the molar refractivity R and the molar volume V. The molar refractivity resembles the density or the specific volume inasmuch as it cannot give us any structural details because it integrates over the whole system. The molar refractivity is an average of the responses to light of all O^{2-} ions in a potassium silicate glass in which the response of the nonbridging O^{2-} ion is considerably greater than that of the bridging ones.

The Lorentz-Lorenz equation, when solved for n reveals that the refractive index decreases with increasing molar volume V or with decreasing density d. This relation accounts for the fact that the n value of many substances decreases with increasing temperature or increasing volumes because of the lower electron density. Some substances, glasses and crystals, show the opposite trend, their n values increase on heating in spite of their expansion which decreases the number of responding electrons in unit volume. Among crystals MgO is a good example. The molar refractivity R or the polarizability which is vested primarily in the O^{2-} anion increases as the lattice expands because the tightening effects which the Mg^{2+} ions exert upon the O^{2-} ions decreases with increasing Mg—O distance. The number of electrons per unit volume which respond to the alternating electric field of light decreases but their response increases.

As far as glasses are concerned, the relationship between refractive index and temperature can be summarized as follows:

1. Fluor crowns contain a substantial concentration of F^- ions. These anions are not strongly deformed because of their low polarizability. Hence, on heating a fluor crown, the state of polarization of the anions undergoes little change; therefore, these glasses have a negative temperature coefficient of refractive index. The effect of the electron density change predominates.

2. For most glasses, however, the refractive index increases with increasing temperature up to the softening range.

3. Above the softening range the volume of glasses expands more rapidly on heating and the refractive index of all glasses decreases. In all cases, however, the refractive index—up to the highest temperature for which measurements are available—remains higher than that value which would be expected on the basis of the density change.

The expansion of the composition fields of glasses was primarily the result of an increasing demand for optical elements with a wider range of optical properties, in particular, refractive index and dispersion. Hence, numerous data have been accumulated in the literature concerning the refractive index as a function of the composition of simple and complex glasses.

Refractive index measurements can be made with great ac-

accuracy if the glass is sufficiently homogeneous. The major contributions to the constitution of glasses made by refractive index measurements concern those changes which take place during annealing. It was primarily the change of the refractive index of glasses with temperature and thermal treatment which enabled A. A. Lebedeff (230) to conclude that the changes of glass properties during annealing are not primarily the result of the removal of mechanical stresses but must be the result of structural changes comparable with the transformation of high quartz into low quartz.

The first three rules governing the mutual interaction of ions (see Chapter III) reveal that the electron cloud of an anion is tightened by:

1. An increase of the nuclear charge
2. A penetration of one or more protons into the anion
3. Adjacent cations

There is no simple relation between the refractive index of a glass and its composition and structure. There are special cases in which the n_D values can give valuable hints about structural changes in glasses. As an example we will cite the work of J. F. Schairer and N. L. Bowen (115) who determined the isofracts (lines of equal n_D value) of glasses in the ternary system Na_2O-SiO_2-Al_2O_3. This diagram reveals that the addition of Na_2O to silica increases the refractive index as one would expect. In vitreous silica all O^{2-} ions are tightened strongly by two adjacent Si^{4+} ions (n_D for SiO_2 = 1.458). The introduction of nonbridging, more polarizable O^{2-} ions through the addition of Na_2O increases the average polarizability of the anions, and with it the n_D value of the glass. Corundum has a higher refractive index (n_D = 1.76) than the different forms of silica because of the lower charge of the Al^{3+} ion. Hence, we would expect the addition of Al_2O_3 to SiO_2 to raise the n_D value. However, the addition of Na_2O to a mixture of Al_2O_3 and SiO_2 in the molar ratio 1:2 lowers its n_D value. This unexpected effect of the alkali is interpreted as resulting from the change of the AlO_6 octahedra into AlO_4 tetrahedra. The smaller Al-O distance in the tetrahedra leads to a stronger tightening of the electron clouds of the O^{2-} ions which in turn lowers the n_D value. The isofracts in the ternary diagram Na_2O-SiO_2-Al_2O_3 reveal that the nonbridging O^{2-} ions are eliminated when Al_2O_3 is added to a sodium silicate glass. They also reveal that alumina participates in such a glass primarily as AlO_4 tetrahedra. Thus the isofracts of the system

Na_2O-Al_2O_3-SiO_2 suggest constitutional changes in a sodium silicate glass upon the addition of Al_2O_3 which are in good agreement with other properties of these glasses, in particular, the increase in modulus of elasticity, viscosity, and chemical resistivity.

A. Dietzel (114) deduced from the increment of the refractive index of Al_2O_3 as determined from binary glasses in the system Al_2O_3-SiO_2 that these glasses contain Al^{3+} ions in fourfold as well as in sixfold coordination. The basis of his reasoning is the low increment of Al_2O_3 in feldspars (1.50) in which the Al^{3+} ions are in fourfold coordination as compared with the higher increment (1.76) for Al^{3+} in sixfold coordination and the intermediate increment (1.6) in binary Al_2O_3-SiO_2 glasses.

There is no need to enter into a detailed discussion of the effect which the composition of a glass has upon its refractive index because these relations are very well covered by G. W. Morey (6). He gives diagrams of the isofracts of several ternary systems which are presented in addition to the optical properties of commercial optical glasses. The atomistic interpretation of the refractive index of a glass is difficult and ambiguous.

For example, the n_D value of vitreous GeO_2 (1.607) is considerably larger than that of vitreous SiO_2 (1.458). We attribute this difference primarily to the stronger tightening of the O^{2-} ions by the stronger fields of the smaller Si^{4+} cores. However, we also have to take into consideration the fact that the larger Ge^{4+} ion itself makes a greater contribution to the n_D value than the Si^{4+} ion, the polarizability of which is neglibible.

In spite of the field strength of the P^{5+} core being higher than that of the Si^{4+} core, the n_D value of P_2O_5 (1.517) is higher than that of SiO_2 (1.458). The P_2O_5 glass contains some nonbridging O^{2-} ions because its oxygen ratio is greater (2.5) than that of SiO_2 (2.0). Vitreous silica does not contain nonbridging, highly polarizable O^{2-} ions.

The evaluation of the molar refractivities of glasses in the systems Li_2O-P_2O_5 and Na_2O-P_2O_5 by E. Kordes and H. Becker (229) reveals the tightening effect which these ions have upon the nonbridging O^{2-} ions. If the molar refractivity is calculated on the basis of increments, the Na^+ and Li^+ ions would have to be given negative molar refractivities, i.e., $R_{Na^+} = -0.38$ and $R_{Li^+} = -0.92$. However, only protons have zero polarizability and no ion can have a negative value. These deviations from additivity are the result of the tightening effect of the Na^+ and Li^+ ions upon the electron clouds of the nonbridging O^{2-} ions.

The first measurements of the temperature dependence of the refractive index of optical glasses were made by C. Pulfrich in 1892 and by J. O. Reed in 1898. Their results and the later work in this field are fully discussed by G. W. Morey (6). Among the newer contributions the work of L. Prod'homme (231) offers some very interesting additions. He found very high negative values for the temperature coefficient of the refractive index of vitreous B_2O_3 which no doubt are the result of the extremely high thermal expansion of this glass combined with a low n_D value. The most interesting feature, however, is the fact that vitreous P_2O_5 shows exactly the same behavior. This speaks very strongly for a structural similarity between the two glasses and suggests that vitreous P_2O_5 may have a high coefficient of thermal expansivity similar to that of vitreous B_2O_3.

Summarizing, we may say that the index of refraction of a glass represents the response of all electrons and that its temperature coefficient reflects two antagonistic effects. Raising the temperature decreases the electron density per unit volume due to thermal expansion but it increases the response of the electrons of the anions because the increased internuclear distance loosens their electron clouds.

The complexity of the effect of structural changes on the refractive index of a glass limits its usefulness as a method for studying the constitution of the glass. However, the accuracy with which the n_D value of a glass can be measured makes it useful for following structural changes even if the latter cannot be given an unambiguous interpretation. Hence, scientists interested in the equilibria and their changes in glass with temperature and time frequently use the n_D value because in many cases an atomistic interpretation is not essential.

There is, for example, the fundamental question: Is the property of a glass a function of the temperature at which it has been melted or is the structural (chemical) equilibrium established fast in the molten state? A. Dietzel and O. W. Flörke (232) answered this question for simple alkali silicates and a soda lime silica glass by measuring the n_D values of glasses which were melted at widely different temperatures, in particular in temperature regions where quartz is the stable phase (below 870°C) and other regions where tridymite is stable. No matter what the melting history of these glasses had been, their n_D value was the same. Hence, they concluded that their structures were identical and independent of the melting history.

This answers an important question and contributes to our knowledge of glass melting. The index of refraction is used here only as a sensitive indicator for structural changes in a general way.

Optical glasses are catalogued according to their index of refractions for the D-line, n_D, and their Abbe numbers. The latter is the reciprocal value of the relative dispersion:

$$\gamma = (n_D - 1)/(n_F - n_C)$$

The wavelengths of the Fraunhofer lines which have been chosen for characterizing the dispersion are:

$$C = 656\ \mu$$
$$D = 589\ \mu$$
$$F = 486\ \mu$$

According to this key a glass typed 517:645 means that its refractive index for the D-line has the value of 1.517 and its Abbe number is 64.5.

The density of a glass can be measured easily with a fair degree of accuracy. Hence, we find numerous efforts to evaluate density measurements in terms of atomic structure. The use of extreme values of the density-composition curve of glasses for detecting the formation of compounds was one of the favorite subjects before the arrival of X rays. The densities or the specific volumes of glasses were among the first properties that were calculated on the basis of the composition. "Factors" for the calculation of the specific volume were determined by A. Winkelmann and O. Schott (233) as early as 1894. When W. E. S. Turner started his fundamental and systematic studies of the properties of glasses as functions of the composition, he, too, in collaboration with S. English (234), established "factors" for calculating densities of glasses.

We look upon density as one of those properties which can be used only for confirming those conclusions concerning the structure of glasses that are based on other properties. Even if the density or the specific volume alone cannot tell us what is going on in a glass, they are still very useful as supporting information for the understanding of other properties. The deviations from additivity of the density of a soda lime silicate glass when Na_2O is replaced by Li_2O or by K_2O, the occurrence of maxima in the density of mixed alkali glasses, are important indications of the influence of alkalies upon the glass structure. A knowledge of this "packing effect" is important for an understanding of the ionic conductivity of mixed alkali glasses even if its interpretation cannot be entirely unambiguous.

S. C. Waterton and W. E. S. Turner (235) found that the substitution of Li_2O for Na_2O in a soda lime silicate glass increases the density up to a Li_2O:Na_2O ratio of 1:2. Beyond this ratio the density decreases with further Li_2O substitution.

The substitution of Li_2O for K_2O in a potash lime silicate glass causes the density to increase strongly until the ratio of Li_2O:K_2O = 1:2 is reached. Further substitution of Li_2O still increases the density but only slightly.

Glasses containing only Na_2O have a higher density than those containing only K_2O. Glasses containing both Na_2O and K_2O have a higher density than that calculated on the basis of additivity.

Waterton and Turner (235) also found that Na_2O-K_2O glasses which contain BaO or PbO in the place of CaO have densities that are more closely additive.

The nature of the alkali in a silicate glass determines the polarizability and, with it, the screening power of the O^{2-} ions, as can be seen from the colors of Ni^{2+} ions in corresponding alkali silicate glasses. It seems reasonable, therefore, to assume that the presence of one alkali ion in the glass may affect the coordination of another alkali ion. This could explain maxima in the density. However, there are other structural changes that are equally probable and that provide equally sound explanations. One has to consider, for example, the fact that a lithium silicate glass in annealed condition is heterogeneous in a subcolloidal range and it is very likely that this heterogeneity will decrease if K_2O is introduced. We know that the polarizable O^{2-} ions of K_2O increases the compatibility of oxides with silica (see Chapter XII).

Density measurements, for example those made in the system B_2O_3-Na_2O, cannot give us a definite suggestion concerning the nature of the structural changes which take place when Na_2O is added to B_2O_3. However, for judging the validity of our interpretation it is most important to consider the densities of these glasses. The transition of a spacious molecular structure (Stewart liquid) into a more compact Bernal liquid is supported by the density of these glasses.

E. Kordes and H. Becker (229) made extensive measurements

of the densities and molar refractivities of binary phosphate glasses. They report that the densities of the sodium phosphate glasses with less than 20 mole % Na_2O were lower than expected and they attribute the discrepancy to the retention of H_2O. Very likely the density of these glasses is low because their structures resemble those of the sodium borate glasses for which the density drops sharply when the Na_2O content becomes less than 20 mole %.

Density measurements are well established in the technological laboratories and are widely used for quality control. Precision methods have been worked out for the purpose of discovering the minute deviations in density which are introduced by faulty changes in the batch composition, inhomogeneities, and even by different degrees of annealing. Density measurements reflect the change of constitution during annealing as well as during crystallization. This applies to both inorganic and organic glasses.

The degree of crystallinity in polymers can be estimated on the basis of X-ray diffraction, density, or refractive index. Dacron that has been chilled has a density of 1.35 and a refractive index of 1.574. The values for a crystalline product are considerably higher; 1.46 for the density and 1.627 for the refractive index. Dacron with intermediate densities can be produced by appropriately varying the heat treatment.

The subject of density of glasses is well covered in G. W. Morey's book (6), *The Properties of Glasses*. Some of the most elaborate attempts to replace the use of "factors" for calculating the density of glasses and to find equations which allow one to correlate density with the chemical compositions of a wide variety of glasses will be found in the publications of M. L. Huggins (236) and of J. M. Stevels (237).

J. M. Stevels (237) used a formula which is based upon the volume of a glass that contains 1 gram atom of O^{2-} ions. This volume, V, is related to a universal constant, V_0, and the oxygen ratio, R, i.e., the number of O^{2-} ions divided by the number of network forming cations (Si^{4+}, B^{3+}, Al^{3+}). The universal constant, V_0, however, is not entirely empirical; its value comes very close to that volume which is occupied by 1 gram atom of closely packed O^{2-} ions (8.5 cm.^{3}). This volume compares well with the molecular volume of BeO (8.4 cm.^{3}) or that of Al_2O_3 (8.5 cm.^{3}). The formula suggested by Stevels

$$V = V_0/(1 - RX)$$

also contains a constant, X, which depends upon the nature of the network-formers. However, in the first approximation, it is affected neither by the nature nor the concentration of the network modifiers. The value of X decreases with increasing charge and decreasing size of the network formers. A decrease in the numerical value of X increases the value of $(1 - RX)$ and decreases the value of V. This means that highly charged network formers tighten the electron clouds of the O^{2-} ions to such an extent that the volume of the glass shrinks.

Glasses which obey this formula were called "normal" glasses by Stevels. Most remarkable is the fact that for a large number of glasses the density can be calculated on a basis which ignores the nature of the network modifiers. Introducing Li_2O or MgO into a glass, however, leads to "abnormal" glasses and Stevels discusses their deviations on the basis of their "contracting effects" upon the O^{2-} ions.

The limitation of any formula for calculating densities that is based upon the distinction between network-modifiers and network-formers is the arbitrariness of this distinction. Nevertheless, the relationship which seems to exist between the volume of a glass and its contraction by network forming cations as well as by Li^+ and Mg^{2+} ions, according to Stevels' formula, can become a source of interesting discussions, for example, on the effect of the simultaneous participation of several kinds of network-formers. For these details the writings of Stevels should be consulted.

In order to fully appreciate the difficulty of this problem we must remember that even for the well organized crystalline state no simple quantitative approach is available that allows one to correlate the "degree of packing" or the density of silicates with their refractive indices, etc. The work of H. W. Fairbairn (238) represents such an effort and indeed, he found a far-reaching parallelism between his "index" values and the index of refraction for numerous silicates. However, as soon as the minerals contain cations of the non-noble gas-type (e.g., Ti^{4+} and Fe^{2+} ions), this correlation fails. When L. Shartsis, W. Capps, and S. Spinner (239) made their systematic studies on alkali borates they also made a serious attempt to correlate their data with the calculations of Huggins and Stevels but they came to the conclusion that: "Neither the Huggins' nor the Stevels' method was suitable for the calculation of the densities of binary alkali borate glasses."

There are many reasons for the failure to find a scientific basis for the evaluation of the density or the specific volume of a glass. Firstly, the anions that fill the major part of the volume of a glass are neither spheres nor do they have a constant size. The description of vitreous silica as having a certain amount of empty space or as a structure in which the oxygen ions fill only about one half of the volume might be convenient for certain purposes, but it bears no relationship to the facts. An examination of silica by electron diffraction methods does not reveal any places in which the electron density comes close to zero.

Furthermore, there is the question of the temperatures at which one should compare the specific volumes of two glasses. The widely different thermal expansions of glasses is another reason which makes it impossible to use the density as a tool for examining structures. Density measurements in the high temperature region by H. F. Shermer (240) reveal that the high silica glasses have the highest densities. At ordinary temperature the high alkali glasses have the highest densities. The temperature at which the cross-over occurred was $\sim$800°C. for Li_2O glasses and 1300°C. for Na_2O glasses.

Refractive index, molar refractivity, and density are properties that do not yield detailed information concerning the constitution of glasses but ought to be considered in all structural interpretations. The fact that quartz is denser than cristobalite can only mean that the average Si—O bond energy in quartz exceeds that of cristobalite. The fact that quartz can melt at a temperature around 200°C. below the melting point of cristobalite indicates that it is not the average bond energy that is overcome by the thermal motion. These pieces of information are important for our over-all picture of the constitution of glasses. The fact that both high temperature cristobalite and vitreous silica have similar low densities does not prove that their structures are very similar, but it lends strong support to this conclusion gained from other properties such as the low heat of fusion and the low coefficient of thermal expansion.

A similar situation applies to the molar refractivity of the oxygen. When applied to analogous systems the value of $R_{O^{2-}}$ can give us much valuable information. The work of K. Fajans and N. J. Kreidl (26) on orthosilicates may be cited as a good example. They found good agreement between the value of $R_{O^{2-}}$

and the field strength or the tightening power of the cations. K. Fajans and S. W. Barber (241) used the value of $R_{O^{2-}}$ of vitreous B_2O_3 (3.50) which is close to that of corundum (3.48) for supporting their views that vitreous B_2O_3 must be a molecular liquid. If the average B—O interaction is even stronger than the Al—O interaction in corundum it can only mean that the average B—O bond must be the result of some very strong B—O interactions and some much weaker interactions, otherwise one cannot understand the difference in the melting points of crystalline B_2O_3 and Al_2O_3.

This reasoning of Fajans and Barber is of extreme importance for our structural picture and for an understanding of the chemical properties of vitreous B_2O_3. Why is B_2O_3 so hygroscopic?

Earlier we learned that the state of polarization of the anion is one of the most important factors controlling the rate of hydrolysis (see Chapter V). The penetration of a proton from an acid aqueous system into an oxide is fast if the value of $R_{O^{2-}}$ is high. Tightening the electron clouds of the O^{2-} ions by cations of high field strengths lowers the value of $R_{O^{2-}}$ and slows down proton penetration. How, then, can we account for the fact that Al_2O_3 does not hydrate readily whereas B_2O_3 does so in spite of its small value of $R_{O^{2-}}$? This apparent contradiction can be resolved easily if we assume that the value of $R_{O^{2-}}$ measured for B_2O_3 represents an average over at least two widely different groups of $R_{O^{2-}}$ values, one being much smaller than the average and the other much larger. There is no method for measuring this distribution of the values of $R_{O^{2-}}$ within a system, but one can speculate. Because of the importance of this relationship we shall present our ideas on the subject in the form of a qualitative scheme, a pictorial presentation of the conditions which must prevail in glasses, and one which we found very useful.

We plot the distribution of the polarizability of the oxygens in Figure 21. Only for the highly symmetrical crystals of corundum and of cristobalite do the measured values of $R_{O^{2-}}$ have a physical reality because in these cases all oxygens are equivalent. Due to the thermal motion there will be a fluctuation of the polarizability with time but essentially the value of $R_{O^{2-}}$ represents the state of polarization of all anions. The two bars (Fig. 21*a*) represent the idealized state of polarization of the oxygens in corundum (3.48) and in cristobalite (3.65).

The value of $R_{O^{2-}}$ for vitreous silica is nearly the same as that

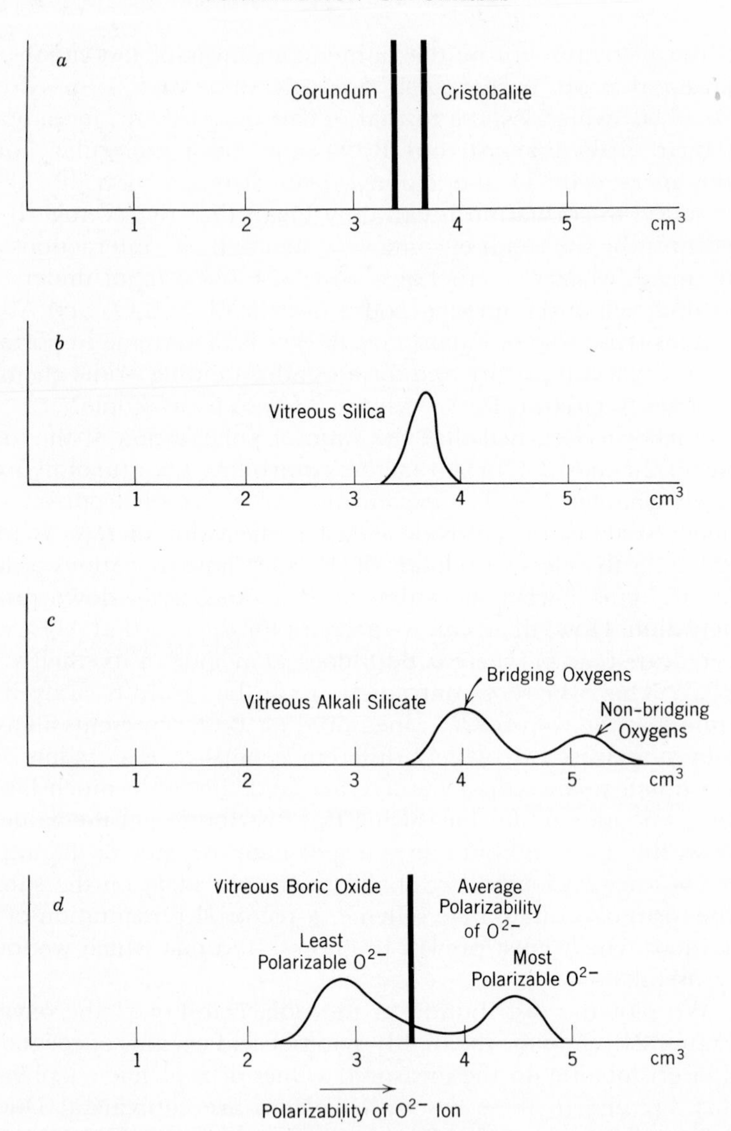

FIG. 21. Scheme representing the polarizabilities of anions in different systems. *a*, Corundum and cristobalite; *b*, vitreous silica; *c*, alkali silicate glass; *d*, vitreous boric oxide.

of cristobalite (3.66) but the lack of periodicity means that not all O^{2-} ions are equal. Hence, we plot an arbitrary distribution curve that gives us the relative concentration of the O^{2-} ions with their slightly different polarizabilities (Fig. 21*b*). This curve gives the average of the polarizability of all O^{2-} ions as being the same as that in cristobalite but it indicates that there is a variation, i.e., a spread, because of the nonequality of the anions. Such a curve would reflect the different thermal history of the glass if it were possible to obtain it experimentally.

In contrast to conventional descriptions of the structure of the alkali silicates we emphasize the asymmetry of forces, especially the strong disturbance of the flawless liquid of the Bernal type which accompanies the introduction of the first 10 to 15% alkali. We cannot accept the conventional picture that a small number of "broken bonds" in an otherwise rigid framework would produce such a spectacular change. We assume that the formation of non-bridging O^{2-} ions disproportionates all binding forces into some weaker and some stronger forces because of the asymmetry that they introduce into the tetrahedra. We assume that the introduction of alkali increases the polarizability of all O^{2-} ions, even the bridging oxygens. This depth action of chemical binding can be pictured (Fig. 21*c*) in our scheme.

Our schematic picture of the distribution of the $R_{O^{2-}}$ in boric oxide (Fig. 21*d*) should be interpreted as follows: What we measured is the average state of polarization of the O^{2-} ions. This value, in contrast to that of Al_2O_3 and SiO_2 (Fig. 21*a*) has no physical reality just as the average B—O bond energy in vitreous B_2O_3 has no reality. In order to understand the properties of B_2O_3 we assume with Fajans and Barber (241) that there is a very strong intramolecular interaction between B^{3+} and some O^{2-} ions and a much weaker intermolecular interaction. The former is responsible for the mechanical strength and the toughness of vitreous B_2O_3, and the latter is responsible for the ease of flow and the hygroscopicity of B_2O_3.

When we discuss the constitution of the alkali silicates, aluminosilicates, borosilicates, and other complex glasses we shall use this scheme because it affords a simple manner by which to express our ideas on this subject. Even if these curves cannot be quantitatively derived experimentally from optical measurements, at least their shapes can be derived indirectly from other properties.

6. Specific Heat

The classical kinetic approach to the specific heat of solids at constant volume, c_v, leads to the relation

$$c_v = 3R$$

in which R is the gas constant. This relation, the law of Dulong and Petit, is valid only in the high temperature region and it requires the atomic vibrations to be treated as harmonic oscillations. (See the book of F. Seitz (242).)

The classical kinetic approach to the specific heats of simple solids failed to explain that the specific heats of most solids, e.g., of metallic silver, approach zero monotonically when the temperature approaches 0°K. A. Einstein, in 1906, offered an explanation for this discrepancy by pointing out that classical mechanics assumes a continuity of energy states, but according to the quantum theory this assumption is not valid. A simple solid may be described as a three-dimensional array of atomic oscillators that vibrate with the same characteristic frequency. Einstein postulated that a change in temperature can change the energy states of these oscillators only by integer multiples of $h\gamma$ wherein h is Planck's constant and γ the frequency characteristic for the atom.

In 1912, P. Debye elaborated on Einstein's qualitative explanation of the deviation of c_v from the law of Dulong and Petit by introducing a refinement; namely, a more accurate analysis of the modes of atomic vibrations. He suggested a modification of Dulong and Petit's law which applies to the temperature region close to 0°K.:

$$c_v = R(T/T_{\mathrm{D}})^3$$

T_{D} is a constant which is characteristic for the solid and which is called the "Debye characteristic temperature."

The heat capacity of a simple solid can be related to the frequencies of vibrations and the latter are reflected in the Raman spectrum and in the infrared absorption of the solid. The vibrational frequency of an oscillating atom is a function of its vibrating mass and the force constant; namely

$$\gamma = \tfrac{1}{2}\pi \text{ (force constant/mass)}^{\frac{1}{2}}$$

For simple solids such as Al_2O_3 (only one kind of Al—O distance) these theoretical approaches to specific heat and infrared spectra can be used as good approximations.

K. Fajans and S. Barber (241) used the low temperature specific heat of Al_2O_3 (sapphire), crystalline and vitreous B_2O_3, and some molecular compounds (glucose, benzene) for deriving a structural picture of vitreous B_2O_3. The heat capacity of Al_2O_3 is reproduced in good approximation by a single Debye function with an average Debye characteristic temperature of $T_D = 950°K$. In the case of vitreous B_2O_3, the values for T_D that were obtained were much too low for a structure analogous to Al_2O_3. The low temperature specific heat values of vitreous B_2O_3 can be interpreted much better as the result of inter and intramolecular heat capacities which show a close resemblance between vitreous B_2O_3 and molecular organic glasses such as glucose.

C. L. Babcock, S. W. Barber and K. Fajans (243) used the low temperature specific heat data for discussing possible structures of vitreous silica. They arrived at the conclusion that only the highest frequencies of atomic vibrations can be attributed to oscillations of Si^{4+} and O^{2-} ions but that some lower frequencies must be attributed to the presence of larger masses or to forces which are weaker than those acting between ion pairs.

Earlier (see Chapter XIV) we learned that A. L. Day and E. T. Allen (160), in 1905, as well as K. Quasebart (161), in 1910, discovered heat effects during the cooling of vitreous borax and of a commercial soda lime glass. These effects revealed a certain similarity between the softening range of a glass and the melting point of a crystal.

The endothermic and exothermic effects that occur when glasses are heated or cooled through the region of t_g were studied by several scientists. S. B. Thomas and G. S. Parks (244) studied the specific heat at constant pressure c_p for vitreous B_2O_3 on heating and cooling at different rates. There is a close similarity between the specific heat of vitreous B_2O_3 in its softening range (250 to 300°C.) and that of an organic compound (glycerol, alcohols, glycols) which forms a glass at low temperature. G. S. Parks and H. M. Huffman (245) measured the specific heats of a number of organic materials that could be supercooled to a glass. G. Tammann and H. Elsner v. Gronow (246) measured the specific heat and the thermal conductivity of vitreous selenium in the softening range.

As far as technical glasses are concerned, A. Q. Tool (247) and associates examined anomalies in the specific heats of borosilicate glasses in connection with changes of density and thermal expansivity. These properties were found to depend strongly on the previous heat treatment. Tool reached the conclusion that some borosilicate glasses are composed of two components.

A more rigorous structural evaluation of the specific heats of glasses in the softening range is not possible because of the complexity of the modes of vibrations of the constituents. Several publications deal with the heat contents of glasses and the corresponding crystals. This information makes it possible to calculate the heats of crystallization of a glass. We will not discuss these data because we share the opinion voiced by G. W. Morey (137) in his criticism of Zachariasen's concept. There is no valid relation between the energy content of a glass or the heat of fusion of a crystalline compound and its tendency toward glass formation. Data on specific heat have also been gathered because they are needed as a basis for calculating the economy of glass-melting furnaces.

Ever since the classical work in 1893 of A. Winkelmann (248) on the specific heat of glass at ordinary and higher than ordinary temperatures, it has been well understood that this property is nearly additive so that it can be calculated in good approximation from the oxides. For details and for the factors that have been suggested by different authors in order to calculate the specific heat of multicomponent glasses, the chapter in G. W. Morey's book (6) should be consulted.

We have seen that even in the low temperature region an absolute interpretation of the specific heat is extremely difficult. In the last decade an interesting approach to the constitution of glasses has been made by comparing the specific heats of glasses with those of crystals of known structures.

V. V. Tarasov (249) and his school developed a quantum theory of heat capacity that enabled them to distinguish chain structures and layer structures from three-dimensional networks. A system of N-connected atoms can vibrate with $3N$ different characteristic frequencies and these frequencies form a vibrational spectrum. Tarasov showed that the frequency distribution within such a spectrum is structure sensitive and that it is characteristic for chain structures, layer structures, and three-dimensional networks regardless of whether the solid has a long range order.

At low temperatures, chain-, layer-, and three-dimensional structures will conform to different functions of heat capacity versus temperature. For the interpretation of the heat capacity curves one must remember that chains or layers are not completely independent structural units but that they interact. The greater the lateral interaction of the chain, the more does the heat capacity versus temperature curve approach that of the Debye theory. Through intensified interaction, the heterodynamic structure changes toward a homodynamic structure. The three-dimensional structure is reached when the interaction between the chain reaches the same magnitude as that of the atoms within the chain.

In 1946, Tarasov and his school applied this theory of heat capacity to the chain structures of selenium, tellurium, arsenic, antimony, and bismuth. Metallic gallium, for example, was found to have a layer structure.

Pyroxene chains vibrate collectively; i.e., the metasilicate chain and the Mg^{2+} ions act as one unit. In sodium metasilicate, however, the sodium ions act as independent oscillators that are attached to the metasilicate chain. The binding forces within the $(SiO_3)_{\infty}^{2-}$ chains are much stronger than those between the chains and the Na^+ ions. Using K. K. Kelley's (250) data on the heat capacities of sodium metasilicate, disilicates, and orthosilicates and the characteristic frequencies of the sodium ions, Tarasov subtracted the contributions of the Na^+ vibrations to the heat capacity of a sodium metasilicate glass and thus obtained a curve that is characteristic for chain structures of SiO_4 tetrahedra.

One group of glasses is represented by the three-dimensional networks of SiO_2 or GeO_2. A second group is comprised of chain-like polymers. The chainlike polymers can be subdivided into two subgroups. Subgroup A contains those glasses which consist only of chains, so that the chains determine the low temperature heat capacity. This subgroup includes As_2S_3 and B_2O_3. Subgroup B includes Na_2SiO_3 and fused borax; i.e., glasses in which the chains are coupled by Na^+ ions.

Band and chain glasses differ from three-dimensional glasses in their mechanical and thermal properties; they are less brittle. Some sulfide glasses free of oxygen can be cut with a saw. Their expansivities are higher than those of glasses with three-dimensional networks.

Tarasov emphasized that glasses of low brittleness, capable of withstanding considerable deformations, must be sought in the group that has the chain structure.

The validity of Tarasov's interpretation of the low-temperature heat capacity of solids has been questioned by several scientists. One of the objections is based on the use in the theory of too many empirical parameters, thus making it possible to describe anything.

We prefer to look upon the interpretation of the low-temperature heat capacity of glasses as an empirical approach based primarily on the comparison of glasses with crystals of known structures. Such an approach can become a valid tool when based on experimental data that are derived from known crystalline structures. This is exactly what Tarasov does: he links together the heat capacities of glasses with those of crystals for which three-dimensional and chain structures have been established by X-ray diffraction work. It is significant that Tarasov finds a chain structure for vitreous B_2O_3 whereas crystalline B_2O_3 has no chain structure.

7. Thermal Conductivity

Shortly after Debye had developed a theoretical approach to the low-temperature specific heat of solids, he applied his ideas toward a theory of the thermal conductivity of solids that are electrical insulators. His model is a continuum in which elastic waves are propagated. The fact that most solids expand on heating proves that these waves are not purely harmonic oscillations. Debye postulated that because of their anharmonicity these waves will mutually interact and scatter. Thermal vibrations do not propagate with the speed of sound through a solid. Their propagation is not comparable with the propagation of light through a clear glass. Thermal vibrations undergo a strong attenuation comparable to the light that penetrates into an opacified glass. The intensity of the thermal waves decreases quickly within a solid, so that a temperature gradient is established. Debye introduced the mean free path of the waves; i.e., the distance that the wave had to travel in order to attenuate its intensity by the factor e. If the mean free path of the elastic wave is Δ, the thermal conductivity λ can be expressed by the formula

$$\lambda = \text{Const}\cdot d\cdot c_v\cdot U\cdot\Delta$$

in which d is the density, c_v the specific heat, and U the velocity of sound. The velocity of sound in an isotropic crystal is inversely proportional to the square root of the product of compressibility and density:

$$\text{Velocity of sound} = (\text{compressibility} \times \text{density})^{\frac{1}{2}}$$

This relation can be very useful because the compressibility is related to the interatomic forces acting within a solid. We are interested primarily in the fact that the mean free path is sensitive to the symmetry of the structure. The free path decreases when foreign atoms or defects are present. Decreasing temperature decreases the thermal motion of the atoms, and as the amplitude decreases, the anharmonicity of the vibrations also decreases. With decreasing anharmonicity, the mean free path and the thermal conductivity increase. For this reason the thermal conductivity of many solids is approximately proportional to the inverse absolute temperature:

$$\lambda = \text{Const. } 1/T$$

At liquid hydrogen temperature (15 to 20°K.) the thermal conductivity of ionic crystals reaches values that are of the same order of magnitude as those of metallic copper at ordinary temperature. In this temperature region the mean free path of the elastic waves in an ionic crystal is very sensitive to defects. The influence of defects or centers of asymmetry in a crystal is particularly pronounced at low temperatures because the interference of atomic vibrations is at a minimum.

The mean free path of the thermal waves in ionic crystals is high when the oscillators in the lattice have the same mass. A. Eucken and G. Kuhn (251, 252) found that the highest thermal conductivity among the alkali halides is possessed by those crystals in which anions and cations have nearly the same atomic weights. Table XXX shows that the thermal conductivity in these groups reaches a maximum when the ratio of the two masses comes close to unity.

The low-temperature thermal conductivities of crystals that have a more complicated composition, e.g., potassium dichromate, are only one tenth of that of KCl. The propagation of heat is governed by the crystal symmetry in very much the same way as is the propagation of light. The absolute value of the thermal conductivity in different crystallographic directions is determined by the interatomic forces. Diamond has a much higher conductivity (0.41 cal./cm. sec. °K.) than potassium chloride (0.024 cal./cm. sec. °K.).

The thermal conductivity of a quartz crystal in the direction of the chain (parallel to the c-axis) is approximately twice as great as that perpendicular to the chain. Layer lattices show even more drastic differences. Within the layer of a mica crystal, the con-

TABLE XXX

Thermal Conductivities of Some Alkali Halides at 83°K. and Atomic Weights (251)

Salt	Atomic weight		Thermal conductivity (cal./cm. sec. °K.)
	Alkali	Halogen	
NaF	23	19	0.124
NaCl	23	35	0.090
NaBr	23	80	0.012
KF	39	19	0.057
KCl	39	35	0.138
KBr	39	80	0.023
KI	39	127	0.030
RbCl	85	35	0.007
RbBr	85	80	0.016
RbI	85	127	0.014

ductivity is 5 to 6 times greater than that perpendicular to the layer.

The effect of foreign atoms upon the thermal conductivity of ionic crystals is well illustrated by A. Eucken's work on the thermal conductivity of the solid solution of KCl-KBr. The presence of 10 mole % KBr in KCl causes the thermal conductivity at −190°C. to be only one tenth of the value of the pure KCl crystal. At 0°C. the effect is less drastic, but still the thermal conductivity of the KCl crystal is lowered to one half. A similar effect is observed when 10 mole % KCl is incorporated into the KBr lattice. The thermal conductivity of a series of solid solutions goes through a minimum.

Minute concentrations of impurities cause rock salt to have a lower thermal conductivity (0.015 cal./cm. sec. °K.) than an artificial NaCl crystal of highest purity (0.021 cal./cm. sec. °K.).

In addition to P. Debye's classical approach to thermal conductivity based on the scattering of elastic waves, a quantum mechanical description can also be used in which heat quanta are treated as particles called "phonons." This treatment of the thermal conductivity is analogous to the dualistic treatment of light which can be described in terms of electromagnetic waves as well as in terms of particles, the light quanta. The electron density around a nucleus can be described on the basis of waves or electrons.

When a piece of metal is connected with the poles of a battery, an electrical current is observed due to the flow of electrons. The same treatment can be applied to the thermal conductivity. One can assume that a stream of phonons flows from a heat reservoir through a solid to the colder parts of the system.

The phonon is the particle that is associated with unit quantum excitation of one of the modes of elastic vibrations of an ideal crystal. The normal modes of vibration can be described by their wavelength, frequency of vibration, and the direction of propagation. For obvious reasons, the minimum possible wavelength is of the order of the internuclear distances in the solid. Crystalline and amorphous solids permit the propagation of both longitudinal and transverse waves of low frequency. However, liquids in this frequency range can propagate only longitudinal waves. If classical mechanics were valid, one could assume the existence of waves of any amplitude. However, the restrictions imposed on these processes by quantum mechanics limit the amplitude of a wave to discrete values. A crystal at a certain temperature contains a wide spectrum of phonons, the distribution of which follows the laws of quantum mechanics and statistics.

If the forces between atoms would obey Hooke's law exactly, two waves would pass through one another without undergoing a change. In the language of quantum mechanics one would say that in such a lattice phonons cannot interact. However, the anharmonicity of the interatomic forces makes it possible for phonons to interact and to change their wave lengths and their direction of propagation. Because of the anharmonicity of the interatomic forces, this interaction (scattering) increases with increasing amplitude of vibration or with increasing energy of the phonons.

If a solid is brought into contact with a source of heat, phonons will flow into the solid. Because of their interaction among themselves and with those phonons that are present, the phonons can diffuse only slowly into the interior. The phonons that carry the highest energy have a mean free path which at ordinary temperature is of the order of ten atoms. Phonons of a much smaller energy, acoustical phonons, interact to a much lesser extent and their mean free path is, therefore, much longer. Sound can travel several hundred meters per second in a solid: its attenuation is negligible at ordinary temperature and so is the energy that is transmitted.

The close similarity between the values of the specific heat of a crystal and the specific heat of the corresponding glass suggests that the phonon spectrum in a rigid glass resembles that in the crystal. However, the lower symmetry or the lack of periodicity in the glass tends to eliminate the high energy phonons faster in that glass than in a crystal. The absence of high energy phonons in the vibrational spectrum of glasses might have some significance with respect to their chemical reactivity. As a rule, glasses are not as catalytically active as crystals for gas reactions.

With respect to the low energy phonons, there should be no major difference between glasses and crystals. The propagation of long waves in a solid is governed by the elastic constants that are characteristic of the continuum. The atomic structure is not a major factor.

We assume that the phonon spectrum of a glass in thermal equilibrium resembles that of a crystal, with the exception that the high energy phonons are absent in the glass. However, a considerable difference exists between crystals and glasses with respect to the propagation of phonons; i.e., under conditions in which these solids are not in thermal equilibrium. The free path of a phonon in a glass is much smaller than that in the crystal because of the lack of long range order in the glass. Glasses have a much lower thermal conductivity than crystals. The measurements of R. Berman (253) and P. G. Klemens (254) reveal that the thermal conductivity of crystalline silica (quartz) is fairly high when compared with vitreous silica. Neutron bombardment decreases the thermal conductivity of quartz in very much the same way as fusion and glass formation decrease it.

The thermal conductivity, more than any other property, sets apart the vitreous solids from corresponding crystals. A. Eucken (252) pointed out that glasses, in contrast to crystals, have conductivities that decrease with decreasing temperature. The thermal conductivity is not as influenced by the chemical nature of the solid as by its structure. The thermal conductivity is a structure-sensitive property that responds strongly to defects and heterogeneities. The temperature coefficients of the thermal conductivities of the alkali halides are negative. A crystal, which is more complex and which contains water of crystallization, behaves with respect to the thermal conductivity as a more heterogeneous medium. The temperature coefficient of λ is zero for $K_4Fe(CN)_6 \cdot 3H_2O$ and assumes even positive values for alum, $K_2SO_4 \cdot Al_2(SO_4)_3 \cdot 24H_2O$.

Measurements of the thermal conductivities of 12 technical glasses by E. H. Ratcliffe (255) reveal that all conductivities decrease with decreasing temperature. Vitreous silica has the highest conductivity, two sodium borosilicates come next, a lead silicate has the lowest conductivity.

The thermal conductivity of fused silica was determined by K. L. Wray and T. J. Connolly (256):

$2.6–2.9 \times 10^{-3}$ cal./cm. sec. °K. at room temp.
$4.5–5.5 \times 10^{-3}$ cal./cm. sec. °K. at 1000 to 2000°K.

C. Kittel (257) explains this behavior of glasses by assuming a temperature-independent, constant free path of the phonons. The decrease in the conductivity with decreasing temperature is then due to the decrease in the specific heat.

The mean free path for vitreous silica at −190°C. is 12 A., whereas that of quartz parallel to the c-axis at the same temperature is of the order of 700 A. With respect to the absolute length of the mean free path, glasses resemble liquids in which the mean free path is of the order of the size of the molecules.

8. Thermal Expansivity

The anharmonicity of the vibrations of the atoms, which is responsible for the complexity of the specific heat (in particular for the deviations from the law of Dulong and Petit), is also responsible for the fact that the volume of a solid changes with the temperature; i.e., with the amplitude of the vibrations. Most solids expand on heating. The thermal expansion is a complex property that is connected with the magnitude and the distribution of forces acting in the system and that reflects any change of the distribution of forces with increasing thermal vibrations.

The thermal expansivity is one of the first properties found to be characteristic for the glassy state. The expansion curves of glasses are very similar and have been used for determining t_g, the temperature at which the supercooled liquid changes into a glass.

Even when a glass is thoroughly annealed one finds that its thermal expansion is not uniform over a large temperature range so that one has to give values for α for different temperature regions. The coefficient α represents the change in length dl per unit of length per degree rise in temperature within a given temperature region.

Sometimes one finds that the differential dl/dt is used, the true coefficient of expansion at the temperature t. At other times it is more convenient to measure the volume expansion of a glass in a dilatometer, for example, a thermometer bulb. In our discussion we will refer only to the mean coefficient of linear expansion α. The numerical value of the cubical expansion is approximately three times that of α.

We assume that the volume change of solids on heating is the result of the following three different phenomena:

1. Increasing the temperature causes the mutual polarization of the ions (over a time average) to decrease so that they behave more like excess point charges. For this reason many crystals that have a small molecular volume and a low symmetry at ordinary temperature, due to strong mutual polarization of their ions, change into more symmetrical and less dense modifications if the temperature is raised.

The different modifications of silica provide a typical example. At high temperature Si^{4+} and O^{2-} ions form the high form of cristobalite, the structure of which has the highest symmetry and the largest molar volume. On cooling, the decreasing amplitude of the atomic vibrations permits a stronger mutual interaction of the ions and the cubic cristobalite changes into less symmetrical modifications of silica. At ordinary temperature and pressure the denser and less symmetrical quartz is the stable phase.

2. A similar volume change can occur in crystals that do not change their geometry. The alkali halides have thermal expansivities that increase with increasing mutual deformation (see W. Klemm (258)). For the fluorides the thermal expansivity increases from LiF to KF and for the sodium halides it increases from NaF to NaI (Table XXXI).

3. The volume also changes because the vibration of the atoms around their equilibrium positions are not harmonic oscillations. A lattice consisting of harmonic oscillators would not expand if the amplitudes increase as the temperature increases. Atoms that are bonded together by strong forces have vibrations with small amplitudes and, therefore, they resemble harmonic oscillators. Atoms with weaker binding forces have larger amplitudes of vibration at the same temperature than strongly bonded atoms. Their anharmonicity is greater and this relationship led to the statement which can be found in the literature that strong bonds result in low expansivities.

TABLE XXXI

Volume Expansion of the Alkali Halides at Room Temperature (258)

	$\alpha \times 10^6/°C.$			
	F	Cl	Br	I
Li	102	132	150	177
Na	108	120	129	145
K	110	115	120	135
Rb	—	108	114	129
Cs	105	(136)	(139)	(146)

Values in parentheses refer to halides with CsCl structure. All other halides have NaCl structure.

The anharmonicity, however, is not only a function of the bond strength or amplitude of the vibrations but also is dependent upon the symmetry of the environment of the oscillator. We may assume that the lower, metastable, melting point of quartz as compared with cristobalite results from the fact that the binding forces differ noticeably in different crystallographic directions. It is primarily this asymmetry of the lattice and of the forces that causes the thermal vibrations in quartz to be less harmonic than vibrations of the same amplitude or energy in high cristobalite or in silica glass. In spite of the average binding forces in quartz being stronger than in the glass, quartz has a much higher thermal expansivity than glass. We attribute the low thermal expansivity of vitreous silica to a combination of three features: (1) low polarizability of all ions (NaF has a lower expansivity than NaI); (2) strong binding forces; and (3) highly symmetrical structural units. The thermal expansivity of vitreous B_2O_3 is very high in spite of this compound having a low polarizability and strong binding forces. This reveals the importance of the asymmetry of the structural units in determining thermal expansivity.

The density of quartz is considerably higher than that of cristobalite or of the glass. On this basis, one might be inclined to attribute the high thermal expansivity of quartz to its anticipating, so to speak, the more spaceous atomic structures that are stable at higher temperature. This explanation, however, is not acceptable. At ordinary temperature a chilled glass can have a higher thermal expansivity than the same glass in annealed condition, in spite of having a more spaceous structure and a tendency to contract as soon as the mobility permits such a change of volume. The higher expansivity of chilled glasses at ordinary temperature must be the result of the lower symmetry of their structural units or, as we like to express it, of their higher defect concentration. The experiments of J. B. Saunders and A. Q. Tool (259) provide ample evidence for the change of the thermal expansivity with the thermal history of a glass.

We attribute the increase in thermal expansion of well-annealed glasses in their softening range to the formation of defects such as vacant anion sites or incomplete coordination. Defects introduce asymmetries into the short range order of glasses and increase the thermal expansion by increasing the anharmonicity of the thermal vibrations. This explanation applies equally well to silicate glasses with their ionic networks and to organic or molecular glasses such as a phenolphthalein glass.

The relation between thermal expansivity and symmetry of the polyhedra can be used for solving structural problems. M. Karkhanavala and F. A. Hummel (260) found that the substitution of a non-noble gas-type cation for a noble gas-type cation of the same size and charge, e.g., of a Cu^{2+} for a Mg^{2+} or a Pb^{2+} for a Sr^{2+} ion, did not change the thermal expansivities of glasses of the composition Na_2O, MgO, $5SiO_2$ and Na_2O, SrO, $5SiO_2$, at least not in the low temperature region. This similarity in the low temperature expansion reveals that Cu^{2+} ions and Mg^{2+} ions or Pb^{2+} ions and Sr^{2+} ions assume positions in these glasses which are equivalent with respect to the nature and the symmetry of the polyhedra. It becomes reasonable, therefore, to assume that non-noble gas-like cations participate in the structure of these glasses as highly symmetrical polyhedra analogous to the oxides MgO and SrO. The light absorptions of CuO and PbO crystals are very different from those of the Cu^{2+} and Pb^{2+} ions in glasses because of the asymmetries of the crystal structures, in particular the defects in CuO and the different Pb^{2+}—O^{2-} distances in PbO.

Replacements such as Cu^{2+} for Mg^{2+} or Pb^{2+} for Sr^{2+} ions lower the viscosity because the more polarizable electron clouds of Cu^{2+} and Pb^{2+} ions can adjust themselves more readily to an asymmetrical environment than can the noble gas-type ions of the same charge and similar sizes; i.e., Mg^{2+} and Sr^{2+} ions.

The thermal expansivity reveals the difference between glasses containing noble gas-type and non-noble gas-type ions with respect to the ease of defect formation. Firstly, glasses which contain non-noble gas-type ions increase their configurational and vibrational entropy at lower temperatures than the corresponding glasses containing noble gas-type ions. The defect concentration, and with it the coefficients of thermal expansion in the CuO and PbO glasses, increases at a lower temperature and increases more rapidly than those in the corresponding MgO and SrO glasses.

The volume changes of glasses have been studied for numerous compositions and over wide temperature ranges. As far as the structural significance of the thermal expansivity is concerned, one has to realize that one deals with a property which integrates over the total volume of the glass and that thermal expansivity responds to all changes in short range and in long range order. We will now review some examples of structural information obtained from thermal expansivity.

1. M. O. Samsoen (261) found a striking similarity in the volume changes of vitreous B_2O_3, and in other glasses that were free of silica. His findings invalidated earlier concepts that the changes which occur in the softening range of silicate glasses, in particular the changes in expansivity, are the result of some polymorphous changes of silica corresponding to the high-low quartz inversion.

This discovery was a milestone in the history of the constitution of glass because it helped to formulate the concept that unrelated substances develop common features when they are brought into the glassy state.

2. The very low thermal expansivity of vitreous silica, 5.0×10^{-7} at ordinary temperature reveals strong forces and highly symmetrical short range order. The slight increase in α with increasing temperature, e.g., $\alpha = 6.7 \times 10^{-7}$ at 400°C., is exactly what we would expect. Increasing amplitudes of vibration increase the anharmonicity of the oscillations and with it the volume. However, the value of α decreases at still higher temperature and becomes 4.2×10^{-7} around 1000°C. W. Souder and P. Hindert (262) found that the value of α for vitreous silica goes through a maximum. This means that the expected normal volume increase on heating must be counteracted by a process which causes the volume of the SiO_2 glass to shrink. Closure of submicroscopic cracks is a possible explanation for this anomaly. The formation of cracks in vitreous silica on cooling and their closure on heating would also explain the anomalous increase of its mechanical strength on heating.

3. Vitreous GeO_2 should have an atomic structure similar to that of SiO_2. The difference between the average bond strength of Si—O and Ge—O should be too small to account for the much higher coefficient of expansion of the GeO_2 glass ($\alpha = 77 \times 10^{-7}$) according to L. M. Dennis and A. W. Laubengayer (263). Hence, the higher expansivity of vitreous GeO_2 must indicate a lower symmetry in the short range order. One can attribute this structural difference to either one or a combination of two causes.

One possibility is to assume a higher defect concentration. The atomic structure of a GeO_2 glass is not as close as that of a silica glass to the structure of a Bernal liquid. The more polarizable Ge^{4+} ion (18 shell) has a less stringent coordination requirement than the Si^{4+} ion. Therefore, the GeO_2 structure permits a higher concentration of defects. This would bring the structure of vitreous GeO_2 somewhere between the points that indicate liquid structures of the Bernal type and those of the Frenkel type.

The alternative explanation is equally probable. GeO_2 at high temperature assumes the structure of quartz. We assume that the metastable liquid that forms when quartz melts at 1500°C. is of the orientable type because it contains remnants of the chain structure that characterizes quartz. We may assume, therefore, that the high value of α is the result of the orientable structure of vitreous GeO_2. This would place the point representing a GeO_2 glass between that of a Bernal liquid and a Stewart liquid.

Neither the X-ray method nor the thermal expansivity can be used to decide which of the two explanations is the correct one. The examination of a drawn fiber of GeO_2 glass would give an answer to this problem.

If the structure of vitreous GeO_2 were to lie between a Bernal liquid and a Frenkel liquid its fibers would not show orientation when examined by X rays, nor would they show diamagnetic anisotropy. Such a structure would be characterized by a higher ionic conductivity than vitreous SiO_2.

If the structure of vitreous GeO_2 were to lie between a Bernal liquid and a Stewart liquid its fibers would show orientation and the glass would have a low ionic conductivity. The relatively low melting point of GeO_2 (1115°C.) as compared with cristobalite (1713°C.) in itself cannot be used as a clue for speculating on the structure of the liquid. Molecular liquids (B_2O_3) as well as fissured liquids can have low freezing points, but the fact that lithium metagermanate has a higher melting point than GeO_2 speaks strongly for its having a structure which to some extent is of the molecular type. In order to ascertain a glass structure, an evaluation of several properties must be made and thermal expansivity can provide valuable hints.

4. The high coefficient of expansion of vitreous B_2O_3 decreases rapidly upon the addition of SiO_2. Some values of α, interpolated from the data given by A. Cousen and W. E. S. Turner (264), are given in Table XXXII.

The average binding forces B—O and Si—O are nearly the same. The high coefficient of expansion of vitreous B_2O_3 reveals that it cannot be a Bernal liquid but that it must contain structural units with a low symmetry or a high concentration of defects. The high expansivity of vitreous B_2O_3 agrees with our concept that vitreous B_2O_3 is an "orientable" liquid of the Stewart type.

The drastic effect of SiO_2 (50% SiO_2 cut the value of α to one third of that of B_2O_3) can be interpreted as the result of a structural change from that of a Stewart model of a liquid toward that of a Bernal model.

5. H. H. Blau (265) developed an equation for the linear coefficient of expansions of sodium silicate glasses based on the volume of that quantity of glass that contained 1 gram atom of oxygen. His equation contained the silicon to oxygen ratio as the parameter for the composition. He found discontinuities in his

TABLE XXXII

Coefficients of Expansion

Weight %		$\alpha \times 10^7$
B_2O_3	SiO_2	
100	—	151
95	5	135
90	10	120
75	25	85
50	50	50

expansivity composition curves. Breaks occurred not only at those Si:O ratios that corresponded to shifts from one to two (0.286), two to three (0.333), and three to four bridging oxygens (0.400), but also at the ratio 0.444 at which one half of all SiO_4 tetrahedra had one bridging O^{2-} ion and the other half no bridging O^{2-} ion. H. H. Blau concluded that there must be a regularity in the arrangement, otherwise it could not produce a break. He assumed that the maximum stability is achieved if all nonbridging O^{2-} ions are equidistant and occupy the most remote positions possible. His conclusion that the nonbridging O^{2-} ions repel one another can be expressed also as follows: Maximum stability of the structure and maximum degree of screening of all silicons are achieved if the distribution of bridging and nonbridging O^{2-} ions is as even as possible throughout the glass structure. We compare the distribution of bridging and nonbridging O^{2-} ions in alkali silicate glasses with the distribution of metal atoms, e.g., Au and Cu, in binary alloys. These binary alloys can assume states which are disordered and others which have a high degree of order: superlattices.

When we discuss the factors that affect the symmetry of the structural units of a given glass, we think first of the increase in the number of defects in the transformation region and the freezing in of a higher defect concentration by chilling a glass. However, we must consider also the fact that structural changes are possible even in the rigid glass. At temperatures below the transformation region we can safely assume that the mutual positions of the Si^{4+} and the O^{2-} ions are essentially fixed. The symmetries and the state of polarization of even the bridging O^{2-} ions, however, depends upon the environment, e.g., the positions of the alkali ions. The strong icepoint depressions of a thermometer made from a mixed alkali glass reveals that even at ordinary temperatures structural changes occur that involve the Na^+ and the K^+ ions. In our discussion of the structure of the alkali silicate glasses we point out that the positions of alkali ions must influence the state of polarization of all O^{2-} ions and, with it, the volume of the glass.

These effects of superlattices involving the alkali ions are not as drastic as those influencing the thermal expansivity in the transformation region, but they are real and have been observed, especially by E. Seddon and W. E. S. Turner (266). Seddon and Turner found transition points in the thermal expansivity of glasses at low temperature (120 to 150°C.) that very likely are related to changes in the symmetry of the distribution of the alkali ions.

6. Our concept that the addition of alkali to a silica glass changes its structure from that of a Bernal liquid toward that of a fissured liquid is supported by an increase in the thermal expansivity.

Replacing in a sodium silicate glass some of the silica by aluminum orthophosphate, e.g., 2 SiO_2 by 1 $AlPO_4$, does not change the concentration of nonbridging oxygens. H. J. Poegel (45) found that this substitution did not affect the softening temperature of the glass noticeably but it did increase its thermal expansivity drastically.

We assume that in the low temperature region the addition of a small amount of alkali to boric oxide modifies its structure away from an orientable liquid and toward a flawless liquid. If much alkali is added, the structure changes so as to assume that of a fissured liquid. This concept is supported by the expansivities of these glasses. The expansivity of B_2O_3 glass first decreases, goes through a minimum, and then increases when increasing amounts of alkali are added.

Our interpretation of thermal expansion as the result of the anharmonicity of thermal vibrations caused by the asymmetry of forces makes this property a valuable tool for studying the constitution of glasses. The low-temperature thermal expansivity reflects the symmetry of the structural units of the glass. M. A. Bezborodov (267) offers numerous examples of the effect of the asymmetry of forces upon the coefficient of expansion of complex glasses.

Low expansion glasses can be found in the system Li_2O—Al_2O_3-SiO_2. The minimum expansivity which could be obtained was 63×10^{-7}. The highest expansivities obtainable in a silicate structure were 190×10^{-7} in the presence of Cs^+ ions.

The ternary system Cs_2O-PbO-B_2O_3 produces glasses with expansivities as high as 288×10^{-7}.

The ternary system K_2O-B_2O_3-P_2O_5, too, lends itself to the preparation of high expansion glasses (245×10^{-7}).

7. The addition of SiO_2 to a lead orthosilicate, Pb_2SiO_4, lowers the linear coefficient of expansion from 112×10^{-7} to 90×10^{-7} (0 to 100°C.) when the glass reaches the composition of the metasilicate, $PbSiO_3$. L. Merker and H. Wondratschek (268) discovered that lead silicate glasses are compatible with lead sulfate. The partial replacement of the $(SiO_4)^{4-}$ group in a lead orthosilicate glass by the $(SO_4)^{2-}$ group introduces an asymmetry which causes the thermal expansivity to increase drastically. A glass of the molar composition 62.5% PbO, 25.0% SiO_2, 12.5% SO_3 was found to have a linear coefficient of expansion of 155×10^{-7}. This increase in the thermal expansivity of these high PbO silicates is largely the result of the vibration of $(SiO_4)^{4-}$ ions, vibrating as a group. The partial replacement of an anion with a fourfold negative charge by one with a twofold charge not only weakens the binding forces but also introduces an asymmetry.

9. Compressibility

P. W. Bridgman (269) in his writings pointed out repeatedly that the examination of the behavior of matter under hydrostatic pressure should be very helpful in obtaining a better understanding of the constitution. This certainly applies to glasses which have been studied ever since the early work of G. Tammann. Tammann found that some glasses may have a pronounced "pressure history" analogous to their thermal history.

If a sodium chloride crystal forms under hydrostatic pressure it has a higher density than one that forms under normal pressure. However, as soon as the pressure is released the NaCl crystal expands and its density becomes the same as that of the crystal that has formed under normal pressure. This is as expected. Glasses, however, are different. G. Tammann and E. Jenckel (270) found that a glass which has formed from the liquid state under a pressure of 6000 atmospheres or one which has been cooled under this pressure from a temperature above t_g to ordinary temperature has a considerably higher density. For example, a glass consisting of V_2O_5 with additions of B_2O_3 and P_2O_5 has a density which is 8% higher than that of the same glass formed under normal pressure. Also, vitreous selenium increases its density by 0.6% whereas other glasses like As_2O_3 show no measurable changes in this pressure range.

The behavior of glasses formed under hydrostatic pressure differs from that of normal glasses. The work of G. Tammann and W. Jellinghaus (271) leaves no doubt that a glass formed under pressure must be considered a "high pressure modification" with distinctly different properties when compared with the 'low pressure modification" of the same composition.

The work of P. W. Bridgman (269) opened up a field of experimentation under much higher pressures than those that were available to Tammann. The compressibility of glasses gives us interesting information, but we face a situation similar to that of the density or the refractive index of glasses, in which no simple relationships can be found between these property values and the glass compositions.

The compressibilities of those alkali halides which have NaCl structures are given in Table XXXIII. These values reveal that the compressibility of an alkali halide increases with increasing size of both the cations and the anions. We may also say that the compressibility is inversely proportional to the strength of the binding forces. A crystal in which the electrostatic forces are strong, e.g., LiF, has only a low compressibility (1.52×10^{-6}) as compared with a crystal in which the binding forces are weak. The compressibility of RbI (9.56×10^{-6}) is six times greater than that of LiF. The compressibility of SrS (2.47×10^{-6}) is only one half of that of NaBr (5.07×10^{-6}). Both substances have the same lattice parameters but the forces are stronger in SrS because of the doubly charged ions. In spite of this obvious dependence of the compressibility upon forces, we prefer to correlate the compressibility with the state of polarization of the ions and emphasize that the more polarizable an ion the greater is its compressibility. The large anions in particular are the most compressible and they lose most

TABLE XXXIII
Compressibilities of the Alkali Halides

	Compressibility ($K \times 10^6$ cm.^{2}/kg.)			
	F	Cl	Br	I
Li	1.52	3.40	4.30	6.00
Na	2.11	4.26	5.07	7.07
K	3.30	5.62	6.70	8.53
Rb	—	6.64	7.93	9.56
Cs	4.23	(5.94)	(7.05)	(8.57)

Values in perentheses refer to halides with CsCl structure.

of their polarizability under hydrostatic pressure. This shift of emphasis permits us to go a little further in explaining the phenomena occurring under high hydrostatic pressure.

We have pointed out repeatedly that in some structures, e.g., quartz, vitreous B_2O_3, and amorphous sulfur, the binding forces acting within the structural elements such as chains can be very different from those acting between these structural elements. The crystal structure of elemental tellurium consists of infinite chains. These chains are oriented with their axes parallel to the c-axis of the crystal.

Correlating the compressibility with the interatomic distances or with the magnitude of the binding forces we can easily understand that a tellurium crystal under pressure will decrease its volume in a way which shows that its compressibility is greater in all directions perpendicular to its c-axis than in the direction of the c-axis. However, on this basis alone we cannot understand why such a crystal should expand under hydrostatic pressure in the direction of the c-axis.

This anomalous behavior becomes understandable only when we discuss it on the basis of our screening concept. The sketch (Fig. 22) shows that each Te^{6+} core is screened by four (e_2^-) quanticules. Two of the four (e_2^-) quanticules are of the bridging type, i.e., they are shared between two Te^{6+} cores, whereas the other two are of the nonbridging type. This scheme makes it obvious that the structure contains two types of (e_2^-) quanticules which differ strongly in their states of polarization and in their screening powers. We treat an electron pair quantized with respect to one Te^{6+} core

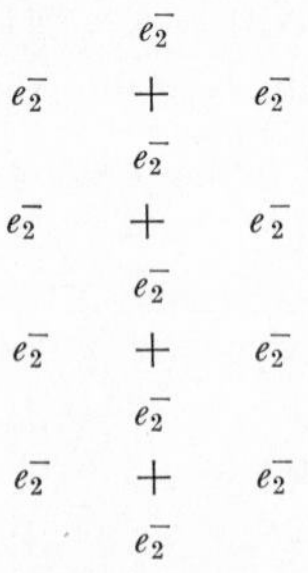

$$\begin{array}{ccc} & e_2^- & \\ e_2^- & + & e_2^- \\ & e_2^- & \\ e_2^- & + & e_2^- \\ & e_2^- & \\ e_2^- & + & e_2^- \\ & e_2^- & \\ e_2^- & + & e_2^- \\ & e_2^- & \end{array}$$

Chain

FIG. 22. Each Te^{6+} core is screened by four quanticules. + = Te^{6+} cores; e_2^- = electron pairs.

(nonbridging quanticule) and the one that is quantized with respect to two Te^{6+} cores (bridging quanticules) in precisely the same manner as we treat the nonbridging and the bridging O^{2-} ions in a silicate. The nonbridging O^{2-} ions and the nonbridging (e_2^-) quanticules are better screeners and are more deformable than the bridging ones. Our assumption that the compressibility of an O^{2-} ion increases with its polarizability is supported by the fact that a K-silicate glass is more compressible than a corresponding Na-silicate glass.

Hydrostatic pressure forces the electrons of the nonbridging (e_2^-) quanticules closer to their Te^{6+} cores. The resulting improvement of the screening of the Te^{6+} cores causes them to interact less with their bridging quanticules. As a result, the Te^{6+} (e_2^-) Te^{6+} distances increase due to a weakening of the forces between the Te^{6+} cores and the bridging (e_2^-) quanticules. The response of elemental tellurium to hydrostatic pressure is interesting because with tellurium one observes an actual expansion of a crystal under hydrostatic pressure. Basically, the same phenomenon occurs in quartz but the effect is not as drastic. The compressibility of quartz parallel to the chains (c-axis) is less (0.718×10^{-6}) than that in the direction perpendicular to the chains (0.995×10^{-6}). This difference, however, can be explained on the basis of conventional approaches but the behavior of tellurium cannot.

P. W. Bridgman rarely concerned himself with the physical and chemical significance of the results of his high pressure work. His book and his papers reveal, however, that he was always aware of the importance of his studies with respect to the theory of the solid state. He pointed out that changing the pressure within experimentally available limits gives us a better insight into the variation of forces between the atoms as a function of the distance than the variation of the temperature can give us. The compressibilities of the elements varies over a wide range. Cesium is 2460 times more compressible than carbon. For many elements the volume change produced by a pressure of 12,000 atmospheres is many times greater than that observed by cooling it under atmospheric pressure from room temperature to absolute zero.

Whereas Tammann was limited in his work to pressures of a few thousand atmospheres, Bridgman and his associates extended the experimental pressure range to 200,000 atmospheres. In his studies of the behavior of a large variety of solids under these high pressures, Bridgman emphasized that it must be of considerable significance that the compressibility of metals and of ionic crystals are of the same order of magnitude. The mechanism responsible for the volume change should be essentially the same. In our approach to the solid state we treat metals, intermetallic compounds, and ionic substances on the same basis, only allowing for the different properties that are introduced when a solid has mobile electrons as anions.

The compressibility of the alkali halides is fairly well understood on the basis of the effect that pressure has upon the equilibrium between attractive and repulsive forces and the resulting internuclear distances.

Some crystals under pressure, e.g., RbBr, undergo changes in their geometry in addition to a decrease in volume. RbBr at ordinary pressure has NaCl structure, but under high pressure it assumes the structure of CsCl; i.e., its coordination increases from 6 to 8. This compacting into a denser structure can be explained on the basis of Le Chatelier's principle. As in so many cases of solid state reactions, an explanation of changes in the equilibrium is easy but the rate phenomena remain a mystery. Why is this change of the coordination of RbBr under hydrostatic pressure a reversible process whereas the formation of silica C under pressure is irreversible so that it leads to a metastable compacted form of SiO_2? Silica C does not change into quartz when the pressure is released.

Formally, this question can be answered by stating that a change of modification is reversible if it takes place at a temperature at which the lattice vibration can supply the necessary activation energy. This statement, however, is merely a description of the facts and not an explanation. Our concept of the screening demand of cations allows us to go further and to give an atomistic interpretation of the energy barrier which separates two modifications of a substance. One can apply to phase transitions the same reasoning which we used for explaining the rates of viscous flow (see Chapter V). If a reaction requires the temporary unscreening of an ion of high charge and low polarizability, the activation energy is high. The degree of unscreening necessary for a regrouping of ions depends among other factors upon the polarizability of the anions. This concept helps us to understand the kinetics of transitions in solids. In the past, emphasis has been placed upon the geometrical relationships between two polymorphous forms of a substance. M. J. Buerger (272) classified phase transformations according to their rates from a geometrical point of view. According to Buerger, a transformation that involves a change in the first coordination should be sluggish (reconstructive transformation), whereas one involving changes only in the second coordination (displacive transformation) can be fast. Buerger's treatment of the rates of these reactions on the basis of the geometry of the lattices is satisfactory only if one restricts oneself to oxide or silicate systems in which the cations have low polarizability and relatively strong force fields. Systems involving highly polarizable anions, e.g., I^- ions, and highly polarizable cations, e.g., Hg^{2+}, Ag^{2+}, Cu^{2+}, can undergo rapid changes even if the two forms are very different with respect to their geometry.

Our approach to the kinetics of phase transformation explains the fast and reversible transitions of RbBr at low temperature as well as its transformation at ordinary temperature under pressure on the basis of the high polarizability of the Br^- ion and the weak field of the Rb^+ ion. These two factors are more important than the geometry because they are conducive to a low energy barrier and high reaction rate. The same applies to the smooth, reversible transition of AgI, which under pressure changes from its ZnS structure into the NaCl structure. Both compounds contain singly charged cations and polarizable anions.

Our approach supplements M. J. Buerger's concepts by considering the forces as well as the geometry. The energy that is necessary to temporarily unscreen the cations provides a physical picture of the activation energy of phase transformations under hydrostatic pressure.

R. B. Jacobs (273) developed a method of taking X-ray diagrams of substances under pressures up to 5000 atmospheres. This made it possible to identify those high-pressure structures that could not be obtained as metastable modifications when the pressure was released. Thus, he found that the high pressure modification of AgI has the structure of NaCl. According to our interpretation, the silver ions that under normal pressure are well screened by four polarizable I^- ions (ZnS-structure), expand their coordination from 4 to 6 under high pressure because the I^- ions lose some of their high polarizability. In the same way R. B. Jacobs proved that under pressure RbI changes from the NaCl structure into a

CsCl structure. These experiments provide the key to the understanding of pressure phenomena. As the polarizability and screening capacity of the anions decreases under pressure, the cations expand their coordination from 6 to 8.

Liquid CS_2 changes irreversibly into a solid when it is exposed to high pressures. Liquid CS_2 consists of single molecules held together by van der Waals' forces. In each molecule the core of carbon, C^{4+}, is neutralized and screened by two strongly deformed S^{2-} ions. Under pressure, the polarizability of the S^{2-} ions decreases to such an extent that two anions can no longer screen the carbon core and, as a result, the single molecules polymerize, forming a three-dimensional structure in which each carbon is surrounded by four S^{2-} ions. The new form remains metastable under ordinary conditions because it contains nonpolarizable cations of high field strength. The same principle can be applied to the discovery of L. Coes (40). The formation of SiO_2 under high pressure below 800°C. either as the result of the oxidation of silicon or the interaction between P_2O_5 and an alkali silicate produces a very dense form of SiO_2.

Glasses resemble crystals with respect to their behavior under pressure. They show reversible compressibility analogous to the alkali halides and they can undergo structural changes that lead to denser metastable structures.

If the low pressure modification of a glass is exposed to a moderately high pressure, say 1000 atmospheres, it will not change its structure unless heated. However, as soon as the constituents have the necessary mobility the glass changes into the new modification and this change is accompanied by a decrease in the volume.

G. Tammann (1) and co-workers showed that glasses can have a "pressure history" just as they have a "temperature history." The absence of long range order makes it possible for a glass to undergo a gradual structural change of a type that in a crystal has to take place abruptly. From a crystal chemical point of view, two glasses with different thermal histories may be considered as different modifications of the same substance. Keeping this in mind, we are not surprised to learn that the compressibility of a glass is a function of its previous heat treatment. This effect on the compressibility was observed by Bridgman and his associates when they measured the compressibility of liquids and found that the compressibility of the glass piezometers depended on their previous thermal treatment.

Several papers on the behavior of glasses under high pressure originated through the interest of geophysicists on the propagation of seismic waves through deeper layers of rocks. Thus, F. Birch and R. R. Law (274) measured the compressibility of a diabase glass up to 300°C. and 10,000 atmospheres. Its compressibility went through a maximum at 150°C. when the temperature was raised.

Extension of the work by F. Birch and R. B. Dow (275) included several technical glasses. This work established the fact that silicate glasses behaved like the low-melting borate glasses of Tammann.

When P. W. Bridgman and I. Simon (276) extended the work on the behavior of glasses under pressure to pressures of the order of 100,000 atmospheres, a new phenomenon was discovered. Silicate glasses, including vitreous silica, undergo structural changes that lead to a permanent compacting even at ordinary temperature if the pressure is sufficiently high. At ordinary temperature vitreous silica begins to compact above 100,000 atmospheres. Vycor glass, i.e., silica containing a few per cent of B_2O_3, begins to compact above 75,000 atmospheres. Pure B_2O_3 glass begins to compact at low pressures and its density approaches a 6% increase asymptotically.

The unequal distribution of pressure in these specimens makes a quantitative evaluation difficult. Nevertheless, the results of this work are sufficient to obtain a clear qualitative picture of what happens in a glass under high pressures. A sample of SiO_2 glass compacted under 200,000 atmospheres showed an average increase in its density of 7%, but due to the high friction the distribution of the pressure in the glass and the resulting volume change was not uniform. When the pressure was released the specimen fractured and pieces were found which showed a density increase of 17.5%.

No structural picture of the high pressure modification of vitreous silica has yet been suggested. Compacting, as a rule, is the result of an increase in the average coordination number. The formation of volume elements which have a structure resembling rutile would be a plausible explanation but no evidence has been found which supports a change of the 4:2 into the 6:3 coordination.

If the coordination number of all Si^{4+} ions remains 4, one can visualize some O^{2-} ions increasing their coordination from 2 to 3 by forming a corresponding number of nonbridging O^{2-} ions.

At present we have no reliable method for estimating the

average coordination of the O^{2-} ions in a glass. Hence, any speculation concerning such a structure has to be checked by indirect evidence. The major difference between vitreous silica in its ordinary form (Bernal-type liquid) and the suggested high pressure form would lie in the asymmetry introduced by the nonbridging O^{2-} ions. If our suggestion is correct, one might find a paradoxical phenomenon; namely, that cooling vitreous silica under high hydrostatic pressure would produce a glass which, in spite of being denser at ordinary temperature, would contract more when cooled further; e.g., to $-50°C.$, than the ordinary, more spacious modification of vitreous silica.

The effect of the presence of alkali in the glass on its compressibility is significant and must be considered in any interpretation of compacting. As one would expect, the addition of alkali lowers the threshold pressure. Alkali silicates began to compact at a pressure of 40,000 atmospheres.

An interpretation of the effect of the alkali on the degree to which a glass can be compacted is not so obvious. The addition of Li_2O to SiO_2 seems to have little effect; i.e., the increase in density is about the same as for vitreous SiO_2 (7%). The addition of K_2O, however, decreases the permanent compacting for a given pressure very strongly. The addition of Na_2O has an intermediate effect as can be judged from the data given by P. W. Bridgman and I. Simon (276) presented in Table XXXIV.

The permanent compacting of a glass under a given pressure decreases with increasing size of the alkali ion, i.e., from Li^+ to K^+ silicate. It also decreases with increasing concentration of the alkali as can be seen from the data in Table XXXIV.

The reversibility of the volume changes due to pressure in-

TABLE XXXIV

Permanent Compacting of Alkali Silicate Glasses

Alkali (mole %)	Pressure (atm.)	Increase in density (%)
22 Li_2O	60,000	6.9
23 Na_2O	75,000	3.5
23 K_2O	133,000	1.2
10Na_2O	100,000	6
23Na_2O	100,000	3
31Na_2O	100,000	0.5

creases with increasing number and polarizibility of the nonbridging O^{2-} ions. The permanent compacting under these high hydrostatic pressures is the result of shear stresses due to unequal loading. Shear stresses lead to a disproportionation of all binding forces and enhance flow. The indentation hardness of a glass is a property of a glass that responds to a combination of pressure and shear forces.

From the viewpoint of the constitution of glasses it would be highly desirable to have more measurements of the compressibilities of glasses whose compositions are varied systematically, as has been done by C. E. Weir and L. Shartsis (277). They found that vitreous B_2O_3 has a much higher compressibility than vitreous SiO_2. They also found that the addition of alkalies decreases the compressibility of B_2O_3 strongly. This agrees with our concept of B_2O_3 having a fundamentally different structure than silica.

10. Hardness

The hardness of a material is one of those evasive properties that is of great practical importance but is extremely difficult to define. The scratch hardness has been used widely by mineralogists for identifying minerals. The simplest way to determine the hardness of a mineral is to compare it with those minerals that were chosen arbitrarily by Mohs when he established his hardness scale. The scratch hardness test is based on the observation that a certain mineral will be scratched by all minerals of the scale which are harder than it is and that it will scratch all minerals which are softer. According to this test, glasses have a hardness of approximately 6 (orthoclase); a few heavy lead glasses are softer than 5 (apatite) and some borosilicate glasses are slightly harder than 7 (quartz). The scratch hardness test has as a prerequisite, the condition that the two minerals which are being compared will not weld together during scratching. This condition, however, is not met with glasses. Glasses are brittle in a macroscopic scale but they can flow under shear stresses in a microscopic scale. The flow and the mutual compatibility of glasses makes it impossible to compare the hardness of glasses among themselves by the scratch test. Even a very soft glass when pressed against a hard one will weld to it. On moving it over the surface of the hard glass it will tear out pieces, thus producing a scratch. This surface vulnerability of even the hardest of glasses is responsible for the fact that all glasses scratch one another. In 1894, F. Auerbach (278) made an attempt to establish a hardness scale for glasses on the basis of the scratch test, but when he found that this was not possible he developed a more precise and an absolute method for measuring the hardness that he called "modulus of indentation." His work was the first of numerous efforts to develop tests that would give absolute numerical values for the hardness of glasses. Very soon it was found, however, that each test was an individual method for comparing the hardness of glasses and minerals but no two experimental methods gave results that were comparable or whose scales of hardness were parallel. Hence, it became customary to speak of the scratch hardness, the indentation hardness, the abrasion hardness, etc. The different experimental approaches for testing the hardness of glasses are well covered by G. W. Morey (6) in his book. Some of the hardness tests give contradictory data. From a practical point of view it is important to realize that in order to protect a "hard" glass from abrasion by sand blasting, it may be coated with a "soft" but resilient layer because such a protective coating is not materially attacked by the sand blast.

Around 1920, scientists attempted to provide a definition of the scratch hardness of the old Mohs scale established in 1812, and to correlate the hardness with the nature of the chemical bond. A. Reis and L. Zimmermann (279), in 1922, were among the pioneers in this effort. Was it possible to attribute the hardness of a crystal to its lattice energy? This was one of the first questions that arose in connection with this work. However, the very soft AgCl has a higher lattice energy (214 kcal.) than the much harder rock salt (180 kcal.).

The effect of the valency of elements upon the hardness was generally recognized and V. M. Goldschmidt (4), correlated hardness and "valence sum" of simple compounds. His ideas of "model substances" applied well to the hardness. The "weakened models," e.g., the fluorides, are softer than the oxides, which have twice the valence sum, e.g., BeF_2 *versus* SiO_2 or CaF_2 *versus* ThO_2, etc.

It seems only logical to expect that the hardness of ionic substances will increase with increasing charge of the particles, as these charges are the cause of the binding forces in the crystal. However, there was a most disturbing feature: the complete lack of any influence of the chemical bond on the hardness. V. M. Goldschmidt listed four compounds with identical crystal structure

(NaCl-structure) and very similar lattice parameters. Their hardness increases steadily with the valency of the elements:

	Hardness	*Valency*
NaF	3.2	1
MgO	6.5	2
ScN	7.5	3
TiC	8.5	4

This relationship was not disturbed by the change of the ionic bond (NaF and MgO) to the covalent bond of the atomic lattices of ScN and TiC. Titanium carbide was considered to be a structure in which the Ti and C atoms were linked together by covalent bonds. V. M. Goldschmidt (4) refers to the work of A. E. Van Arkel (12) in 1926, in which Van Arkel states that the X-ray diffraction pattern of TiC does not exclude the possibility of treating TiC as essentially an ionic lattice, thus showing his doubt concerning the usefulness of the distinction between ionic and atomic structure.

V. M. Goldschmidt discovered that substances AB, in which the sum of the atomic numbers, A and B, is constant, and which crystallize in the ZnS-diamond structure, have the same lattice dimensions. Table XXXV gives some examples which show that in

TABLE XXXV

Scratch Hardness of Some Compounds (4)

Compound	Valence sum	Sum of atomic numbers	Interatomic distance	Hardness
CuBr	2	29 + 35 = 64	2.46	2.4
ZnSe	4	30 + 34 = 64	2.45	3–4
GaAs	6	31 + 33 = 64	2.44	4.2
GeGe	8	32 + 32 = 64	2.43	6
CuCl	2	29 + 17 = 46	2.34	2.5
ZnS	4	30 + 16 = 46	2.35	4
GaP	6	31 + 15 = 46	2.35	5
CuI	2	29 + 53 = 82	2.62	2.4
ZnTe	4	30 + 52 = 82	2.64	3
GaSb	6	31 + 51 = 82	2.64	4.5
AlP	6	13 + 15 = 28	2.36	5.5
SiSi	8	14 + 14 = 28	2.35	7

every group the hardness increases with the valence sum of the compound and that even the elements (Si and Ge) fit into the pattern which had been derived for compounds.

It can be advantageous to treat elements such as silicon, germanium or carbon, the latter in the form of diamond, as Si^{4+} Si^{4-}, Ge^{4+} Ge^{4-}, and C^{4+} C^{4-} because their electronic properties, just as their hardnesses, fit into the same pattern as that of typical compounds of the formula $A^{+}B^{-}$. In the diamond, one must assume that the C^{4+} cores are screened by a tetrahedral group of highly polarizable C^{4-} ions (diamond has a very high index of refraction) the electron clouds of which are pulled toward the C^{4+} cores. From the viewpoint of electron density distribution in the lattice, there need be no difference between this description and the conventional one according to which the diamond consists of carbon atoms because the C^{4-} ions lose and the C^{4+} cores gain electron density through the mutual deformation.

However, the difference in the quantization of the electrons can explain why diamond is hard and has a high melting point. It must require a very strong mechanical force in order to unscreen the carbon cores and move C^{4+} ions past other C^{4+} ions. The unique hardness of diamond becomes obvious if one thinks of the extremely strong force fields of C^{4+} cores analogous to the carbides of silicon or of boron; compounds which are characterized by great hardness.

Our approach to solid state chemistry correlates the hardness with the energy requirement for temporarily unscreening cations or positive cores and for overcoming the repulsive forces between incompletely screened cations. This energy term, the cation-cation repulsion, is singled out among others as being the most important. On moving one crystal plane over another the energy necessary to force cations to pass other cations must be high in most cases because of the low polarizability of cations as compared with anions. We consider the polarizability of an ion as its ability to adjust the symmetry of its force field to suit the environment. When two Cl^{-} ions are brought together they polarize each other and thus lower their mutual repulsive forces. Two Na^{+} ions within the same distance cannot do so, at least not to the same extent. For this reason we find that anions touch one another in many crystal structures, but cations of the noble gas-type are rarely found to be close neighbors in equilibrium positions.

The first conclusion we can draw from our interpretation of

the scratch hardness concerns noble gas-type versus non-noble gas-type ions. If the internuclear distance is approximately the same, the crystal that contains the non-noble gas-type cations must be softer than the one that contains the noble gas-type ones. Indeed, if we compare some Sr^{2+} and Pb^{2+} compounds we find the latter to have the lower hardness (Table XXXVI).

In spite of having a somewhat smaller particle distance, the lead compound is softer than the corresponding strontium compound because the Pb^{2+}-Pb^{2+} repulsion is lowered through mutual polarization. Pb^{2+} ions have the same charge as and a size similar to Sr^{2+} ions but they are more polarizable. Table XXXVII supports this relationship by additional examples.

V. M. Goldschmidt placed particular emphasis upon the packing in a crystal, i.e., on the interatomic distances. Whereas this is, no doubt, an important factor, the screening demand of ions can counteract the effect of packing upon the hardness. A Th^{4+} ion requires more anions in order to be properly screened

TABLE XXXVI

Comparison of Hardness of Sr^{2+} and Pb^{2+} Compounds

Compound	Particle distance (A.)	Hardness
SrS	3.0	3.3
PbS	2.9	2.8
SrSe	3.2	2.9
PbSe	3.0	2.4
SrTe	3.3	2.8
PbTe	3.2	2.3

TABLE XXXVII

Effect of the Electron Configuration of the Cations upon the Hardness of Some Crystals

Noble gas-type ion	Hardness	Non-noble gas-type ion	Hardness
Al_2O_3	9.0	Fe_2O_3	6.0
$MgAl_2O_4$	8.0	$FeFe_2O_4$	6.0
Modifications of SiO_2	6.0–7.0	Modifications of TiO_2	5.7–6.3
Be_2SiO_4	7.5	Zn_2SiO_4	5.5

than the much smaller Si^{4+} ion. As a result, ThO_2 has the same hardness as SnO_2 and TiO_2 (hardness, 6–7) and is nearly as hard as SiO_2 in spite of the variations in the internuclear distances (Table XXXVIII). If the cations have high charges (as shown in Table XXXVIII), the screening demand as expressed by their coordination number dominates their hardness. If the charge is only 1 or 2, the internuclear distance seems to be the determining factor as can be seen from the fact that the hardness of BeO (9.0) is greater than that of MgO (6.5) and CaO (4.5). The hardness decreases with increasing ionic size of the cation. In the same way the hardness of the alkali halides decreases with increasing internuclear distance; i.e., from NaF to NaCl, NaBr, and NaI or from NaCl to KCl and RbCl.

The concept of the "temporary unscreening of cations" during scratching requires an additional consideration if one goes from simple compounds to complex crystals; namely, the determination of which cations have to be unscreened. For example, the compounds $LiKSO_4$ and $LiKBeF_4$ have the same lattice parameters but contain ions of different charges; namely, the S^{6+} core of the sulfate and the Be^{2+} core of the fluoberyllate complex. The two substances have the same hardness which leads to the conclusion that neither the sulfate nor the fluoberyllate complex has to be destroyed during scratching. Apparently, these groups move as units $(SO_4)^{2-}$ and $(BeF_4)^{2-}$ and the unscreening during scratching is limited to the Li^+ and K^+ ions.

In potassium nickel fluoride $KNiF_3$ and potassium niobate $KNbO_3$, the Ni^{2+} and Nb^{5+} ions are screened by six anions each. The K^+ ions are surrounded by 12 anions and the two compounds have the same structure (Perowskite type). In spite of having identical cell dimensions (particle distances) the niobate is con-

TABLE XXXVIII

Effect of Packing and Screening on Hardness

Compound	Internuclear distance, A.	Coordination no.	Hardness
ThO_2	2.42	8	6.5
SnO_2	2.06	6	6–7
TiO_2	1.96	6	6–7
SiO_2	1.61	4	7

siderably harder (hardness, 4.5) than the fluoride (hardness, 3.5) indicating that the scratch hardness is determined by the temporary unscreening of the Nb^{5+} and Ni^{3+} ions, respectively, and that these ions do not move as complexes.

The screening approach to the hardness of simple compounds can be of help to those who are looking for new substances which are hard. Firstly, one has to choose as the cations only those of low polarizability. Mg^{2+} is more suitable than Pb^{2+} or Ba^{2+}; Al^{3+} is more suitable than Ga^{3+} or In^{3+}. Secondly, one has to select anions that have high charges, e.g., N^{3-} or C^{4-}, in order to produce a compound with a low anion-to-cation ratio. In order to keep this ratio low, cations with very high charges, e.g., S^{6+} or Os^{8+}, must be avoided. In order to neutralize these cations, a large number of anions is needed and a large anion-to-cation ratio provides good screening and favors the formation of molecules $S^{6+}O_3^{2-}$ and $Os^{8+}O_4^{2-}$ that have relatively high vapor pressures. This reasoning agrees with the empirical findings that nitrides and carbides are the hardest abrasives. The relationship that exists between the hardness, brittleness, and the ductility of simple crystals and structural parameters such as internuclear distance and the polarizability of all ions has been treated by W. A. Weyl (280). The concept that any hardness test involves a partial unscreening of cations is strongly supported by the observation that liquids which can act as screeners lower the hardness. When W. von Engelhardt (281) determined the abrasion hardness of quartz he found that this mineral was "harder" in hexane than in water but distinctly "softer" when abraded in n-butanol. Table XXXIX gives the apparent hardness of quartz in different liquids in arbitrary units, setting the abrasion hardness of quartz in water equal to 100 units.

This dependence of the hardness of a crystal upon the environ-

TABLE XXXIX

Apparent Abrasion Hardness of Quartz in Different Liquids (281)

Liquid	Hardness	Liquid	Hardness
Hexane	109	Acetone	95
Benzene	103	Methanol	87
Carbon tetrachloride	100	Ethanol	87
Water	100	iso-Pentanol	71
Nitrobenzene	95	n-Butanol	67

ment, e.g., the "cooling liquid," proves that even for a well defined solid such as a single quartz crystal, the abrasion hardness is not only a matter of the structure alone but also involves mechano-chemistry. The most promising tool for studying the hardness of crystalline and amorphous solids seems to be the indentor.

According to H. E. Powell and F. W. Preston (282), glasses should be ideal in many respects for studying the mechanical properties of matter. The hardness is a property that must be closely related to the mechanical strength of a glass and to its low temperature viscosity.

As tested in the form of bottles, laths, plates or rods, glass shows a tensile strength varying from one test to the next, but most values lie between 3000 and 10,000 lbs./in.^{2} The strength varies:

(a) With the duration of the test (static fatigue)
(b) With the humidity of the atmosphere (hydrolysis)
(c) With the degree of abrasion of the surface (flaws as stress raisers)
(d) With the temperature

Glass fibers have been found to show strengths ranging from the order of 10^5 lbs./in.^{2} to 10^6/in.^{2}. However, the high strength of these fibers drops sharply when they are touched.

Using a steel ball pressed against a flat surface, Powell and Preston obtained values of the tensile strength that were 20 to 60 times as great as the macrostrengths of the same glasses.

A window glass (fire-polished) is much stronger (236,000 lbs./in.^{2}) than a plate glass (160,000 lbs./in.^{2}) that during its grinding must develop cracks of a certain depth action.

The maximum radial tension resulting during this indentation test can be calculated from a formula derived by H. Hertz in 1896; it is this tensile stress that initiates fracture. The volume of the highly stressed zone during this test is comparable with that of a glass fiber. Steel balls $\frac{1}{30}$ to $\frac{1}{8}$-inch diameter produce a stressed annulus of the order of 0.02 to 0.06 inches in perimeter and one-thousandths of an inch in width.

The determination of the Vickers hardness, H_V, is based on a similar principle, using a diamond pyramid rather than a steel ball. R. W. Douglas (283) made some valuable comments on the mechanism of this method of determining the hardness of glasses.

The determination of the Vickers hardness, H_V, for glasses by means of diamond indentation (L. Ainsworth (284)) gave the following values:

$$H_V \text{ for polished plate glass} = 540 \pm 3 \text{ kg./mm.}^2$$
$$H_V \text{ for silica glass} = 710 \pm 3 \text{ kg./mm.}^2$$

The evaluation of indentation hardness used the mean pressure which is defined by P (applied load) divided by the total surface area under pressure.

For a diamond pyramid with an angle of 136° between opposite faces, one finds:

$$\text{Mean pressure} = P(2 \sin 68°)/d^2$$

in which P = applied load, and d = diagonal of the impression. The stress system which results from indentation pressure is com plex but it has been shown that approximately two-thirds of the mean pressure appears in the form of hydrostatic pressure that cannot contribute to plastic flow.

R. W. Douglas (283) points out that for shear stresses of the order of 10^{10} dynes/cm.^{2} the viscosity can no longer be treated as being independent of the shear; the viscosity will decrease rapidly with increasing shear. He suggests that when the loaded diamond point first touches the surface, the viscosity of the glass under the intense load is sufficiently reduced to allow flow to take place. This flow will continue until the area of contact between diamond and glass has increased sufficiently to reduce the shear stresses to such magnitude that the viscosity assumes its normal value and no further flow can take place. We describe the effect of shear stresses as a disproportionation of the binding forces and the ability of the system to flow because of the weaker forces.

The asymmetry of the surface layer that causes the structure of any liquid, even of vitreous silica, to deviate from the ideal, flawless Bernal liquid makes it impossible to correlate the flow of surfaces under the indentor with the viscosity of the bulk of the glass extrapolated to ordinary temperature. We will see later (Chapter XVIII, 3) that the ability to flow increases and the brittleness decreases when the particles which are subjected to mechanical forces become very small. Some brittle substances, e.g., coal, will flow if the particle size decreases below a certain value.

The viscosity of a glass at ordinary temperature decreases with increasing "fictive temperature" of the glass.

P. Grodzinski (285) showed that the hardness of a "toughened" glass, often referred to as a "hardened glass," is actually lower than that of the same glass in annealed condition.

F. W. Glaze, D. H. Blackburn, S. S. Osmalov, D. Hubbard and M. H. Black (286) measured the hardness of a sample of vitreous arsenic trisulfide and found that its diamond pyramid hardness was as follows:

100 to 110 kg./cm.^{2} for the chilled glass
120 to 125 kg./cm.^{2} for the annealed glass

L. Ainsworth (284) used a diamond pyramid indentor for studying "microstrength" of glasses under conditions that do not lead to fracture and that involve such a small volume of glass that the chances of avoiding major Griffith flaws were very good. He expresses his diamond pyramid hardness (DPH) by numbers given by the applied load divided by the area of contact. The following figures show variations of the DPH numbers for some representative glasses:

Fused silica	710 kg./mm.^{2}
Pyrex	595 kg./mm.^{2}
Plate glass	540 kg./mm.^{2}
Lead crystal glass	495 kg./mm.^{2}

This method of determining the DPH gave precise and reproducible results that were independent of the applied load. The loads were kept sufficiently small to produce stresses that were small as compared with those stresses which cause fracture.

In a second paper, L. Ainsworth (284) applied his method to glasses whose compositions were varied systematically. A few of his results are cited in Table XL.

For the glasses in the soda-silica system the DPH values drop sharply with the first addition of Na_2O and go through a flat minimum for a glass of the approximate composition Na_2O, $2SiO_2$.

A few values of the DPH for potash glasses (see Table XL) reveal that K_2O on a molar basis exerts a stronger softening effect than Na_2O. The first addition of an alkali was found to produce the most drastic effect in lowering the DPH of silica. Furthermore, the addition of K_2O lowered the hardness of silica more than an equivalent addition of Na_2O. Most interesting is the "mixed alkali effect" in which the DPH goes through a maximum, (Table XLI).

The maximum hardness of a glass which contains two kinds

TABLE XL

Diamond Pyramid Hardness of Glasses of Varied Composition (284)

Glasses (mole %)		DPH (kg./mm.²)
SiO_2	Na_2O	
100	—	710
88	12	505
84	16	442
80	20	405
76	24	375
68	32	354
62	38	376
56	44	388
	K_2O	
100	—	710
88	12	406
84	16	374
80	20	364
72	28	337

TABLE XLI

"Mixed Alkali Effect" on Diamond Pyramid Hardness (284)

Glasses (mole %)			DPH (kg./mm.²)
SiO_2	Na_2O	K_2O	
80	20	—	405
80	16	4	420
80	12	8	429
80	8	12	413
80	4	16	394
80	—	20	364

of alkali agrees with similar "mixed alkali effects" as are revealed in other properties e.g. in the electrical conductivity or the low temperature viscosity.

The replacement of Na_2O by CaO causes the DPH to increase steadily, more so for the first substitution than for later ones as can be seen from the Δ values, the differences between two glasses that differ in CaO content by 5 mole % (Table XLII).

Lead glasses are much softer than soda lime glasses. For this reason it becomes exceedingly interesting to learn from Ainsworth's data that this situation is not quite as simple as it seems. When

TABLE XLII

Effect of Replacement of Na_2O by CaO on Diamond Pyramid Hardness (284)

Glasses (mole %)			DPH (kg./mm.²)	Δ
SiO_2	Na_2O	CaO		
70	30	—	358	
70	25	5	487	129
70	20	10	554	67
70	15	15	605	51
70	10	20	620	15

TABLE XLIII

Effect on Diamond Pyramid Hardness of Addition of Lead Oxide to Sodium Silicate (284)

Glasses (mole %)			DPH (kg./mm.²)
SiO_2	Na_2O	PbO	
80	20	—	405
76	19	5	432
72	18	10	445
68	17	15	447
64	16	20	440
56	14	30	409
40	10	50	270

starting out with a sodium silicate of the composition $Na_2O,4SiO_2$ and adding lead oxide, the DPH values go through a maximum as can be seen from Table XLIII.

In order to compare a greater variety of oxides, L. Ainsworth measured a number of glasses of the molar composition 72 mole % SiO_2, 18 mole % Na_2O, and 10 mole % of some oxide. The following values were obtained:

10 mole % oxide	*DPH*
Na_2O	362
CaO	562
SrO	550
BaO	522
PbO	445
MgO	498
ZnO	510
B_2O_3	554
Al_2O_3	578
SiO_2	426

L. Ainsworth's primary interest in his DPH measurements was to use them as a basis for determining the mechanical strength of glasses via a nondestructive test. For this reason he enters into a detailed discussion of his data and of earlier measurements of the mechanical strength of glasses as affected by their compositions (G. Gehlhoff and M. Thomas (287)). For these discussions, for further details of his technique, and for complete data, his original papers should be consulted.

We are primarily interested in his structural explanation because it is straightforward and reveals how far one can go on the basis of the three-dimensional random network theory including the use of the field strengths of the cations.

According to Ainsworth, the addition of alkali to silica weakens the structure by breaking Si—O—Si bonds. The combination of two alkalies permits a more efficient packing and thus produces a maximum DPH for a certain $K_2O:Na_2O$ ratio. This explanation, based on conventional concepts, is not convincing. For example, why should the first 12 mole % K_2O lower the DPH of silica from 710 to 406 kg./mm.^{2} and the same number of broken bridges in the corresponding Na_2O glass have a lesser effect? The addition of 12 mole % Na_2O lowers the DPH value to 505 kg./mm.^{2}.

According to our approach, the high value of the DPH of vitreous silica is the result of the combination of strong binding forces and the very low polarizability of all ions. The determination of the DPH involves flow under shear stresses and for all flow processes the polarizability is of paramount importance. Alkali ions introduce polarizable O^{2-} ions that disproportionate the binding forces into some stronger and some weaker forces, increasing the polarizability of all O^{2-} ions. K_2O is more effective than Na_2O with respect to both changes.

The fact that the addition of Na_2O causes the DPH values to go through a minimum reveals two antagonistic effects. The first addition of alkali participates in the structure to a large extent in the form of submicroscopic clusters. As the over-all polarizability of the glass increases with further alkali additions, the alkali ions become more evenly distributed and, thus, strengthen the glass structure.

K_2O produces lower DPH values than the corresponding amount of Na_2O. However, by increasing the polarizability of the glass, K_2O causes a more even distribution of the Na^+ ions, hence the mixed alkali effect. The gradual replacement of Na_2O by K_2O causes the DPH values to go through a maximum.

The gradual replacement of Na_2O by CaO in a glass which contains 70% SiO_2 and 30% Na_2O increases the DPH values. We explain this effect on the basis that the Ca^{2+} ions coordinate with the highly polarizable nonbridging O^{2-} ions. This means that the highly polarizable O^{2-} ions are eliminated when Ca^{2+} ions are introduced. This is analogous to the effect of this substitution upon the chemical resistivity.

In a second series of Na_2O-CaO-SiO_2 glasses, Ainsworth keeps the $Na_2O:SiO_2$ ratio constant (1:4) and adds CaO. For these glasses the values of the DPH go through a pronounced maximum. According to our views, the addition of CaO to a glass of the composition 20% Na_2O, 80% SiO_2 has two antagonistic effects: (1) introducing O^{2-} ions that are more polarizable than the bridging O^{2-} ions in pure SiO_2, and (2) eliminating the most polarizable nonbridging O^{2-} ions in the Na_2O silicate.

The same situation occurs if PbO is added to the Na_2O-SiO_2 glass (1:4). Lead glasses are known to be soft but the first addition of PbO eliminates the most polarizable nonbridging O^{2-} ions and hence the addition of PbO to an alkali silicate glass hardens the glass.

The emphasis placed upon the field strength of the cation and sharp distinction between network formers and modifiers leads to contradictions and to difficulties when Ainsworth discussed the effects which the divalent oxides have upon the hardness. The order of decreasing hardness was as follows: CaO, SrO, BaO, ZnO, MgO, PbO. He wrote: "It is suggested that the positions of ZnO, MgO, and PbO in this sequence are explained by the fact that these three oxides all take part in the structure in network-former positions to a considerable extent." It seems perfectly logical to assume that Zn^{2+} and Mg^{2+} ions can form ZnO_4 and MgO_4 groups, respectively. This agrees with the earlier description used by N. J. Kreidl (112) in 1929, when he called MgO an "acidic" oxide because of its effect on the properties of glasses. The emphasis on size or field strength leads to a difficulty when the large Pb^{2+} ion reveals its role as network former.

This difficulty does not arise if one places the emphasis upon the polarizability of the O^{2-} ions. The lower coordination of Mg^{2+} ions can then be interpreted as affecting a smaller number of

O^{2-} ions than the larger Ca^{2+} and Ba^{2+} ions. The size of the Mg^{2+} ion is approximately the same as that of the Ni^{2+} ion and for the latter we know that it forms both NiO_4 and NiO_6 groups depending on the composition of the glass and its temperature (see Chapter XVI). Using the molar refractivity of the O^{2-} ions as a measure of the polarizability, K. Fajans and N. J. Kreidl (26) found that the only ion that decreases the polarizability of the O^{2-} ions more strongly than the Si^{4+} ion is the Be^{2+} ion. This is in perfect agreement with the early findings of F. Eisenloeffel (288) and of C. A. Becker (289) who discovered the beneficial effect of beryllium oxide upon the scratch hardness of glass. Beryllium orthosilicate Be_2SiO_4 is harder (hardness, 7.5) than quartz (hardness, 7.0).

Recently, A. Petzold, F. G. Wihsmann and H. von Kamptz (290) published an extensive study of the indentation hardness of silicate glasses. Using the polarization concept, these authors presented a clear picture of the effect of the chemical composition upon the hardness of glasses. On the basis of the screening concept, these authors were able to correlate the indentation hardness of systematically varied glasses with their molar refractivities, the polarizabilities of the cations, and with the softening temperatures of the glasses.

Our discussion of the hardness of crystals revealed the importance of the polarizability of all ions and of the interatomic distances. Applying these principles to glasses, one would expect the hardness to decrease with increasing temperature analogous to the volume expansion of a glass with increasing temperature, because increasing volume increases both the polarizability of the oxygen ions and the internuclear distances.

J. H. Westbrook (291) determined the hardness of some glasses as a function of the temperature and found some very interesting phenomena. The indentation hardness of quartz decreases with increasing temperature except in the inversion region. In the inversion region the hardness increases not only above that of quartz at ordinary temperature but also above that of corundum. Indentation hardness involves deformation due to the cooperation of atoms over very large distances. Lack of depth action during the inversion of quartz prevents the disproportionation of binding forces and the hardness increases. This phenomenon is utilized in "Pyroceram" glasses which contain particles too small to exhibit depth action. This lack of depth action also causes the "ductility" to go through a sharp minimum. According to Westbrook, quartz is particularly brittle in the inversion region. The indentation hardness, when measured *in vacuo* in order to keep hydrolysis to a minimum, seems to be one of the most powerful tools for studying the effect of long range order.

Vitreous silica made from quartz by fusion showed a weak but distinct irregularity in the region in which quartz undergoes its low-high inversion (573°C.). Vitreous silica made from cristobalite showed a similar irregularity in its indentation hardness around 150°C.; i.e., in the temperature region in which cristobalite undergoes a modification change. These effects support our views that vitreous silica may contain remnants of the crystals from which it has formed. Most interesting, however, is the fact that Corning's vitreous silica also shows a distinct anomaly around 573°C. in spite of the fact that the Corning process does not involve fusion of any crystalline form of silica but hydrolysis of a volatile compound of silicon. Hence, we must assume that during cooling vitreous silica can develop structural elements or quasi-ordered regions which resemble quartz sufficiently to reveal its low-high transition.

11. Electrical Potentials

A. Development of the Oxygen Electrode Using Glass as the Electrolyte

At elevated temperatures, many glasses are electrolytic conductors, in particular the alkali silicates and borates, and they behave in very much the same way as an aqueous solution of an electrolyte at ordinary temperature. When two different metals are brought in contact with an electrolyte they establish a potential difference because of their different tendencies to send ions into the electrolyte. Such a system can produce an electric current, and then it becomes a galvanic cell. A. C. Becquerel (292) performed this experiment with copper and iron in contact with a glass. A similar experiment was made by W. Thomson (293), who studied the combination of copper and zinc with a hot glass in order to prove his theory that even solids can be electrolytic conductors.

B. von Lengyel and A. Sammt (294) used a glass as an electrolyte for studying the electrical potentials between a glass and fused salts of different compositions: e.g.;

$$Pb/PbCl_2 + \text{variable } KCl/Glass/PbCl_2 + \text{constant } KCl/Pb$$

The concentration of alkali chloride was kept constant in one compartment, whereas that in the other compartment was varied. The resulting electrical potentials were measured.

The classical experiment in which a glass served as an electrolyte for studying reactions and equilibria between gases is that performed by F. Haber (295). Haber was interested in the dissociation of H_2O at elevated temperature and in establishing a correlation between the available thermodynamic data and the electrical potentials that should arise between two different gas mixtures. He built a galvanic cell having a mixture of H_2O-H_2 on one side and one of H_2O-O_2 on the other. The cell used a glass tube separated into two chambers by a thin glass plate. The latter became the electrolyte when the cell was operated at temperatures ranging from 330 to 570°C. Today we would call this arrangement a "fuel cell" because its electrical energy originates from the combustion of a fuel, in this case hydrogen. The glass plate was the electrolyte and contacts were made by films of a noble metal. It turned out that the potentials obtained were in good agreement with the thermodynamic data. The electromotive force (emf) of the cell responded to variations of the oxygen pressure over the H_2O-O_2 electrodes as was expected for an oxygen electrode.

At sufficiently high temperatures the O^{2-} ions in glasses and crystalline oxides become mobile and carry electrical charges. A. V. Bleininger (296) observed electrical potentials when he brought pellets of different silicate mixtures in contact with one another and heated them to temperatures between 900 and 1300°C. Mixtures which contained Zn_2SiO_4 assumed a positive potential in contact with pellets which contained the silicates of Mn^{2+}, Cu^{2+}, and Fe^{2+}. The more acidic cations with incomplete shells attracted O^{2-} ions from the better-screened Zn^{2+} compounds. The work of Bleininger was qualitative and lacked reproducibility because the experimental conditions were such that the potential differences were masked by polarization effects.

The application of the Pt-O electrode to fused salts (carbonates) was first used by E. Bauer and R. Brunner (297). P. Csaki and A. Dietzel (298) used the oxygen electrode for studying borates.

A major improvement in the construction of reproducible oxygen electrodes to be used for fused salts was made by scientists in the Norwegian Silicate Institute. H. Flood (299) and his associates began systematic investigations in the field of fused salts in 1947. Using low current densities and working at relatively high temperatures (above 700°C.) they found that the oxygen electrode could function in a reversible reaction.

We showed earlier that the acidity-basicity of a system can be attributed either to the field strength or polarizing power of the cations or to the polarizability of the anions (see Chapter V). Glasses or fused salts containing O^{2-} ions as the only anions can be described as mixtures of O^{2-} ions having different energy states (states of polarization) that are stabilized and neutralized by their cations. On the basis of the polarizability of the anions, H. Flood and his school describe salt formation between two oxides, e.g., SiO_2 and BaO, as a process in which the states of polarization of the O^{2-} ions are equalized.

Therefore, acidity and basicity of fused salts and glasses can be measured if the transfer of O^{2-} ions from one state of polarization into another state of polarization can be carried out in a reversible cell. H. Flood, T. Förland and K. Motzfeldt (300) constructed such a cell of two oxygen electrodes.

The oxygen electrodes consisted of platinum wires immersed in fused salt mixtures. Oxygen gas was bubbled past the platinum wires. The fused salt mixtures were in separate platinum crucibles and these two half cells were connected by a liquid junction consisting of a porous MgO rod impregnated with a fused salt. For systems containing sulfate, carbonate, and small amounts of oxide the EMF measured for the cell was in very good agreement with the values calculated for a cell consisting of oxygen electrodes. The measurements revealed that the liquid junction potential was negligible.

In 1954 the oxygen electrodes became well established as a major tool in high temperature research. R. Didtschenko and E. G. Rochow (301), I. Peychès and P. Le Clerc (302), E. Plumat (303), as well as T. Förland and M. Tashiro (304) developed galvanic cells for studying the constitution of melts, the acidity of glasses in their softening range, and the interaction of glasses with metals and refractory oxides.

For an evaluation of the results obtained by these scientists we will discuss some of the representative experiments. For the experimental details, the original papers should be consulted. In order to present a uniform interpretation of the experiments and to show the nature of the information that can be obtained from working with the oxygen electrode, we will describe the results of the different scientists in our own terminology. As different scientists used the oxygen electrode for different purposes the terminology in the original papers is far from uniform. Some scientists speak of the "free oxygen ion concentration" as characterizing the basicity of the system whereas others use the term "oxygen ion activity". T. Förland and M. Tashiro (304) use the electrostatic approach to the acidity-basicity of glasses and emphasize the intrinsic difficulty that one encounters in formulating a common parameter of acidity-basicity for glasses that contain different kinds of alkali ions. E. Plumat (303) bases his interpretations upon the screening concept because he needed an approach that was equally applicable to glasses and crystalline solids. Plumat developed methods for comparing glasses and crystalline solids with respect to their acidities.

Before discussing this work we shall examine the origin of the electrical potentials in a variety of systems.

B. Fundamentals Concerning the Establishment of Electrical Potentials

The crystallization of fused NaCl below 800°C. improves the screening of the Na^+ ions. At the melting point two phases are in equilibrium. The liquid phase, corresponding to a more probable, less ordered, distribution of highly mobile ions has the higher entropy. The crystalline phase offers better screening because it has the higher density and symmetry. In the crystal electroneutrality is achieved in a smaller volume than in the melt and the symmetry of the crystal provides better screening for the cations. On the basis of this description, one must expect that at the melting point of a crystal a tendency exists for cations to leave the liquid phase and enter the still rather defective crystal. This tendency exists because screening conditions in the crystal are superior and the coulombic attractive forces are stronger. One must also expect that the anions would have a tendency to leave the crystal lattice and participate in the screening of the cations in the melt by increasing the anion-to-cation ratio of the liquid phase. Both processes lead to an uneven distribution of anions and cations between the two phases and give the solid NaCl a positive excess charge (more vacant anion sites than vacant cation sites) in contact with the melt. A. C. Marshall (305) in our laboratory found that a platinum electrode coated with solid NaCl at 800°C.

assumed a positive charge with respect to another Pt electrode immersed in the fused salt.

The participation of excess cations in the crystal or the formation of an excess of anion vacancies over cation vacancies in the lattice of NaCl is limited because these processes raise the energy of the system to a high level.

The unique way in which a proton can be screened (see Chapter I), namely, by its penetration into the electron cloud of an anion, makes it possible for some hydrogen compounds, e.g., water, to accommodate excess protons in their structures. E. J. Workman and S. E. Reynolds (306) found that freezing of water can produce potential differences as high as 60 volts between the liquid and the solid: the ice is positive with respect to the water. Under equilibrium conditions an electrical potential is established because the crystal contains an excess of protons and the liquid contains an excess of anions. The screening of the protons is better in the symmetrical crystal than in the more random liquid structure. We can refer to such a system as consisting of a better screening (basic) solid in contact with an acidic liquid that has a lesser screening power. Hence, protons will move from the liquid phase into the solid and establish a potential difference. Workman and Reynolds (306) also found that the liquid that was separated from the partly frozen water had a different pH value than the original water; namely,

pH of water before freezing, 6.3
pH of the frozen fraction, 6.2
pH of the liquid fraction of the system, 7.0

These pH values indicate that in the partly frozen system the ice contained more protons than the water. The experiments also indicate that ice can form a defective structure of nonstoichiometric composition. As far as the changes in the chemical composition are concerned, the deviation from stoichiometry is small but the electrical potentials which develop under these conditions are high and they are of paramount importance in nature (waterfall electricity, thunder storm electricity).

We have defined acids and bases as systems that differ in the degree of screening of their cations (see Chapter V). The system in which the cations are better screened is a base with respect to the system that contains the lesser screened cations. When mobility of the ions is sufficiently high, the two systems can react. Two oxides may form a salt by rearranging their ions to equalize the degree of screening of all cations. However, if the conditions do not permit a chemical reaction, the two systems will develop a potential difference when brought into contact with one another. A "contact potential" and its intensified form, "friction electricity," result from a transfer of protons from the acidic to the basic system or from a transfer of anions (electrons) from the better screened basic to the less screened acidic phase.

The proton is unique among cations because of its small size and the absence of electrons. When a glass membrane separates two aqueous solutions of different acidities some protons migrate through the membrane from the more acidic into the more basic, better-screening liquid. As the anions cannot follow the protons, a potential difference arises between the two liquids. Equilibrium is reached in such a system if the tendency of the protons to leave the poorly screened part of the system (acid solution) and enter the better screening (basic) solution is balanced by the electrical repulsive forces between the excess positive charge of the basic medium and the protons. The potential difference between two solutions separated by a glass membrane (glass electrode) has been correlated with the hydrogen ion concentration and is widely used for measuring the hydrogen ion concentration. The process is not limited to proton transfer but applies in principle to all cations that can migrate through a glass. Using alkali aluminosilicate glasses, G. Eisenman, D. O. Rudin and J. U. Casby (307), developed glass electrodes that respond specifically to alkali ions (308).

The screening of cations in a solution is a function of the polarizability of the surrounding O^{2-} ions. The polarizability depends on the electrical field of all cations of the system. For this reason the acidity or the degree of screening of the protons in an aqueous system is a function of all constituents. Hence, no simple relation can be expected to exist between the actual concentration of hydrogen ions in two solutions and the potential difference that arises between them. M. Dole (309), one of the pioneers in the field of the application of glass electrodes, once wrote: "We do not know what we measure when we measure pH but we do know that it is very important. We correlate the pH values with other observable properties of the solution, thus giving our pH data practical significance."

The electrical potential difference that originates between two solids on contact or rubbing is affected by their compositions and by their surface structures, particularly by their state of hydration. Glasses, as a rule, assume a positive charge when rubbed with silk or leather. Lead glasses are less suitable for this purpose than soda lime glasses. The presence of highly polarizable cations, e.g., Pb^{2+} ions, lowers the surface free energy and, with it, the chemical reactivity of the glass.

The sign and the magnitude of electrostatic charges resulting from the friction between metals and glasses have been examined repeatedly but the results are not very reproducible. As a rule, noble metals (Au, Pt, Ag, and Cu) assume a positive charge, whereas the more basic metals (Al, Zn, Sn, etc.) assume a negative charge with respect to glasses. The interaction between metals and glasses is complicated by the fact that during friction many metals combine with the glass surface so that metal particles are left sticking to the glass. Because of these complications no attempt will be made to explain the results of the different workers in the field of friction electricity between glasses and metals.

Later (Chapter XXIII) we will return to the formation of electrostatic charges through the diffusion of protons from one medium into another one. We attribute the adhesion of organic polymers to glasses primarily to such a proton transfer which has a finite depth action.

C. Temperature Gradient as a Source of an Electrical Potential

P. Le Clerc (310) observed an electrical potential between two electrodes that were attached to a glass rod when the rod was exposed to a temperature gradient. The electrode at the higher temperature was negative. The potential difference decreased when the temperature of the system was raised. E. Plumat (303) carried out similar experiments with molten glasses and found a potential of 0.09 volts for a soda lime glass when the temperature difference between the electrodes was 100°C. One electrode was in contact with the molten glass at 1100°C. (negative) and the other at 1000°C. (positive). A sodium silicate glass (30% Na_2O) gave a smaller emf at 1000°C. Plumat observed the formation of relatively large gas bubbles at the negative electrode, i.e., the hotter one, when the two electrodes were short circuited.

The lower the temperature of the glass, the greater is the need for its cations to be screened. This statement can be rephrased as follows. In the hotter part of the glass the energy for a partial unscreening of the cations is available. One can also say that the free energy of a glass, which has a uniform composition but is exposed to a temperature gradient, can be lowered by transferring cations from the cold to the hot end or anions from the hot to the cold end. Such a transfer of ions would lead to an equalization of the screening demand of all cations. The same lowering of the free energy can be achieved through the formation of O^{2-} ions from O_2 molecules of the atmosphere at the cold electrode and the discharge of O^{2-} ions and the formation of O_2 molecules at the hot electrode.

If this reaction occurs the hot electrode assumes a negative charge because O^{2-} ions are changed into O_2 molecules (gas bubbles) and electrons become available. The electrons that form

$$\text{hot electrode: } 2O^{2-} \rightarrow O_2 + 4(e^-)$$

move to the cold electrode where they are utilized for the formation of screeners according to

$$\text{cold electrode: } O_2 + 4e^- \rightarrow 2O^{2-}$$

These reactions are not only of interest with respect to the constitution of glass but reactions of this type have important technological implications. As far as the practical significance of these reactions is concerned, the original papers of E. Plumat (303) should be consulted.

D. Oxidation-Reduction Phenomena as Sources of Electrical Potentials

G. E. Rindone, E. C. Marboe, and W. A. Weyl (311) constructed electrolytic cells consisting of two compartments separated by a refractory material, and electrolyzed glasses in order to change their states of oxidation. The reduction of Ti^{4+} to Ti^{3+} ions, of sulfate to sulfide, and of ferric to ferrous ions are typical examples. For this purpose, two platinum electrodes were inserted into the molten glass and an emf was applied. In order to avoid the mixing of the oxidized glass with the reduced part of the glass the anode compartment of the refractory crucible was separated from the cathode compartment by a refractory diaphragm. The current was carried through the diaphragm by O^{2-} ions and some alkali ions. When the electrodes were disconnected from the applied emf source and connected with a voltmeter, a counter emf was observed. We can attribute the emf to a reaction by which the free energy of the system is lowered by equalizing the states of oxidation in the two compartments, i.e., by an electron transfer; e.g.,

$$Fe^{3+} + (e^-) \rightarrow Fe^{2+}$$
$$Fe^{2+} \rightarrow Fe^{3+} + (e^-)$$

The oxidized glass (Fe^{3+}) withdraws electrons from the platinum electrode whereas the reduced glass (Fe^{2+}) donates electrons to the platinum electrode.

The donation of electrons by Fe^{2+} ions and their oxidation to Fe^{3+} ions and similar reactions can be a source of electrons at the hot electrode in a temperature gradient. The reaction

$$2O^{2-} \rightarrow O_2 + 4(e^-)$$

can be replaced by the reaction

$$Cr^{3+} \rightarrow Cr^{6+} + 3(e^-)$$

Both reactions that take place at the hot electrode provide the electrons necessary at the cold electrode for changing oxygen molecules into O^{2-} ions.

E. Acid-Base Reactions as Sources of Electrical Potentials

The oxygen electrode has been used for comparing the acidities of a lead silicate glass in the molten state, which resulted when different additions were made, to the melt by R. Didtschenko and E. R. Rochow (301). A method for measuring glasses in their softening range was developed (T. Förland and M. Tashiro (304)) that made it possible to compare the acidities of glasses in a lower temperature range. This, in turn, opened up the possibility of comparing "acidity" with other properties of glasses. E. Plumat (303) developed several experimental methods that enabled him to compare the acidities of molten glasses with those of solid oxides, particularly refractories. For the experimental details of these three approaches, the original papers should be consulted. We will restrict ourselves to the discussion of some of the results which were obtained.

(*1*) *Liquid-Liquid Interactions*

R. Didtschenko and E. G. Rochow (301) selected a low melting glass of the composition of the lead metasilicate, $PbO \cdot SiO_2$, as their standard melt. They measured the activity of the O^{2-}

ions as affected by foreign oxides by the emf of the cell:

$$Pt:O_2/\text{standard melt}/\text{standard melt} + nR_xO_y/O_2:Pt$$

They correlated their results with Dietzel's values of the field strength of the cations as expressed by the quantity z/a^2 (see Chapter II). Plotting the observed potentials against the value of the field strength of the cations they obtained curves (Fig. 23) that they interpreted as follows:

1. Potentials related to cations with a completed noble gas

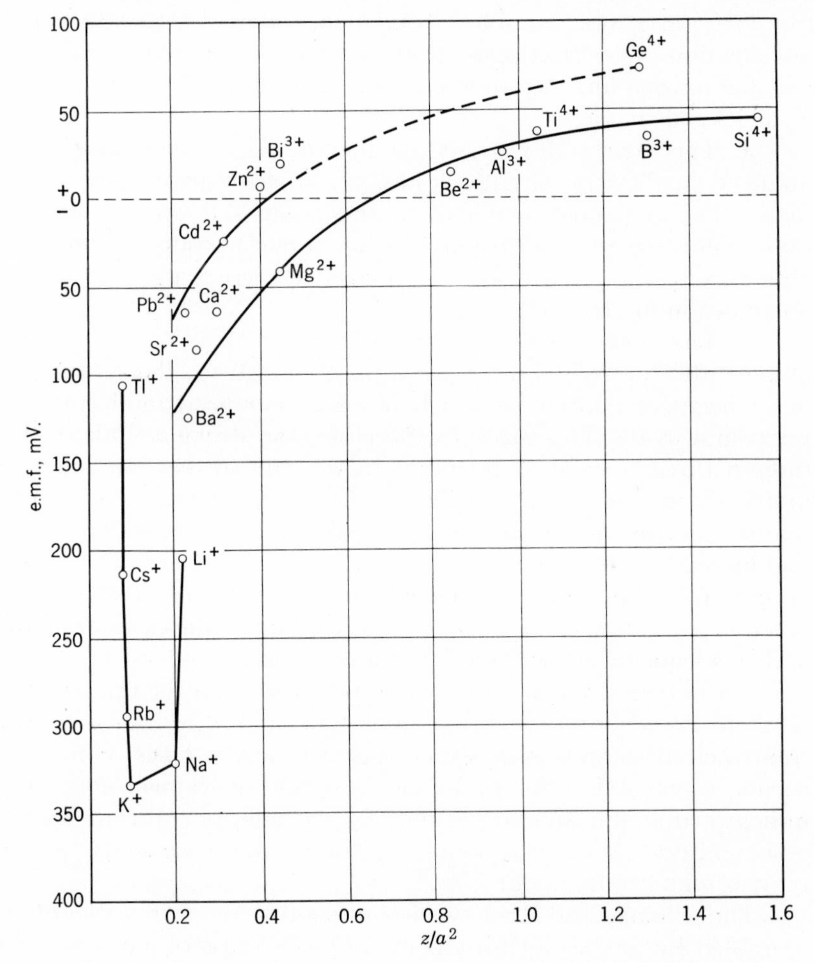

FIG. 23. Potentials as functions of the field strengths of ions. (From (301).)

shell fall on the hyperbolic curve. The Ba^{2+} ion and the Si^{4+} ion are the extremes. The typical alkaline earth oxides give negative potentials, increasing in the order of basicity; i.e., from MgO to BaO. The so-called "acid" oxides, such as beryllium oxide, alumina, boron trioxide, titania and silica, give positive potentials, increasing in that order. Thus, the basic or acidic character of an oxide is due to the increase or decrease of oxygen ion activity in the silicate system in which the oxide is dissolved. For the ions of noble gas type, the change in oxygen ion activity varies with the coulombic fields of these ions as expressed by z/a^2. The fact that the Ti^{4+} ion is not a noble gas-type ion gives rise to additional polarization forces that increase the attraction between the cation and the oxygen ions. Titania acts as a stronger acid than expected from its z/a^2 value.

2. The latter effect observed for titania is even more pronounced in the case of cations having 18 electrons in their outer shells. The respective cell emf of these ions fall upon a second hyperbolic curve that is displaced toward more positive potentials. One may be tempted to see in this displacement a measure of the polarization forces.

3. The potentials for glasses containing alkali oxides do not follow either pattern. They form a parabolic curve, shifted toward more negative potentials, which has a pronounced minimum for potassium oxide. This oxide is, therefore, the strongest base in the molten $PbSiO_3$ since a minimum in the emf means a maximum in the oxygen ion activity. This behavior can tentatively be explained on the basis of two opposing effects: decreasing z/a^2 value, and increasing coordination requirements in the series from lithium to cesium. The increasing coordination affects the oxygen ion activity oppositely to that obtained as a result of the field strength, and this leads to the occurrence of a maximum.

Didtschenko and Rochow (301) point out that the uncertainty of their liquid-liquid junction potentials makes it impossible to treat their data on a more exact thermodynamic basis. However, earlier work of L. Holub, F. Neubert and F. Sauerwald (312) indicates that the junction potentials are only of the same order of magnitude as the reproducibility of the measurements, which they estimate to be about 5 mv.

Didtschenko and Rochow emphasize that their data should be amplified by further measurements in order to be of more general value. Their results apply only to their particular standard melt $PbSiO_3$ and to the one temperature of 900°C.

(2) *Glass-Glass Interactions*

The next step in the application of the O_2-electrode to the constitution of glasses was the development of a cell that permitted the comparison of the acidities of glasses in and below their softening ranges. T. Förland and M. Tashiro (304) constructed a cell that consisted essentially of two rafts made of glass rods. Drawing glass rods provided a convenient method of obtaining glass samples with fresh, uncontaminated, and, therefore, reproducible surfaces. The following cell was adopted for the emf measurements:

Ag (in air)/Glass I/Glass II/Ag (in air)

Heating these cells for an hour established equilibrium and gave reproducible results at temperatures around 400 to 500°C. and higher. The operation of the cell requires ionic conductivity and hence the glasses have to contain alkali. The combination of two glasses free of alkali; namely, MgO, Al_2O_3, $4P_2O_5$ and BaO, Al_2O_3, $4P_2O_5$ gave no emf at 500°C. The change of O^{2-} ions into neutral molecules at one electrode, and the formation of O^{2-} ions from oxygen of the ambient atmosphere, has to be accompanied by a migration of positive carriers within the glass. In the absence of positive carriers, the electrode reactions can build up only a space charge but they can not produce a measurable current. Let us briefly review the results obtained by Förland and Tashiro with their emf measurements on glasses in the softening range.

1. Using a Na_2O, $3SiO_2$ glass as their standard, the effect of changing the silica to alkali ratio was examined. A glass with an SiO_2:Na_2O ratio of 2.0 assumed a negative charge and the glasses with SiO_2:Na_2O ratios of 4.0 and 5.0 respectively assumed positive charges. The results at 400 and 500°C. are plotted in Figure 24. The acidity increased with increasing SiO_2:Na_2O ratio. The difference in acidity seemed to increase with increasing temperature. We assume that this effect is the result of the different thermal expansivities.

2. Replacing Na_2O in a Na_2O,$3SiO_2$ glass gradually by MgO or BaO has an effect similar to that produced by increasing the SiO_2 content; i.e., the acidity of the glass increases (Fig. 25).

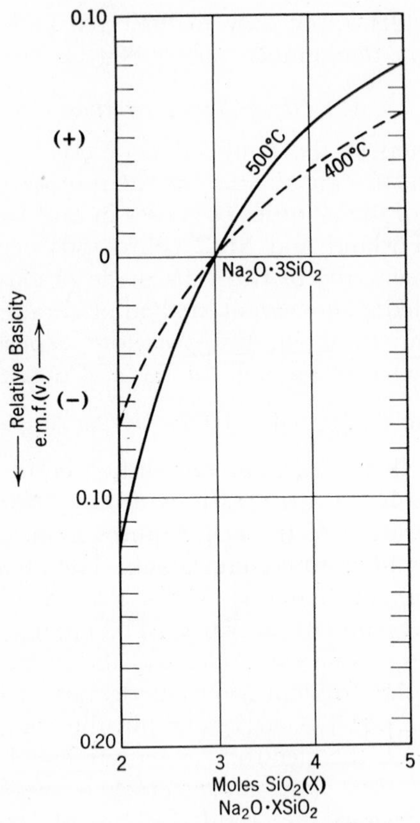

FIG. 24. Potentials of sodium silicate glasses. (From (304).)

3. With respect to the constitution of alkali silicate glasses, the most interesting experiment was a series in which Na_2O was gradually replaced by K_2O (Fig. 26). The $K_2O, 3SiO_2$ glass was more basic than the $Na_2O, 3SiO_2$ glass as might be expected from conventional chemical concepts. However, a glass of the composition $Na_2O, K_2O, 6\,SiO_2$ was much more acidic than both end members. Here Förland and Tashiro encountered some difficulties in finding a suitable explanation and they wrote: "The final interpretation has to await the gathering of additional and more accurate information on the thermal and electrical properties of the glasses." We assume that this effect can be explained on the basis of a closer packing in mixed alkali glasses. The acidity-basicity concept based on the polarizability of the anions leads to the conclusion that the low

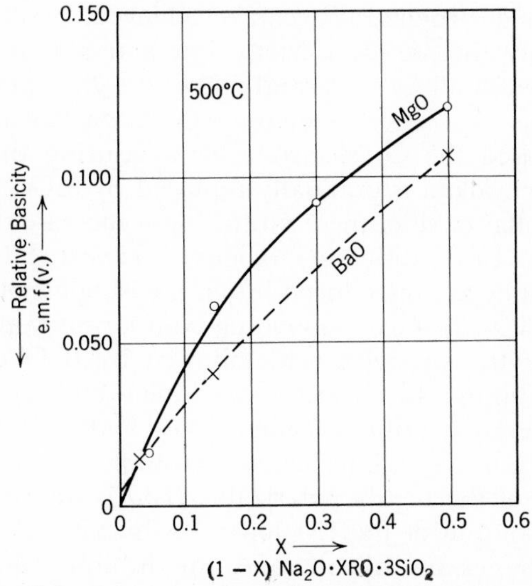

FIG. 25. Potentials of sodium silicate glasses with additions of MgO and BaO. (From (304).)

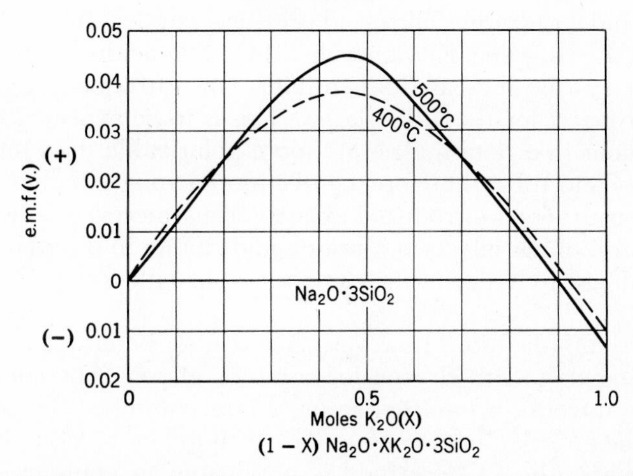

FIG. 26. Potentials of sodium-potassium silicate glasses. (From (304).)

density form of SiO_2, silica W, is more basic and the high density form, silica C, is more acidic than quartz. For a given composition the state of polarization of the O^{2-} ions is affected by the proximity of the cations. Several properties reveal that a mixture of Na^+ and K^+ ions can be distributed in a glass more efficiently than one kind of alkali alone. The more efficient packing leads to a smaller volume, in which electroneutrality can be achieved. In other words, it leads to a more intense electrostatic interaction that decreases the polarizabilities of all O^{2-} ions and makes the glass more acidic.

By the same experimental method G. S. Smith and G. E. Rindone (313) used the O_2 electrode for measuring the basicity of glasses in which alkali is gradually replaced by SiO_2, as well as by MgO and by BaO. All of these substitutions increase the acidity of the base glass. Little difference is found between SiO_2, MgO, and BaO when they are introduced into a potash glass of the composition $K_2O, 3SiO_2$. In a corresponding Na_2O, $3SiO_2$ glass, MgO was found to be the strongest acid followed by BaO and SiO_2. When introduced into a Li_2O, $3SiO_2$ glass, the three oxides showed the strongest differences: SiO_2 was the weakest and BaO the strongest acid; MgO assumed an intermediate position. We assume that the strong effect of the highly polarizable BaO is the result of the more even distribution of the Li^+ ions in a barium silicate glass. The lithium magnesium silicate and the lithium silicate glass favor subcolloidal immiscibility.

The effect of Al_2O_3, SiO_2, and TiO_2 on the acidity of sodium silicate and potassium silicate glasses was studied by G. E. Rindone, D. E. Day and R. Caporali (314). The acidity of all glasses was found to be increased when TiO_2 was introduced, the effect being strongest for the K_2O glasses. This is to be expected because the O^{2-} ions in a potash glass are more polarizable than those in a soda glass and they, therefore, can be more strongly tightened if an acidic constituent is introduced. The rigorous interpretation and the comparison of the effects of alumina and titania in different glasses is difficult. Any change in the composition of a glass changes several factors.

This complication, however, should not discourage a scientist from using this method even for complex glasses. The complexity of a glass introduces into the picture a larger number of unknowns, which means that one needs a larger number of equations. In other words, the O_2 electrode is applicable to complex systems such as K_2O-Al_2O_3-SiO_2 glasses, but the method has to be supported by other methods such as the evaluation of viscosity, thermal expansion, chemical resistivity, using the same series of glasses. The thermal expansion of a glass changes the internuclear distances and, thus, affects the average polarizability of the O^{2-} ions even if no other structural changes occur on heating.

(3) *Liquid-Solid Interactions*

E. Plumat (303) carried out extensive work on the potentials that arise between liquid glasses and refractory materials at about the same time as I. Peychès and P. Le Clerc (302) studied the electrical potentials between glasses of different composition, between glasses and metals, and between glasses and refractory oxides. The interest of these scientists was not primarily the elucidation of the constitution of glasses, but was to find the answers to urgent technological problems such as the corrosion of refractories, formation of gas bubbles in the glass refractory-contact zone, effect of a temperature gradient on oxidation-reduction equilibria, and related problems. The unusual diversity of interactions to be studied and the wide temperature range that had to be covered required the construction of cells of very different design. The publications of Plumat as well as those of Peychès and Le Clerc are full of important details that should be of interest to those who experiment in this field. We will restrict ourselves to a description of the basic relation between the chemical reaction of a molten glass and a refractory oxide. This relation is of fundamental importance for the understanding of the chemical reactivity of glasses and for refractory problems.

Our acidity-basicity concept (see Chapter V) makes it possible to compare Al_2O_3 or BaO with soda lime silicate glass. One arrives at the conclusion that Al_2O_3 is more acidic and BaO more basic than a representative glass. The fact that Al_2O_3 as well as BaO can react with the molten glass has to be interpreted as follows: Ignoring in the first approximation any entropy changes, we may state that Al_2O_3 goes into solution because it can improve the screening of the Al^{3+} ions by surrounding them with more polarizable O^{2-} ions. BaO goes into solution because its polarizable O^{2-} ion can improve the screening of the Si^{4+} ions of the glass. Both oxides react with the molten glass, i.e., they are corroded, but for different reasons.

E. Plumat (303) measured this tendency of an oxide to react chemically with the glass by constructing a suitable galvanic cell. Using aluminum oxide as the refractory, he found that electrons flow from the Pt electrode to the oxide. The electrons are needed for producing O^{2-} ions according to the following formula:

$$O_2 + 4e^- \rightarrow 2O^{2-}$$

The source of the electrons depends upon the composition of the glass. For a pure soda lime silicate glass the electrons are formed from O^{2-} ions according to:

$$2O^{2-} \rightarrow O_2 + 4e^-$$

One may describe the electrode processes which take place at the refractory-glass and at the glass-platinum interface as follows: O^{2-} ions of the glass are taken to improve the screening of the Al^{3+} ions; e.g., by forming AlO_4 tetrahedra:

$$Al_2^{3+}O_3^{2-} + 5O^{2-} = 2(Al^{3+}O_4^{2-})$$

This reaction interferes with the electroneutrality principle (see Chapter I) because it leads to a negatively charged layer around the refractory and to a positively charged glass. This development of a space charge is eliminated by the migration of alkali ions from the glass that surrounds the Pt electrode into the layer surrounding the refractory oxide.

Taking the migration of Na^+ ions into consideration we can now write the galvanic reaction as follows:

$$\text{Pt electrode: } Na_2O \rightarrow 2Na^+ + \tfrac{1}{2}O_2 + 2e^-$$

$$\text{Refractory-glass: } Al_2O_3 + \tfrac{1}{2}O_2 + 2e^- + 2Na^+ \rightarrow 2NaAlO_2$$

This equation represents the scheme of the reaction but it is not supposed to mean that Al_2O_3 dissolves in the glass by forming sodium aluminate molecules. We write this molecular species only in order to show that Al_2O_3 can form AlO_4 groups which then participate in the structure of the silicate glass.

If the glass contains constituents in addition to the O^{2-} ions which may serve as a source of electrons, e.g., Mn^{2+}, Fe^{2+}, Cr^{3+}, etc., the latter may become the electron donors by changing into Mn^{3+}, Fe^{3+}, and Cr^{6+} ions, respectively.

Using BaO as the reacting solid in contact with a soda lime silicate glass, the opposite process can be observed; i.e., electrons flow from the refractory to the platinum electrode. The screening of the Si^{4+} ions of the glass is improved by the formation of O^{2-} ions from O_2 and electrons at the Pt electrode. The electrons are derived from the dissociation of O^{2-} ions at the refractory according to

$$BaO \rightarrow 2e^- + \tfrac{1}{2}O_2 + Ba^{2+}$$

The electrons flow from the refractory to the platinum electrode where they react with the atmosphere, producing O^{2-} ions. The Ba^{2+} ions diffuse into the molten glass in which they restore the electroneutrality that has been disturbed by the formation of O^{2-} ions in that volume of glass which surrounds the Pt electrode.

F. Summary

The electrochemical approach to the constitution of glasses, in particular the use of the O_2-electrode for determining the acidity-basicity of glasses, does not provide an absolute method. The O_2-electrode enables us to compare the acidity-basicity of related glasses. The importance of the electrochemical method lies in the possibility of linking important properties that are of practical interest, such as the chemical resistivity of a glass or its corroding action upon certain refractories, to the traditional concept of acid-base reactions. At the same time this method demonstrates the fundamental difference that exists between acidity-basicity of aqueous solutions on the one hand and fused salts or glasses on the other. In aqueous solutions we deal with protons and oxygen ions as the major constituents. The screening of the proton (see Chapter I.3.E.) is unique inasmuch as it can enter the electron clouds of O^{2-} ions. We explained the unique solvent power of water (water is the only solvent that can dissolve and ionize a compound such as $Al_2(SO_4)_3$ or $Th(NO_3)_4$) on the basis of its ability to restore electroneutrality around highly charged cations by a shift of protons away from the cation (see Chapter IX.5.C). This leveling effect does not exist in a glass, at least not to the same extent. We postulate that the introduction of Na_2O into vitreous silica increases the polarizability of all O^{2-} ions but we still assume that there are two kinds of anions, one being more polarizable than the other. The chemistry of glasses is governed by those O^{2-} ions that have the highest polarizability. As long as a sodium silicate glass contains nonbridging O^{2-} ions it reacts readily with water. Al_2O_3, CaO, and even BaO are acids with respect to a sodium silicate glass because they tighten the electron clouds of these highly polarizable O^{2-} ions and lower their polarizabilities. After they have been eliminated, for example, in a soda lime silicate glass, the BaO behaves as a base. The effectiveness of a cation in eliminating the highly polarizable O^{2-} ions is a function not only of its field strength (see Chapter II.3), as is the case for aqueous systems, but also of its average coordination number. This is brought out drastically by the measurements of Didtschenko and Rochow (301) who found that the Rb^+ ion is more acidic than the Na^+ ion and that the Cs^+ ion is nearly as acidic as the Li^+ ion. The field strength and the polarizing power of a Li^+ ion is far greater than those of a Cs^+ ion, but one Li^+ ion may affect an average of four nonbridging O^{2-} ions whereas one Cs^+ ion may affect eight of them.

G. E. Rindone, D. E. Day, and R. Caporali (314) found that the addition of Al_2O_3, TiO_2, and SiO_2 increased the acidity of all sodium and potassium silicate glasses, but the order of their efficiency in doing so was not the same. The order reversed with increasing concentration. The unambiguous evaluation of the emf is limited to glasses of simple composition but the O_2-electrode remains an important tool for comparing glasses that differ with respect to one variable only. It is important that one realizes both the strength and the limitation of the method. One should not try to generalize results obtained for one kind of alkali silicate or for one alkali to silica ratio.

The temperature ranges and the composition ranges for which the method is applicable depends upon the mobility of positive and negative ions. It cannot be applied in a temperature region in which the O^{2-} ions are not mobile. For glasses in the softening range it also depends upon the presence of mobile alkali ions. The mechanism of the cell reactions is based upon the mobility of the O^{2-} ion and of at least one kind of cation.

12. Review of the Major Contributions of the Different Methods to the Constitution of Glasses

Prior to the application of X rays, speculations concerning the structure of glasses had to be based on a comparison of glasses with other systems; e.g., solutions, colloids. The application of X rays to simple glasses, in particular the Fourier analysis of their diffuse patterns, was the first absolute approach to the constitution of glass. This method revealed that neither vitreous SiO_2 nor alkali silicate glasses contained molecules. The interpretation of the structure of these glasses as consisting of subcolloidal crystals was ruled out. Among all methods used, the X-ray method made by far the most important contribution to our present concept of the constitution of glass. Unfortunately, some of the early results obtained by X rays were generalized in spite of repeated warnings by B. E. Warren. Thus, the early X-ray work on the structure of glasses led to a pattern, i.e., the three-dimensional, continuous, and random network of tetrahedra, that was widely accepted as the only possible structural picture of inorganic glasses. This pattern is also responsible for the terminology used for describing glasses and for the changes that occur when "network modifiers" such as the alkalies are added to a "network former" such as silica. If the X-ray work had started with a TeO_2 glass instead of SiO_2 glass or with one of G. W. Morey's TiO_2-Ta_2O_5 glasses, which probably contain TiO_6 and TaO_6 octahedra as the structural elements, the interpretation of the structure of glasses would have taken a very different course. Lead orthosilicate glasses would not have been looked upon as exceptions. Octahedra and tetrahedra would have been treated on a par as structural units in oxide glasses.

If B. E. Warren had examined a sodium metaphosphate glass instead of the calcium phosphate, he would have discovered chains in alkali phosphate glasses and the three-dimensional network would not have been considered the only pattern for oxide glasses. The fact that the molecular structure of vitreous sodium phosphate resembles some organic polymers whereas vitreous silicates have a three-dimensional structure might have directed the interpretation of the structure of vitreous B_2O_3 and of borate glasses into different channels. In science, a discovery is important in itself, and is also important with respect to the time at which it is made. It is the sequence of discoveries that molds the minds of scientists and is largely responsible for the terminology that develops in a new field.

The X-ray methods provided a structural picture of the average geometry. This picture directed the thinking much more into channels of geometry than into the consideration of forces. A. Dietzel with his concept of the "field strength" of ions directed our attention to forces. However, no experimental methods were available for determining the forces. Therefore, it is important that at the present time infrared methods are being developed for studying glass structures.

This new approach has provided some startling results. Firstly, a silica glass is not quite as random as it was thought to be. Such a glass may contain structural elements that resemble quartz, in other words, crystals that were not completely randomized during the melting. Secondly, a sodium silicate glass contains SiO_4 tetrahedra that are asymmetrical. The nonbridging O^{2-} ions are held by stronger (20%) forces to the Si^{4+} core than are the bridging ones.

The use of color indicators, e.g., Ni^{2+} ions, revealed that chilled glasses contain Ni^{2+} ions in a lower state of coordination than the same glasses in annealed conditions. This observation related glasses to crystals, in which the coordination of the cations is frequently lower in the high temperature form than in the low temperature modification (CsCl).

Color indicators also revealed that cations with a charge of 2 or more surround themselves symmetrically with O^{2-} ions if the composition of the glass permits this condition. The sharpness of the Nd^{3+} spectrum in a glass can be used as a direct indication for its compatibility, homogeneity, and stability. Glasses in which the Nd^{3+} ion gives only diffuse absorption spectra are either heterogeneous in subcolloidal dimensions or they have a strong tendency to crystallize. The fact that Pb^{2+} ions in glass are colorless reveals the similarity between glasses and aqueous solutions.

Using paramagnetic ions as indicators, magnetic measurements, can give information similar to that given by color indicators. The main contribution of the magnetic methods lies in detecting orientations in structures. The diamagnetic anisotropy distinguishes vitreous B_2O_3 from vitreous SiO_2. It would be desirable to extend this method to other simple glasses, e.g., GeO_2, in order to find out whether they contain orientable molecules.

Density and refractive index measurements have contributed much to our understanding of the thermal history of glasses. Lebedeff's study of the refractive index of chilled glasses revealed that it is not the mechanical stress that determines the property of glasses as a function of their heat treatment, it is that their structures undergo changes. A chilled glass and the same glass in annealed condition are different from a chemical or structural point of view.

Measurements of thermal effects (specific heat, differential thermal analysis) have also contributed to our understanding of the thermal history of glasses.

At the present time, V. V. Tarasov is applying a method based upon the low temperature specific heat of glasses to the constitution of glass. The specific heat is a fundamental property of matter, but it is so complicated that it is not yet understood except in the temperature region close to absolute zero and even there only for very simple solids. C. L. Babcock, S. W. Barber and K. Fajans used the specific heat of B_2O_3 and SiO_2 for developing ideas on the structures of these glasses. Tarasov has been criticized for the invalidity of some assumptions he made with respect to the theoretical relations that are involved. We do not believe that this criticism is a valid argument against Tarasov's reasoning. It is not pertinent for the evaluation of the low temperature specific heat whether the mathematical treatment of the theory is beyond reproach. Tarasov's reasoning is based on the comparison of glasses with crystals of known structure (chains or layers of SiO_2 tetrahedra) and the modes of vibrations in these systems are much too complicated in their interactions to be treated rigorously.

The most important feature of any method lies in its use in correlating phenomena occurring in glasses with corresponding phenomena in systems that are better understood. In order to derive the structure of a glass, one has to correlate the results of different methods applied to the same series of glasses.

The thermal conductivity of vitreous silica is higher than that of other glasses. This strongly supports our concept that in vitreous silica we have a structure closely resembling that of a flawless liquid.

Measurements of the thermal expansivity was one of the first experimental approaches to reveal the similarity of otherwise unrelated substances in the vitreous state. The increase in thermal expansivity in the softening range was widely used for determining t_g of substances. Our concept that t_g is the temperature at which a glass develops "defects" or asymmetries, i.e., disturbances around which the binding forces disproportionate into stronger and weaker ones, is supported by the increase in the thermal expansivity in the softening range. When H. H. Blau examined the expansivities of alkali silicate glasses as a function of the composition, he ruled out "randomness" as a characteristic feature of their structures. Thermal expansion and specific volume revealed structural changes in glasses that had undergone different heat treatments.

In his writings P. W. Bridgman emphasized that the behavior of matter under hydrostatic pressures should contribute substantially to our knowledge of the solid state. Glasses can have a "pressure history" analogous to their "thermal history." A glass that has formed under a hydrostatic pressure is a different chemical individual because of the lower polarizability of its anions. The screening concept of chemical binding is well suited for understanding the behavior of matter under pressure. We explain the phenomenon that a crystal (tellurium) can expand in one direction under hydrostatic pressure on the basis of the screening concept. No conventional treatment can account for this "anomaly."

Closely related to the behavior of glasses under hydrostatic pressure is their flow under shear stress. The use of the indentation method for determining what is usually called the hardness of a glass is most interesting because it reveals the paramount importance of the polarizability of the O^{2-} ions in this kind of deformation processes.

We did not include in this discussion of methods any of the strictly chemical approaches to the constitution of glass. These chemical methods are restricted to phosphate glasses of the type that is soluble in water, i.e., hydrogen-alkali phosphates. We shall refer to these methods in our later discussion of phosphate glasses.

Electrochemical methods, in particular the application of oxygen electrodes to glasses, have made major contributions to understanding the constitution of glasses. This method helped to establish the relationship between the chemical description of an oxide as an acid or a base and the role of the oxide in the glass structure. The fundamental difference that exists between the acidity-basicity relationships in glasses and those of aqueous systems could be understood only when the oxygen electrode was used. The superior chemical resistivity of soda lime glasses as compared with sodium silicates is explained on the basis that Ca^{2+} ions are very "acidic" when introduced into a sodium silicate glass because they interact with the most polarizable nonbridging O^{2-} ions and make them resist the penetration of protons.

References

1. G. Tammann, *Kristallisieren und Schmelzen* (1905); *Aggregatzustande* (1922); *Der Glaszustand* (1933); Leonard Voss, Leipzig.
2. W. E. S. Turner, reviewed in: G. W. Morey, *Properties of Glass*, Ed. 2, Reinhold Publishing Corp., New York, 1956.
3. W. H. Zachariasen, *J. Am. Chem. Soc.*, **54,** 384 (1932); *J. Chem. Phys.*, **3,** 162 (1935); *Glastech. Ber.*, **11,** 120 (1933).
4. V. M. Goldschmidt, "Geochemical Distribution Laws No. 8.," *Skifter Norske Videnskaps. Akad. Mat. Naturv. Kl.* (1926); *Trans. Faraday Soc.*, **25,** 253 (1929).

5. B. E. Warren, *J. Appl. Phys.*, **8,** 645 (1937); **13**, 602 (1942).
6. G. W. Morey, *Properties of Glass*, Ed. 2, Reinhold Publishing Corp., New York, 1954.
7. K. Fajans, *Chem. Eng. News*, **27,** 900 (1949); *Ceram. Age*, **54,** 288 (1949); *Chimia*, **13,** 349 (1959). (These papers contain references to earlier publications of Fajans and his associates.)
8. P. Debye and H. Menke, Physik. Z., **31,** 797 (1930).
9. R. Brill, *Z. angew. Chem.*, **51,** 277 (1938).
10. L. Pauling, *Nature of the Chemical Bond*, Cornell University Press, Ithaca, N. Y., 1940.
11. A. F. Wells, *Structural Inorganic Chemistry*, Clarendon Press, Oxford, 1945.
12. A. E. van Arkel, *Molecules and Crystals in Inorganic Chemistry*, Interscience, New York, 1949.
13. K. Fajans and N. Bauer, *J. Chem. Phys.*, **10,** 410 (1942).
14. R. S. Mulliken, *J. Chem. Phys.*, **2,** 782 (1934); **3,** 573 (1935).
15. W. A. Weyl, *Glastech. Ber.*, **10,** 541 (1932).
16. K. Endell and H. Hellbrügge, *Beih. Z. Ver. deut. Chemiker*, **18,** (1940).
17. B. E. Warren and A. G. Pincus, *J. Am. Ceram. Soc.*, **23,** 301 (1940).
18. A. Dietzel, *Z. Elektrochem.*, **48,** 9 (1942).
19. K. Fajans, *Encyclopedia of Chemistry*, Reinhold Publishing Corp., New York, 1957, p. 763, 803.
20. M. Born and W. Heisenberg, *Z. Physik*, **23,** 388 (1924).
21. W. A. Weyl and E. C. Marboe, *Trans. Soc. Glass Tech.*, **43,** 417–437 (1959).
22. J. M. Stevels, *Glass Ind.*, **35,** 657 (1954).
23. L. F. Audrieth, *Priestley Lecture*, The Pennsylvania State University, University Park, Penn., 1949.
24. J. A. A. Ketelaar, *Chemical Constitution*, Elsevier Publishing Co., Amsterdam, 1953, p. 2.
25. H. Flood and T. Förland, *Acta Chem. Scand.*, **1,** 592, 781, 790 (1947).
26. K. Fajans and N. J. Kreidl, *J. Am. Ceram. Soc.*, **31,** 105 (1948).
27. E. Kordes, *Glastech. Ber.*, **17,** 65 (1939); *Z. anorg. u. allgem. Chem.*, **241,** 1 (1939); *Z. physik. Chem. B*, **43,** 119 (1939); **43,** 173 (1939); **50,** 194 (1941).
28. D. P. Enright, P. A. Marshall and W. A. Weyl, "Decomposition of Hydrogen Peroxide by Lead Peroxide," *Office Naval Research Tech. Rep.* No. 15, Contract N6 onr 269 Task Order 8 (1950), Penn. State University, University Park, Pa.
29. W. A. Weyl, *Coloured Glasses*, Society of Glass Technology, Sheffield, 1951.
30. D. A. Stuart and O. L. Anderson, *J. Am. Ceram. Soc.*, **36,** 27 (1953).
31. R. W. Douglas, *J. Soc. Glass Technol.* **31,** 74 (1947); **33,** 138 (1949).
32. O. L. Anderson and D. A. Stuart, *Ind. Eng. Chem.*, **46,** 154 (1954).
33. W. A. Weyl and E. C. Marboe, *J. Soc. Glass Technol.*, **39,** 16 (1955).
34. G. F. Hüttig, *Handbuch der Katalyse*, Springer, Wien, 1943.
35. J. D. MacKenzie, *J. Chem. Phys.*, **25,** 187 (1956).
36. A. Dietzel and E. Deeg, *Glastech. Ber.*, **30,** 282 (1957).
37. J. A. Prins, *Non-Crystalline Solids*, V. D. Frechette, Editor, John Wiley & Sons, New York, 1960, p. 322.
38. E. A. Moelwyn-Hughes, *The Kinetics of Reactions in Solution*, Clarendon Press, Oxford, 1947.

39. A. Ferrari and L. Sessa, *Gazz. chim. ital.*, **67,** 501 (1937).
40. L. Coes, *Science*, **118,** 131 (1953).
41. A. Weiss and A. Weiss, *Z. anorg. u. allgem. Chem.*, **276,** 95 (1954).
42. M. Born and J. E. Mayer, *Z. Physik*, **75,** 1 (1932).
43. L. Pauling, *J. Am. Chem. Soc.*, **51,** 1010 (1929).
44. A. Dietzel and H. J. Poegel, *Naturwissenschaften*, **40,** 604 (1953).
45. H. J. Poegel, *Glastech. Ber.*, **29,** 266 (1956).
46. C. Wagner and P. Hantelmann, *J. Chem. Phys.*, **18,** 72 (1950).
47. W. A. Weyl, *J. Phys. & Colloid Chem.*, **55,** 507 (1951).
48. W. A. Weyl and N. A. Terhune, *Ceram. Age*, **62**(2), 23 (1953).
49. W. A. Weyl and E. C. Marboe, *J. Soc. Glass Technol.*, **43,** 191 (1959).
50. A. Pabst, *Am. Mineralogist*, **37,** 137 (1952).
51. W. Primak, L. H. Fuchs and P. Day, *J. Am. Ceram. Soc.*, **38,** 135 (1955).
52. I. I. Kitaigorodski, *Technologie des Glasses*, V. E. B. Verlag, München, 1957.
53. G. Hägg, *J. Chem. Phys.*, **3,** 42 (1935).
54. J. Frenkel, *Kinetic Theory of Liquids*, Clarendon Press, Oxford, 1946.
55. J. D. Bernal, "Structure and Molecular Forces in Pure Liquids." *Discussions Faraday Soc.*, p. 27, 1936; *Nature*, **183,** 141 (1959).
56. J. Zarzycki, *Non-Crystalline Solids*, John Wiley & Sons, New York, 1960, p. 117.
57. H. Eyring, *J. Chem. Phys.*, **4,** 283 (1936).
58. G. W. Stewart, *Kolloid-Z.*, **67,** 130 (1934); *Am. J. Phys.*, **12,** 321 (1944); "Structure and Molecular Forces in Pure Liquids," *Discussions Faraday Soc.*, p. 238, 1936.
59. D. Vorländer, *Chemische Kristallography der Flüssigkeiten*, Leipzig, 1924.
60. C. Weygand, *Hand u. Jahrb. Chem. Physik*, **2,** 17 (1941).
61. W. Kast, *Physik. Z.*, **38,** 627 (1937); *Z. Elektrochem.*, **45,** 184 (1939).
62. J. J. Trillat and H. Forestier, *Bull. soc. chim. France*, **51,** 248 (1932).
63. K. H. Meyer and Y. Go, *Helv. Chim. Acta*, **17,** 1081 (1934).
64. M. Goldstein and T. H. Davies, *J. Am. Ceram. Soc.*, **38,** 223 (1955).
65. B. K. Banerjee, *J. Am. Ceram. Soc.*, **36,** 296 (1953); *Bull. Nat. Inst. Sci. India*, **14,** 62 (1959).
66. W. Skaliks, *Z. anorg. u. allgem. Chem.*, **183,** 263 (1929).
67. A. P. Rostkowsky and A. G. Bergmann, *J. Russ. Chem. Soc.*, **62,** 2055 (1930).
68. T. Bååk, *Acta Chem. Scand.*, **9,** 1406 (1955).
69. A. Einstein and L. Infeld, *The Evolution of Physics*, Simon and Schuster, New York, 1938.
70. G. Tammann, *Z. anorg. u. allgem. Chem.*, **158,** 1 (1926).
71. J. D. Bernal and R. H. Fowler, *J. Chem. Phys.*, **1,** 515 (1933).
72. L. Havestadt and R. Fricke, *Z. anorg. u. allgem. Chem.*, **188,** 357 (1930).
73. G. F. Wells, *Structural Inorganic Chemistry*, Ed. 2, Clarendon Press, Oxford, 1950, p. 429.
74. J. Morgan and B. E. Warren, *J. Chem. Phys.*, **6,** 666 (1938).
75. F. E. Bartell and K. E. Bristol, *J. Phys. Colloid Chem.*, **44,** 86 (1940).
76. O. Ruff and B. Hirsch, *Z. anorg. u. allgem. Chem.*, **173,** 14 (1928).
77. W. A. Weyl, *Structure and Properties of Solid Surfaces*, Edited by R. Gomer and C. S. Smith, Univ. of Chicago Press, Chicago, 1953, p. 147.
78. W. A. Weyl and W. C. Ormsby, *Rheology—Theory and Applications*, Vol. III, Edited by F. R. Eirich, Academic Press, New York, 1960, pp. 249–298.

79. W. A. Weyl, *Glastech. Ber.*, **9,** 641 (1931).
80. C. R. Kurkjian and L. E. Russell, *J. Soc. Glass Technol.*, **42,** 130 (1958).
81. H. S. Frank and M. W. Evans, *J. Chem. Phys.*, **13,** 507 (1945).
82. H. W. B. Roozeboom, *Z. Phys. Chem.*, **5,** 198 (1890).
83. I. Koppel, *Z. anorg. u. allgem. Chem.*, **41,** 377 (1904).
84. A. Kleinhaus, *Arch. Wärmewirtsch.*, **17,** 127 (1936).
85. A. Eucken, *Lehrbuch der Chemischen Physik*, Ed. 3, Vol. II, Akademische Verlagsgesellschaft, Leipzig, 1949, p. 239.
86. O. Fuchs, *Z. Elektrochem.*, **47,** 101 (1941).
87. R. Willstätter, H. Kraut, and K. Lobinger, *Ber. deut. chem. Ges.*, **62,** 2027 (1929).
88. C. J. van Nieuwenburg and H. B. Blumendahl, *Rec. trav. chim.*, **49,** 857 (1930).
89. M. von Stackelberg, F. Quatram, and J. Dressel, *Z. Elektrochem.*, **43,** 14 (1937).
90. E. Lennard-Jones and A. F. Devonshire, *Proc. Roy. Soc.* (*London*), **169,** 317 (1938); **170,** 464 (1939).
91. N. V. Sidgwick, *The Electronic Theory of Valency*, Clarendon Press, Oxford, 1929.
92. L. Pauling, *J. Am. Chem. Soc.*, **54,** 988 (1932).
93. A. Bondi, *Rheology, Theory and Application*, Vol. I, Edited by F. R. Eirich, Academic Press, New York, 1956, p. 342.
94. W. Jander and E. Hoffmann, *Z. anorgan. u. allgem. Chem.*, **174,** 16 (1928); **218,** 211 (1934).
95. W. Ostwald, *Lehrbuch der Allgemeinen Chemie*, Leipzig, 1902.
96. I. N. Stranski and D. Totomanow, *Z. phys. Chem. A*, **163,** 399 (1933).
97. E. C. Marboe, *Chem. Eng. News*, **27,** 2198 (1949).
98. M. Volmer and H. Flood, *Z. phys. Chem.* (Leipzig), *A* **170,** 273 (1934).
99. H. Reiss, *Ind. Eng. Chem.*, **44,** 1284 (1952).
100. S. D. Stookey, U. S. Pat. 2920971, 1960.
101. R. Smoluchowski, *Phase Transformations in Solids*, John Wiley & Sons, New York, 1951, p. 149.
102. E. C. Marboe and W. A. Weyl, *J. Soc. Glass Technol.*, **32,** 281 (1948).
103. M. Volmer and I. Estermann, *Z. Physik*, **7,** 13 (1921).
104. E. Zschimmer, E. Zimpelmann, and L. Riedel, *Sprechsaal*, **59,** 411 (1926)
105. F. Krüger, *Glastech. Ber.*, **16,** 233 (1938).
106. C. Eden, *Glastech. Ber.*, **25,** 83 (1952).
107. W. Eitel, *The Physical Chemistry of the Silicates*, Univ. of Chicago Press, Chicago, 1954.
108. E. Zschimmer and A. Dietzel, *Glastech. Ber.*, **6,** 579 (1928).
109. P. Othmer, *Z. anorg. u. allgem. Chem.*, **91,** 209 (1915).
110. D. E. Harrison and F. A. Hummel, *J. Electrochem. Soc.*, **103,** 491 (1956).
111. F. Feigl, *Chemistry of Specific, Selective and Sensitive Reactions*, Academic Press, Inc., New York, 1949, p. 162.
112. N. J. Kreidl, *Glastech. Ber.*, **7,** 313 (1929).
113. W. A. Weyl and E. Thümen, *Glastech. Ber.*, **11,** 113 (1933).
114. A. Dietzel, *Ber. deut. keram. Ges.*, **24,** 283 (1943).
115. J. F. Schairer and N. L. Bowen, *Am. J. Sci.* **254,** 129 (1956).
116. W. C. Taylor, *Glass Ind.*, **7,** 90 (1925).

117. A. Hilsenrod and B. Gehauf, *J. Chem. Phys.*, **24**, 914 (1956).
118. N. V. Solomin, N. M. Galdina, and V. V. Lapin, Abstracted in *Verres et Réfractaires*, **10**, 370 (1956).
119. H. Jebsen-Marwedel, *Glastechnische Fabrikationsfehler*, Ed. 2, Springer, Berlin, 1959, p. 236.
120. R. B. Sosman, *Properties of Silica*, Reinhold Publishing Co., New York, 1927.
121. J. B. Murgatroyd, *J. Soc. Glass Technol.*, **32**, 291 (1948).
122. G. Tammann, *Z. Elektrochem.*, **36**, 665 (1930).
123. O. R. Wulf, *Proc. Nat. Acad. Sci.*, **14**, 609 (1938).
124. W. Wahl, *Z. physik. Chem.*, **84**, 112 (1913).
125. E. J. Shaw and T. E. Phipps, *Phys. Rev.*, **38**, 174 (1931).
126. G. Heyne, *Z. angew. Chem.*, **46**, 473 (1933).
127. J. E. Stanworth, *J. Soc. Glass Technol.*, **30**, 54 (1946).
128. J. M. Stevels, *J. Soc. Glass Technol.*, **30**, 64 (1946).
129. A. G. Smekal, *J. Soc. Glass Technol.*, **35**, 411 (1951).
130. A. Smekal, *Nova Acta Leopold*, **11**, 511 (1942); *Verhandl. deut. physik. Ges.*, **23**, 39 (1942).
131. A. Dietzel, *Naturwissenschaften*, **31**, 22 (1943).
132. K. H. Sun, *J. Am. Ceram. Soc.*, **30**, 279 (1947).
133. P. L. Baynton, H. Rawson, and J. E. Stanworth, *Trav. IV Congrès International du Verre*, Paris, 1956, p. 52.
134. H. Rawson, *Trav. IV Congrès International du Verre*, Paris, 1956, p. 62.
135. A. Dietzel, *Glastech. Ber.*, **22**, 41, 81, 212 (1948).
136. H. G. Grimm and P. Huppert, U. S. Pat. 1964629, 1934; 2100396, 1937; 2227082, 1940.
137. G. W. Morey, *J. Am. Ceram. Soc.*, **17**, 315 (1934).
138. W. H. Zachariasen, *J. Chem. Phys.*, **3**, 162 (1935).
139. G. Hägg, *J. Chem. Phys.*, **3**, 363 (1935).
140. B. E. Warren, *J. Am. Ceram. Soc.*, **24**, 256 (1941).
141. K. Grjotheim, *Glass Ind.*, **39**, 201 (1958).
142. J. M. Stevels, *Glass Ind.*, **35**, 657 (1954).
143. H. J. L. Trap and J. M. Stevels, *V. Internationaler Glas Kongress, München, VI*, 23 (1959).
144. E. Berger, *Glastech. Ber.*, **5**, 393 (1925/26); **8**, 339 (1930).
145. G. Tammann and A. Elbrächter, *Z. anorg. u. allgem. Chem.*, **207**, 268 (1932).
146. S. M. Brekhovskich, *Glastech. Ber.*, **32**, 437 (1959).
147. G. W. Morey and H. E. Merwin, *J. Am. Chem. Soc.*, **58**, 2252 (1936).
148. R. Zsigmondy, *Zur Erkenntnis der Kolloide*, Jena, 1905.
149. H. Siedentopf, *Ann. Physik*, **10**, 1 (1903).
150. G. L. Clark, *The Encyclopedia of Microscopy*, Reinhold Publishing Co., New York, 1961.
151. A. F. Prebus and I. W. Michener, *Phys. Rev.*, **87**, 201 (1952).
152. F. Oberlies, *Naturwissenschaften*, **43**, 224 (1956).
153. W. Vogel and K. Gerth. *Glastech. Ber.*, **31**, 15 (1958); *Silikat Tech.*, **9**, 353, 495 (1958).
154. W. Vogel, *Silikat Tech.*, **10**, 241 (1959).
155. W. Vogel, *The Structure of Glass*, Vol. 2, (trans. from Russian), Consultants Bureau, N. Y., 1960, p. 17.

156. M. Faraday, *Trans. Roy. Soc.* (*London*), **1,** 1 (1930).
157. H. Hovestadt, *Jenaer Glas und seine Verwendung in Wissenschalt und Technik*, Gustav Fischer, Jena, 1900. Report of the early work by O. Schott and his associates carried out in the Jena Glass Works.
158. F. Eckert, *Jahrb. Radioakt. u. Elektronik*, **20,** 93 (1923).
159. W. Hittorf, *Ann. Phys. u. Chem.*, **84,** 214 (1852).
160. A. L. Day and E. T. Allen, *Carnegie Inst. Wash. Publ.*, **31,** 34 (1905).
161. K. Quasebart, *Sprechsaal*, **49,** 18 (1916).
162. G. Tammann and A. Kohlhass, *Z. anorg. u. allgem. Chem.*, **182,** 51 (1929).
163. E. Berger, *J. Am. Ceram. Soc.*, **15,** 647 (1932). This paper contains numerous references to earlier work on the glassy state.
164. R. W. G. Wyckoff and G. W. Morey, *J. Soc. Glass Technol.*, **9,** 265 (1925); *Am. J. Sci.*, **12,** 419 (1926).
165. G. W. Parmelee, G. L. Clark, and A. E. Badger, *J. Soc. Glass Technol.*, **13,** 285 (1929).
166. G. L. Clark and C. R. Amberg, *J. Soc. Glass Technol.*, **13,** 290 (1929).
167. J. T. Randall, H. P. Rooksby, and B. S. Cooper, *J. Soc. Glass Technol.*, **15,** 54 (1931).
168. W. A. Weyl, *Coloured Glasses*, Society of Glass Technology, Sheffield, 1951, p. 77.
169. N. S. Kurnakov, *Z. anorg. u. allgem. Chem.*, **135,** 81 (1924).
170. G. Tammann and M. E. Pillsbury, *Z. anorg. u. allgem. Chem.*, **172,** 243 (1928).
171. B. E. Warren, H. Krutter, and O. Morningstar, *J. Am. Ceram. Soc.*, **19,** 202 (1936).
172. W. A. Weyl, *Glastech. Ber.*, **30,** 269 (1957).
173. J. Biscoe, M. A. A. Druesne, and B. E. Warren, *J. Am. Ceram. Soc.*, **24,** 100 (1941).
174. B. E. Warren and J. Biscoe, *J. Am. Ceram. Soc.*, **21,** 259 (1938).
175. G. Hartleif, *Z. anorg. u. allgem. Chem.*, **238,** 353 (1938).
176. G. W. Brady, *J. Chem. Phys.*, **27,** 300 (1957).
177. T. Ito and H. Sawada, *Z. Krist.*, **102,** 13 (1939).
178. G. W. Brady, *J. Chem. Phys.*, **28,** 48 (1958).
179. E. A. Porai-Koshits, *The Structure of Glass*, Vol. 1, (trans. from Russian), Consultants Bureau, Inc., N. Y., 1958, p. 25.
180. S. Urnes, "*X-ray Diffraction Studies of Glass*," In: *Modern Aspects of the Vitreous State*, J. D. MacKenzie, Editor, Butterworth & Co., London, 1961, p. 10.
181. H. Z. Brugel, *Z. Physik*, **128,** 255 (1950).
182. V. A. Florinskaya and R. S. Pechenkina, *Doklady Akad. Nauk S. S. S. R.*, **85,** 1265 (1952); **89,** 37 (1953); *Glass Ind.*, January–March, 1958.
183. I. Simon and H. O. McMahon, *J. Chem. Phys.*, **21,** 23 (1953); *J. Am. Ceram. Soc.*, **36,** 160 (1953).
184. B. I. Stepanov and A. M. Prima, *Optiko i Spektroskopiya*, **4,** 734 (1958); **5,** 15 (1958).
185. J. Zarzycki and F. Naudin, *Verres et Réfractaires*, **14,** 113 (1960).
186. J. A. Hedvall, *Reaktionsfähigkeit Fester Stoffe*, Joh. Ambrosium Barth, Leipzig, (1938).
187. F Weidert, *Z. wiss., Phot.*, **21,** 254 (1922).

188. R. Hill and O. R. Howell, *Phil. Mag.*, **48,** 833 (1924).
189. W. Feitknecht, *Helv. Chim. Acta*, **20,** 659 (1937).
190. L. E. Orgel, *An Introduction to Transition-Metal Chemistry, Ligand Field Theory*, Methuen & Co., Ltd., London, 1960.
191. W. R. Brode, *J. Am. Chem. Soc.*, **55,** 939 (1933); *Proc. Roy. Soc.* (*London*) *A*, **118,** 286 (1928).
192. H. S. Linwood and W. A. Weyl, *J. Opt. Soc. Am.* **32,** 443 (1942).
193. A. Dietzel and M. Coenen, *Glastech. Ber.*, **34,** 49 (1961).
194. W. Stegmaier and A. Dietzel, *Glastech. Ber.*, **18,** 297 (1940).
195. A. A. Kefeli, *The Structure of Glass*, Vol. 2 (trans. from Russian), Consultants Bureau, New York, 1960, p. 336.
196. N. M. Parikh and H. E. Simpson, *J. Am. Ceram. Soc.*, **35,** 99 (1952).
197. I. J. Piccard and E. Thomas, *Helv. Chim. Acta*, **6,** 1040 (1923).
198. J. Meisenheimer, *Z. Phys. Chem.*, **97,** 304 (1921).
199. K. Fajans, *Z. Krist.*, **66,** 321 (1928).
200. G. R. McCarthy, *Am. J. Sci.*, **12,** 16 (1926).
201. R. R. Shively, Jr., and W. A. Weyl, *J. Phys. & Colloid Chem.*, **55,** 512 (1951).
202. P. W. Selwood, *Nature*, **161,** 883 (1948).
203. E. J. W. Verwey, P. W. Haayman, and F. C. Romeyn, *Chem. Weekblad*, **44,** 705 (1948).
204. W. A. Weyl, G. H. Johnson, W. Capps, and T. Förland, *Office Naval Research, Tech. Reps.*, No. **24–29** (1951), Contract N6 onr 269 Task Order 8, Pennsylvania State University, University Park, Pennsylvania.
205. J. A. Hedvall and P. Sjöman, *Z. Elektrochem.*, **37,** 130 (1931).
206. J. H. Weymouth and W. O. Williamson, *Mineral. Mag.*, **23,** 573 (1951).
207. W. O. Milligan, *J. Phys. Chem.*, **38,** 797 (1934).
208. G. O. Bagdykyants and A. G. Alekseev, *The Structure of Glass*, Vol. 2 (trans. from Russian), Consultants Bureau, New York, 1960, p. 198.
209. K. Rosenhauer and F. Weidert, *Glastech. Ber.*, **16,** 51 (1938).
210. C. Kühl, H. Rudow, and W. A. Weyl, *Glastech. Ber.*, **16,** 37 (1938).
211. W. Büssem and C. Schusterius, *Wiss. Veröffentl. Siemens-Werken*, **17,** 59 (1938).
212. E. V. Anufrieva and M. V. Volkenshtein, *The Structure of Glass*, Vol. 2 (trans. from Russian), Consultants Bureau, New York, 1960, p. 117.
213. W. D. Smiley and W. A. Weyl, *Glass Sci. Bull.*, *VI*, 1 (1947).
214. W. A. Weyl, J. H. Schulman, R. J. Ginther, and L. W. Evans, *J. Electrochem. Soc.*, **95,** 70 (1949).
215. K. O. Otley and W. A. Weyl, U. S. Pat. 2,722,519, 1955; *J. Appl. Phys.*, **23,** 499 (1952).
216. G. E. Rindone, *Trav. du IV Congrès International du Verre*, Paris, **VII**, 4 (1956).
217. W. A. Weyl, *Sprechsaal*, **93,** 128 (1960).
218. H. S. Williams, *Glass Sci. Bull.*, **I,** 1 (1944).
219. E. C. Marboe and W. A. Weyl, *J. Appl. Phys.*, **20,** 124 (1949).
220. A. W. Bastress, *J. Am. Ceram. Soc.*, **30,** 42 (1947); *Glass Sci. Bull.*, **IV,** 140 (1947).
221. O. Schmitz-DuMont, H. Brokopf, and K. Burkhardt, *Z. anorg. u. allgem. Chem.*, **295,** 7 (1958).
222. O. Schmitz-DuMont, H. Gossling, and H. Brokopf, *Z. anorg. u. allgem. Chem.*, **300,** 159 (1959).

223. C. Andresen-Kraft, *Glastech. Ber.*, **9,** 577 (1931).
224. K. Breit and R. Juza, *Glastech. Ber.*, **27,** 117 (1954).
225. P. W. Selwood, *Magnetochemistry,* Edition 2, Interscience, New York, 1956, p. 182ff.
226. E. Weir Toor, quoted by P. W. Selwood, *Magnetochemistry*, Ed. 2, Interscience, New York, 1956, p. 189.
227. P. W. Selwood, J. A. Parodi, and A. Pace, Jr., *J. Am. Chem. Soc.*, **72,** 1269 (1950).
228. W. Blitz, F. Weibke, and L. Schrader-Traeger, *Glastech. Ber.*, **16,** 131 (1938).
229. E. Kordes and H. Becker, *Z. anorg. u. allgem. Chem.*, **260,** 185 (1949).
230. A. A. Lebedeff, *Trans. Opt. Inst., Petrograd,* **2,** No. **10,** 1 (1921).
231. L. Prod'homme, Thesis for Doctor of Science, University of Paris, 1957.
232. A. Dietzel and O. W. Flörke, *Glastech. Ber.*, **28,** 423 (1955).
233. A. Winkelmann and O. Schott, *Ann. physik & Chem.*, **51,** 730 (1894).
234. S. English and W. E. S. Turner, *J. Soc. Glass Technol.*, **6,** 228 (1922).
235. S. C. Waterton and W. E. S. Turner, *J. Soc. Glass Technol.*, **18,** 268 (1934).
236. M. L. Huggins, *J. Opt. Soc. Am.*, **30,** 420, 495, 514 (1940).
237. J. M. Stevels, *Progress in the Theory of the Physical Properties of Glass*, Elsevier Publ. Co., Amsterdam, 1948.
238. H. W. Fairbairn, *Bull. Geol. Soc. Am.*, **54,** 1305 (1943).
239. L. Shartsis, W. Capps, and S. Spinner, *J. Am. Ceram. Soc.*, **36,** 35 (1953).
240. H. F. Shermer, *J. Research Nat. Bur. Standards,* **57,** 97 (1956).
241. K. Fajans and S. W. Barber, *J. Am. Chem. Soc.*, **74,** 2761 (1952).
242. F. Seitz, *The Modern Theory of Solids,* McGraw-Hill, New York, 1960, p. 99.
243. C. L. Babcock, S. W. Barber, and K. Fajans, *Ind. Eng. Chem.*, **46,** 161 (1954).
244. S. B. Thomas and G. S. Parks, *J. Phys. Chem.*, **35,** 2091 (1931).
245. G. S. Parks and H. M. Huffman, *J. Phys. Chem.*, **31,** 1842 (1927).
246. G. Tammann and H. Elsner v. Gronow, *Z. anorg. u. allgem. Chem.*, **192,** 193 (1930).
247. A. Q. Tool, *J. Am. Ceram. Soc.*, **31,** 177 (1948). This paper contains references to the earlier publications of the author and his associates.
248. A. Winkelmann, *Ann. Physik u. Chem.*, **49,** 401 (1893).
249. V. V. Tarasov, *The Structure of Glass*, Vol. 2 (trans. from Russian), Consultants Bureau, New York, 1960, p. 64. This paper contains references to earlier publications by the author and associates.
250. K. K. Kelley, *J. Am. Chem. Soc.*, **61,** 471 (1939).
251. A. Eucken and G. Kuhn, *Z. Phys. Chem.*, **134,** 193 (1928).
252. A. Eucken, In: *Lehrbuch der Chemischen Physik*, Ed. 3, Vol. II, Akademische Verlagsgesellschaft, Leipzig, 1949, p. 752.
253. R. Berman, *Advances in Physics*, **2,** 103 (1953).
254. P. G. Klemens, *Non-Crystalline Solids*, Edited by V. D. Fréchette, John Wiley & Sons, New York, 1960, pp. 508–530.
255. E. H. Ratcliffe, *Phys. and Chem. Glass*, **1,** 103 (1960).
256. K. L. Wray and T. J. Connolly, *J. Appl. Phys.*, **30,** 1702 (1959).
257. C. Kittel, *Phys. Rev.*, **75,** 972 (1949).
258. W. Klemm, *Z. Elektrochem.*, **34,** 523 (1928).
259. J. B. Saunders and A. Q. Tool, *Bur. Standards J. Research* **11,** 799 (1933).
260. M. D. Karkhanavala and F. A. Hummel, *J. Am. Ceram. Soc.*, **35,** 215 (1952).

261. M. O. Samsoen, *Compt. rend.*, **182,** 517 (1926).
262. W. Souder and P. Hindert, *Sci. Papers Bur. Standards*, **21,** 1 (1926).
263. L. M. Dennis and A. W. Laubengayer, *J. Phys. Chem.*, **30,** 1510 (1926).
264. A. Cousen and W. E. S. Turner, *J. Soc. Glass Technol.*, **12,** 169 (1928).
265. H. H. Blau, *J. Soc. Glass Technol.*, **35,** 304 (1951).
266. E. Seddon and W. E. S. Turner, *J. Soc. Glass Technol.*, **17,** 324 (1933).
267. M. A. Bezborodov, *The Structure of Glass*, Vol. 2 (trans. from Russian), Consultants Bureau, New York, 1960, p. 46.
268. L. Merker and H. Wondratschek, *Glastech. Ber.*, **32,** 54 (1959).
269. P. W. Bridgman, *Physics of High Pressure*, G. Bell & Sons, London, 1949; *Rev. Modern Phys.*, **18,** 1–93 (1946).
270. G. Tammann and E. Jenckel, *Z. anorg. u. allgem. Chem.*, **184,** 416 (1929).
271. G. Tammann and W. Jellinghaus, *Ann. Physik*, **2,** 264 (1929).
272. M. J. Buerger, *Phase Transformations in Solids*, John Wiley & Sons, Inc., New York, 1951, p. 183.
273. R. B. Jacobs, *Phys. Rev.*, **51,** 999 (1937); **54,** 325, 468 (1938).
274. F. Birch and R. R. Law, *Bull. Geol. Soc. Am.*, **46,** 1219 (1935).
275. F. Birch and R. B. Dow, *Bull. Geol. Soc. Am.*, **47,** 1255 (1936).
276. P. W. Bridgman and I. Simon, *J. Appl. Phys.*, **24,** 405 (1953).
277. C. E. Weir and L. Shartsis, *J. Am. Ceram. Soc.*, **38,** 299 (1955).
278. F. Auerback, *Ann. Physik. u. Chem.*, **53,** 1000 (1894).
279. A. Reis and L. Zimmermann, *Z. phys. Chem.*, **102,** 298 (1922).
280. W. A. Weyl, *Glastech. Ber.*, **23,** 174 (1950).
281. W. von Engelhardt, *Nachr. Akad. Wiss., Göttingen, mathm.-naturw. Kl. Heft*, **2,** 7 (1942); *Kolloid-Z.*, **102,** 217 (1943); *Naturwissenschaften*, **33,** 195 (1946).
282. H. E. Powell and F. W. Preston, *J. Am. Ceram. Soc*, **28,** 145 (1949).
283. R. W. Douglas, *J. Soc. Glass Technol.*, **42,** 145 (1958).
284. L. Ainsworth, *J. Soc. Glass Technol.*, **38,** 479, 501 (1954).
285. P. Grodzinski, *Glastech. Ber.*, **26,** 309 (1953).
286. F. W. Glaze, D. H. Blackburn, J. S. Osmalov, D. Hubbard, and M. H. Black, *J. Research Nat. Bur. Standards*, **59,** 83 (1957).
287. G. Gehlhoff and M. Thomas, *Z. tech. Physik*, **7,** 105 (1926).
288. F. Eisenloeffel, German. Pat. 444, 749 Kl.32b.
289. C. A. Becker, *Sprechsaal*, **67,** 137 (1934).
290. A. Petzold, F. G. Wihsmann, and H. von Kamptz, *Glastech. Ber.*, **34,** 56 (1961).
291. J. H. Westbrook, *Phys. and Chem. Glass*, **1,** 32 (1960).
292. A. C. Becquerel, *Compt. rend.*, **38,** 905 (1854).
293. W. Thomson, *Proc. Roy. Soc.* (London), **23,** 468 (1875).
294. B. von Lengyel and A. Sammt, *Z. phys. Chem.*, **181,** 55 (1938).
295. F. Haber, *Z. Elecktrochem.*, **12,** 415 (1906).
296. A. V. Bleininger, *Trans. Am. Ceram. Soc.*, **17,** 218 (1915).
297. E. Bauer and R. Brunner, *Z. Elecktrochem.*, **41,** 794 (1935).
298. P. Csaki and A. Dietzel, *Glastech. Ber.*, **18,** 33 (1940).
299. H. Flood and T. Förland, *Discussions Faraday Soc.*, **1,** 302 (1947).
300. H. Flood, T. Förland, and K. Motzfeldt, *Acta Chem. Scand.*, **6,** 257 (1952).
301. R. Didtschenko and E. G. Rochow, *J. Am. Chem. Soc.*, **76,** 3291 (1954).
302. I. Peychès and P. Le Clerc, *Verres et Réfractaires*, **7,** 339 (1953).

303. E. Plumat, *Office Naval Research, Techn. Rep.* No. **60** (1954), Contract N6 onr 269, Task Order 8, NR032–265, The Pennsylvania State University, University Park, Penn.; *Silicates inds.*, **19,** 141 (1954).
304. T. Förland and M. Tashiro, *Glass Ind.*, **37,** 381 (1956).
305. A. C. Marshall, *Office Naval Research, Tech.* No. **48,** Contract N6 onr 269, Task Order 8, NR032–265, April, 1952, Pennsylvania State University, University Park, Penn.
306. E. J. Workman and S. E. Reynolds, *Phys. Rev.*, **78,** 254 (1950).
307. G. Eisenman, D. O. Rudin, and J. U. Casby, U.S. Pat. 2,829,000; *Science*, **126,** 831 (1957).
308. J. O. Isard, Report on a Research Colloquium on the Alkali Ion Determination by Means of Glass Electrodes, *Nature*, **184,** 1616 (1959).
309. M. Dole, *Am. Dyestuff Reptr.*, **30,** 231 (1941).
310. P. Le Clerc, *Chim. Ind.*, **69,** 653 (1953).
311. G. E. Rindone, E. C. Marboe, and W. A. Weyl, *J. Am. Ceram. Soc.*, **30,** 314 (1947).
312. L. Holub, F. Neubert, and F. Sauerwald, *Z. phys. Chem. A*, **174,** 161 (1935).
313. G. S. Smith and G. E. Rindone, *Glass Ind.*, **37,** 437 (1956).
314. G. E. Rindone, D. E. Day, and R. Caporali, *J. Am. Ceram. Soc.*, **43**, 571 (1960).

NAME INDEX

SUBJECT INDEX